The Open University

MST209 Mathematical methods

els

C000226016

Block 7

Contents

The Open University, Walton Hall, Milton Keynes, MK7 6AA.

First published 2005. Second edition 2008.

Copyright © 2005, 2008 The Open University

All rights reserved. No part of this publication may be reproduced, stored in a retrieval system, transmitted or utilised in any form or by any means, electronic, mechanical, photocopying, recording or otherwise, without written permission from the publisher or a licence from the Copyright Licensing Agency Ltd. Details of such licences (for reprographic reproduction) may be obtained from the Copyright Licensing Agency Ltd, Saffron House, 6–10 Kirby Street, London EC1N 8TS; website http://www.cla.co.uk.

Open University course materials may also be made available in electronic formats for use by students of the University. All rights, including copyright and related rights and database rights, in electronic course materials and their contents are owned by or licensed to The Open University, or otherwise used by The Open University as permitted by applicable law.

In using electronic course materials and their contents you agree that your use will be solely for the purposes of following an Open University course of study or otherwise as licensed by The Open University or its assigns.

Except as permitted above you undertake not to copy, store in any medium (including electronic storage or use in a website), distribute, transmit or retransmit, broadcast, modify or show in public such electronic materials in whole or in part without the prior written consent of The Open University or in accordance with the Copyright, Designs and Patents Act 1988.

Edited, designed and typeset by The Open University, using the Open University TEX System.

Printed and bound in the United Kingdom by Charlesworth Press, Wakefield.

ISBN 978 0 7492 5287 8

1.1

UNIT 25 Multiple integrals

Study guide for Unit 25

For your study of this unit you should be familiar with the definition of the definite integral as a limit. You will also need to be familiar with polar coordinate systems. The plane polar coordinate system was introduced in *Unit 4*, and the cylindrical and spherical polar coordinate systems were introduced in *Unit 23*. You will also need to remind yourself about finding the centre of mass of a system of particles from *Unit 19*.

The sections should be studied in order. As a rough guide, you should expect to spend about the same amount of time on Section 1 and Section 2, and slightly less on the remaining sections.

Many of the results in this unit will be used in *Unit 27*.

You will need to use your computer to carry out the activities in Section 5.

Introduction

You know that in one dimension the *definite integral* of a function $f(x)$ on an interval of the x-axis can be defined as the limit of a sum of function values on the interval. In *Unit 24* you saw how this idea could be generalized to line integrals, and used to calculate properties of vector fields. In this unit we shall generalize the idea of an integral still further to deal with two and three dimensions by introducing two new kinds of integrals, called *area integrals* and *volume integrals.*

Area integrals arise in calculations of populations over regions. For example, suppose you know the number of bacteria per unit area at each point on a glass plate. More generally, the total number of bacteria on any region of the plate is the product of the surface density and the area of that region. If the population density is non-uniform then the total number of bacteria on a region of the plate can be expressed as an *area integral of the population density* over that region. Because a surface is a two-dimensional region, an area integral involves integrating with respect to two independent variables. Section 1 shows how area integrals can be evaluated as combinations of two ordinary integrals, while Section 2 describes applications of area integrals, including the evaluation of centres of mass of planar (i.e. two-dimensional) objects.

Centres of mass were discussed in *Unit 19.*

Volume integrals arise in the calculation of the mass of an object. For example, suppose you know the mass per unit volume of a solid body. If the density is uniform, the total mass of the body is the product of its density and its volume. More generally the mass of the body is the *volume integral of the density* over the three-dimensional region occupied by the body. Section 3 shows how volume integrals can be expressed as combinations of three ordinary integrals.

Area integrals and volume integrals are examples of *multiple integrals*, the title of this unit. One of the major applications of multiple integrals is the calculation of *moments of inertia.* If you haven't come across this term before, don't worry. *Unit 27* will give a full treatment of moments of inertia and will describe the role played by moments of inertia in the rotational dynamics of solid bodies. In this unit we shall give a definition of the moment of inertia but thereafter we shall be concerned only with the techniques of calculating moments of inertia as multiple integrals.

Section 4 shows how area integrals can be used to compute the area of a curved surface.

In Section 5 you will have the opportunity to compute area and volume integrals using the computer algebra package for the course.

1 Area integrals

In *Unit 24* you saw that a scalar line integral involves integrating with respect to just one variable along a path. We now turn to *area integrals* in which the function being integrated is defined over an area, rather than along a path, so that it is a function of two variables. We can use an area integral to calculate, for example, the mass of a thin plate when the composition of the plate is non-uniform. We can also use area integrals to calculate populations. The distribution of, say, bacteria on a microscope slide can be described by a *population density* function giving the number of individuals per square metre at each point. Then the total population on the slide is the area integral of the population density over the slide. We shall consider this and other applications of area integrals in Section 2. In this section we shall define area integrals (in Subsection 1.1) and see how to compute them using Cartesian coordinates (in Subsections 1.2 and 1.3).

This variable is usually the path parameter.

1.1 Defining area integrals

Materials such as plate glass are usually sold by the square metre. By ignoring the fact that the material is a three-dimensional solid and treating it instead as an infinitely thin sheet, or **lamina**, we can describe the 'weight' of such a material by a *surface mass density* or mass per unit area of the sheet. The surface mass density, or **surface density** for short, is a constant for a uniform sheet, but will vary with position when the material is of non-uniform composition. If we imagine the lamina placed in the (x, y)-plane then the surface density is a **surface density function** $f(x, y)$ defined on the region S of the (x, y)-plane occupied by the lamina.

Suppose we wish to find the mass of this lamina. We know that when $f(x, y)$ is a constant, the total mass of the lamina is simply the constant density (in $\text{kg}\,\text{m}^{-2}$) times the total area (in m^2) of the lamina. When the surface density varies we can divide the region S into N small **area elements** such that the density can be considered constant on each element (see Figure 1.1). Let the area of the ith element be δA_i and in this element select a point with coordinates (x_i, y_i). Then the mass of this element of the plate is approximately $f(x_i, y_i)\delta A_i$, and the total mass of the lamina is approximately the sum of the masses of all the elements

We assume we are carrying out a theoretical investigation rather than simply weighing the lamina to find its mass.

$$\sum_{i=1}^{N} f(x_i, y_i)\delta A_i.$$

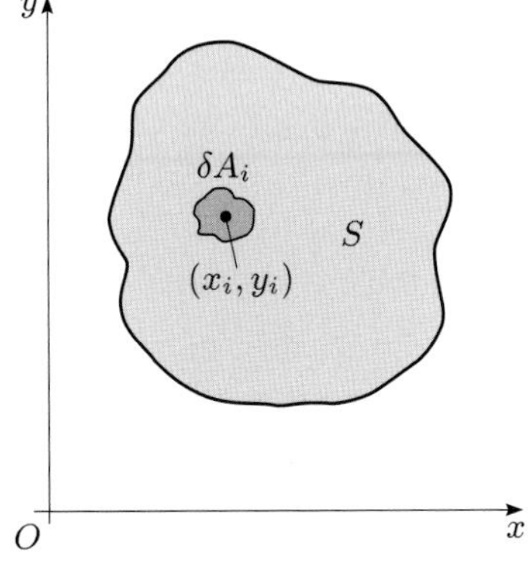

Figure 1.1

Now if we take the limit of this sum, as the number N of area elements increases indefinitely and the size of the elements tends to zero, we obtain an integral called an area integral which we denote by $\int_S f(x, y)dA$. This area integral gives the mass of the lamina.

We can define an area integral for any function of two variables over a region S in its domain.

> ***Definition***
>
> The **area integral** of $f(x, y)$ over a **region of integration** S in the (x, y)-plane, subdivided into N area elements where element i contains the point (x_i, y_i) and is of area δA_i, is
>
> $$\int_S f(x, y)dA = \lim_{N\to\infty} \sum_{i=1}^{N} f(x_i, y_i)\delta A_i, \qquad (1.1)$$
>
> where $\delta A_i \to 0$ for each i as $N \to \infty$.

We shall look at other applications of area integrals in Section 2. Next we consider how to evaluate area integrals, first over rectangular regions and then over non-rectangular regions. Since $f(x, y)$ is a function of two variables, we shall find that the evaluation of an area integral involves evaluating *two* definite integrals, one after the other.

Area integrals are sometimes referred to as *double integrals* or *surface integrals.*

1.2 Area integrals over rectangular regions

In this subsection we shall consider how to apply Equation (1.1) to evaluate an area integral and, in particular, how to subdivide the region of integration S in a convenient way when working with Cartesian coordinates.

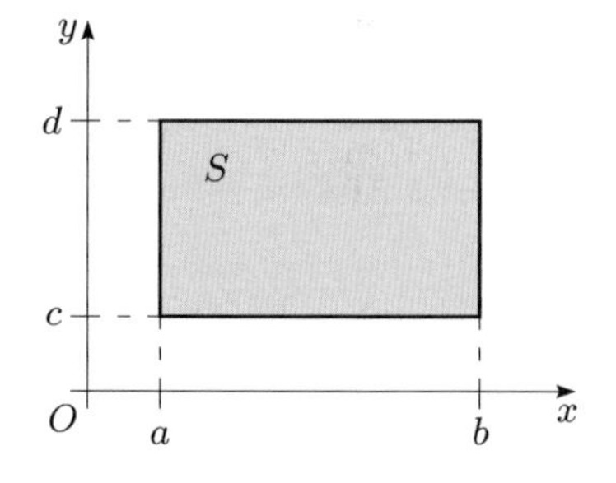

Figure 1.2

We begin by considering the case when the region S is the rectangle formed by the lines $x = a$, $x = b$ and $y = c$, $y = d$, as in Figure 1.2. The most natural way to evaluate the sum in Equation (1.1) is to divide the rectangle into small rectangular elements. We proceed as follows (see Figure 1.3).

(a) Divide the interval $[a, b]$ of the x-axis into n subintervals of width $\delta x_1, \delta x_2, \ldots, \delta x_j, \ldots, \delta x_n$ and choose numbers $x_1, x_2, \ldots, x_n$ such that x_j is in the jth subinterval;

(b) Divide the interval $[c, d]$ of the y-axis into m subintervals of width δy_1, $\delta y_2, \ldots$, $\delta y_k, \ldots, \delta y_m$ and choose numbers $y_1, y_2, \ldots, y_m$ such that y_k is in the kth subinterval;

(c) The area elements are the small rectangles so formed; the general element has side lengths δx_j and δy_k, area $\delta x_j \delta y_k$, and contains the point (x_j, y_k).

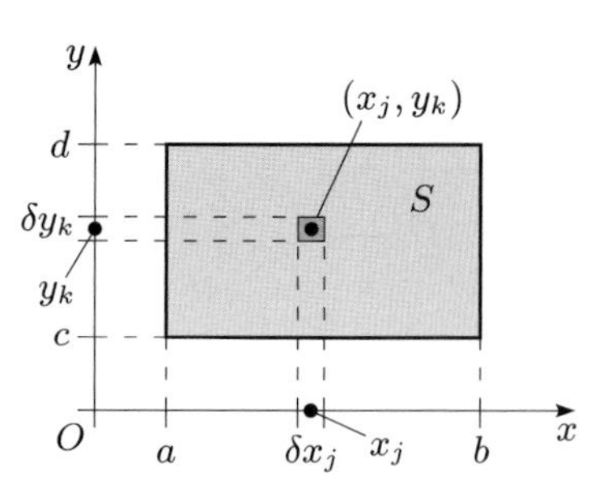

Figure 1.3

The rectangle S has been divided into $n \times m$ rectangular area elements each one identified by a point (x_j, y_k) and we need to find a systematic way of including all $N = n \times m$ of them in the summation. Let us organize the rectangular area elements into thin strips. There are two straightforward ways. One is to consider vertical strips of width $\delta x_1, \delta x_2, \ldots, \delta x_j, \ldots, \delta x_n$ (as in Figure 1.4) counting all the segments of length δy_k within each strip, or to use horizontal strips of width $\delta y_1, \delta y_2, \ldots, \delta y_k, \ldots, \delta y_m$ (as in Figure 1.5) counting all the segments of length δx_j in each.

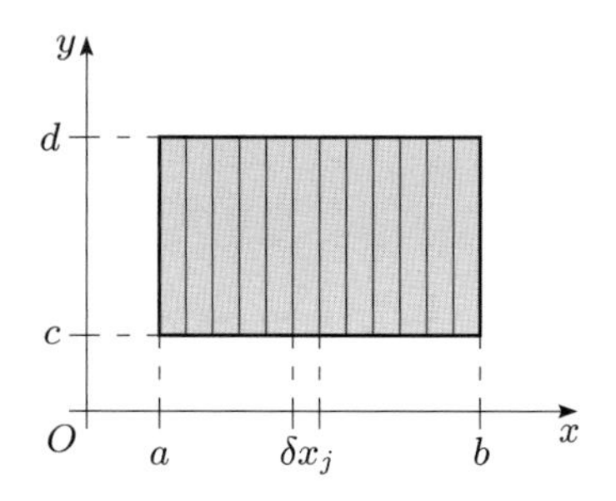

Figure 1.4

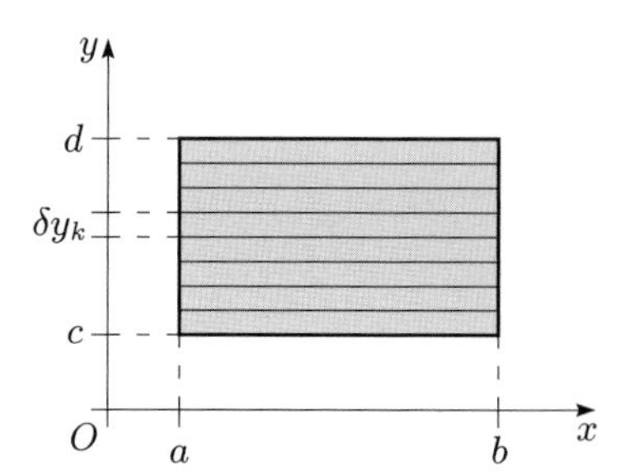

Figure 1.5

We choose vertical strips. The jth vertical strip (of width δx_j) is shown shaded in Figure 1.6. So a typical element with subscript i in Equation (1.1) is included by virtue of its position y_k in the strip and the label x_j for the strip. Thus a typical term in the sum in Equation (1.1) is $f(x_j, y_k)\delta x_j \delta y_k$. So the contribution to the sum from the m rectangular area elements in the jth vertical strip, of width δx_j is

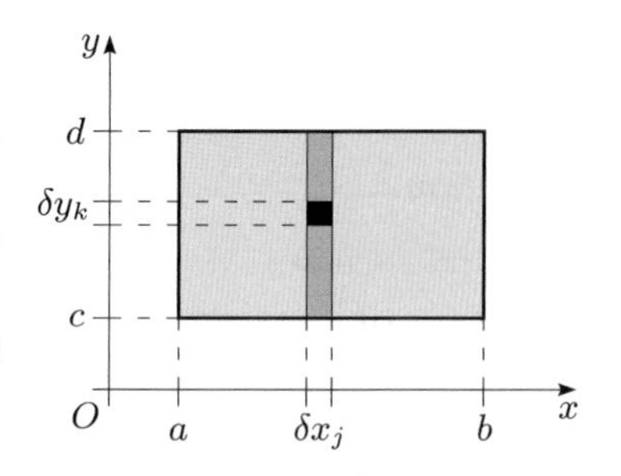

Figure 1.6

$$\left(\sum_{k=1}^{m} f(x_j, y_k)\delta y_k \right) \delta x_j.$$

In this summation x_j and δx_j remain unchanged and we are summing over the ys, i.e. over the subscript k. Now we need to add the contributions of the n vertical strips which lie between $x = a$ and $x = b$, so we are summing over the xs, i.e. over the subscript j. We then have an expression involving two summations

$$\sum_{j=1}^{n} \left(\sum_{k=1}^{m} f(x_j, y_k)\delta y_k \right) \delta x_j.$$

The summation over k is called the *inner summation* and the summation over j is the *outer summation.* The area integral of the function f over the region S is the limit of this double summation as the number of rectangles increases indefinitely, i.e. as n and m increase indefinitely. So

$$\int_S f(x,y)dA = \lim_{n\to\infty} \left(\sum_{j=1}^{n} \left(\lim_{m\to\infty} \sum_{k=1}^{m} f(x_j, y_k)\delta y_k \right) \delta x_j \right). \tag{1.2}$$

First let us look at the inner summation over k, remembering that x_j is constant here. In the limit as the lengths δy_k go to zero, this summation equals the definite integral of $f(x_j, y)$ between $y = c$ and $y = d$, i.e. between the bottom and top of the jth vertical strip. We write

$$\lim_{m\to\infty} \sum_{k=1}^{m} f(x_j, y_k)\delta y_k = \int_{y=c}^{y=d} f(x_j, y)\, dy. \tag{1.3}$$

Remember that x_j is a constant in the summation and is held constant when we evaluate the integral. So the value of the integral will depend on x_j but not on y: that is, the value of the integral is a function of x_j. We shall illustrate this with an example.

You can think of the integration over y as *partial integration* by analogy with partial differentiation. You are integrating with respect to one variable while keeping the other variable fixed.

Example 1.1

Find the value of the definite integral $\displaystyle\int_{y=1}^{y=2} x_j y\, dy$ where x_j is a constant.

Solution

The function to be integrated is $f(x_j, y) = x_j y$. In the integration we are varying y (between the limits 1 and 2) but keeping x_j fixed. Then

$$\int_{y=1}^{y=2} x_j y\, dy = x_j \int_{y=1}^{y=2} y\, dy = x_j \left[\tfrac{1}{2}y^2\right]_{y=1}^{y=2} = \tfrac{3}{2}x_j. \quad \blacksquare$$

Suppose that we denote the value of the integral $\int_{y=c}^{y=d} f(x_j, y)\, dy$ in Equation (1.3) by $g(x_j)$. Equation (1.2) then becomes

$$\int_S f(x,y)dA = \lim_{n\to\infty} \sum_{j=1}^{n} g(x_j)\delta x_j.$$

In this summation we are adding vertical strips between $x = a$ and $x = b$ (see Figure 1.7) and in the limit the summation approaches the definite integral of $g(x)$ between the limits $x = a$ and $x = b$,

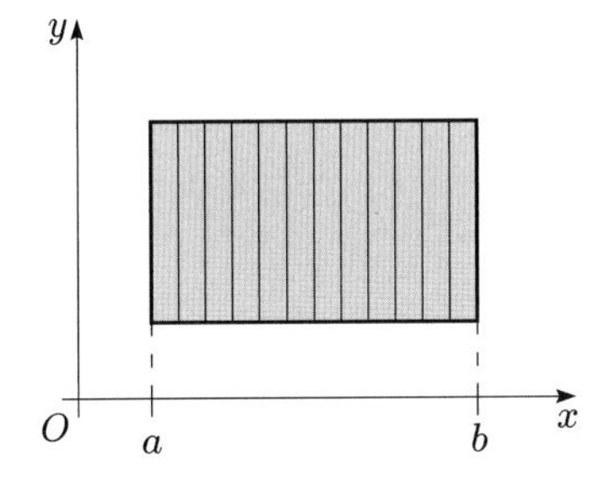

Figure 1.7

$$\int_{x=a}^{x=b} g(x)\, dx = \lim_{n\to\infty} \sum_{j=1}^{n} g(x_j)\delta x_j.$$

In the limit of the double summation, as δx_j and δy_k go to zero in Equation (1.2), the value of the area integral, in terms of two single integrals, the first over y and the second over x, is

$$\int_S f(x,y)dA = \int_{x=a}^{x=b} g(x)\, dx \quad \text{where } g(x) = \int_{y=c}^{y=d} f(x,y)\, dy. \tag{1.4}$$

The two integrals in Equation (1.4) can be evaluated using standard techniques.

Area integral over a rectangular region

The area integral of a function $f(x,y)$ over a rectangular region S contained between the lines $x=a$, $x=b$ and $y=c$, $y=d$ is obtained as two successive integrals as follows:

$$\int_S f(x,y)dA = \int_{x=a}^{x=b}\left(\int_{y=c}^{y=d} f(x,y)\,dy\right)dx.$$

Remember that in the integral over y we treat x as a constant.

Example 1.2

Find the value of the area integral of the function $f(x,y)=xy$ over the rectangle bounded by the lines $x=0$, $x=3$ and $y=1$, $y=2$.

Solution

The region of integration is shown in Figure 1.8. The area integral is

$$\int_S xy\,dA = \int_{x=0}^{x=3}\left(\int_{y=1}^{y=2} xy\,dy\right)dx.$$

The integral over y was evaluated in Example 1.1, so

$$\int_S xy\,dA = \int_{x=0}^{x=3}\left(\int_{y=1}^{y=2} xy\,dy\right)dx = \int_{x=0}^{x=3} \tfrac{3}{2}x\,dx = \left[\tfrac{3}{4}x^2\right]_0^3 = \tfrac{27}{4}.$$

The value of the area integral of xy over the rectangle is $\frac{27}{4}$. ■

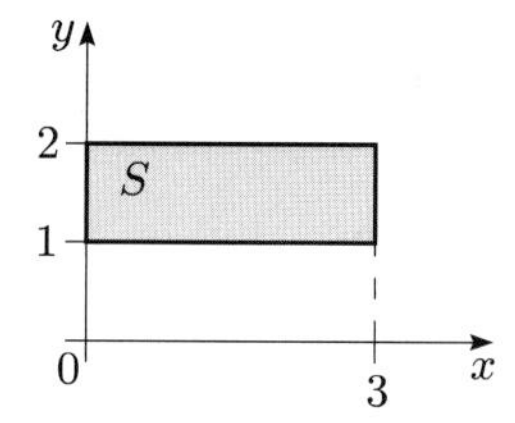

Figure 1.8

***Exercise 1.1**

Find the value of the area integral of the function $f(x,y)=x^2y^3$ over the square bounded by the lines $x=0$, $x=2$ and $y=1$, $y=3$.

So far we have evaluated area integrals by first integrating over y and then integrating over x. In the summations this is equivalent to summing first over k and then over j. However, we could have used another order for the summations, by first drawing a strip parallel to the x-axis of width δy_k containing y_k and summing over the rectangles of width δx_j for all the js from 1 to n (see Figure 1.9). The result would be

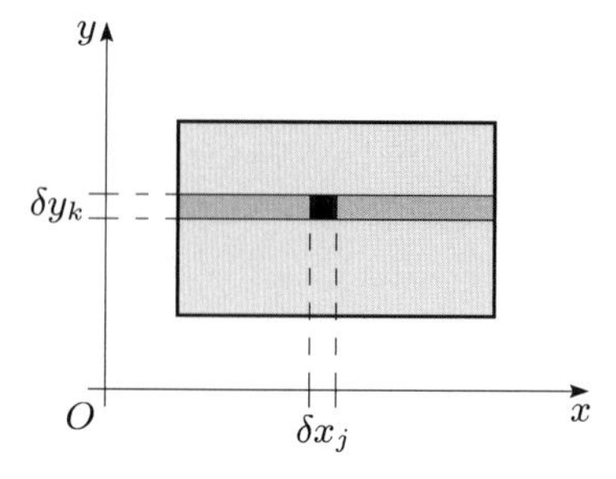

Figure 1.9

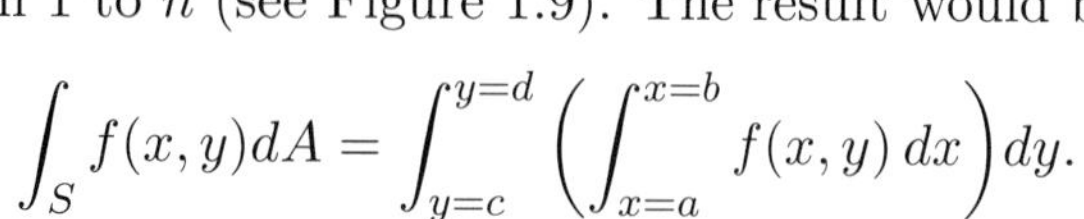

$$\int_S f(x,y)dA = \int_{y=c}^{y=d}\left(\int_{x=a}^{x=b} f(x,y)\,dx\right)dy.$$

This time in the inner integral we integrate over x, treating y as a constant, to give a function of y, and then we integrate over y, to complete the evaluation of the integral.

Exercise 1.2

Find the value of the area integral in Example 1.2 but integrate over x first and then over y.

The value of the area integral in Exercise 1.2 is the same as in Example 1.2 which you may have expected since the function and the region of integration are the same. Either order of evaluating the single integrals will give the same answer.

1.3 Area integrals over non-rectangular regions

The area integral of a function over a rectangular region involves two single integrals for which the limits of integration are constants. For non-rectangular regions we have to be more careful in setting up the integrals because the strips are no longer of the same length and the limits on the inner integral depend on the variable in the outer integral. To illustrate this consider the following example.

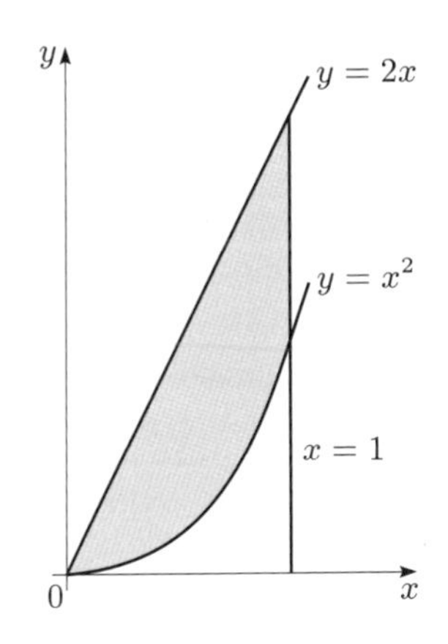

Figure 1.10

Example 1.3

Find the value of the area integral of the function $f(x, y) = xy$ over the region bounded by the curves $y = 2x$, $y = x^2$ and the line $x = 1$.

Solution

We begin by drawing a diagram to show the region of integration. It is the shaded region in Figure 1.10. We choose to integrate first over y and then over x.

To decide on the limits of the integration over y, consider a vertical strip drawn at an arbitrary value of x, as shown in Figure 1.11. The ends of the strip lie on the curves $y = x^2$ and $y = 2x$. Hence the lower and upper limits for the y-integration are (the functions) $y = x^2$ and $y = 2x$ respectively. The y-integration sums all area elements in the strip of Figure 1.12.

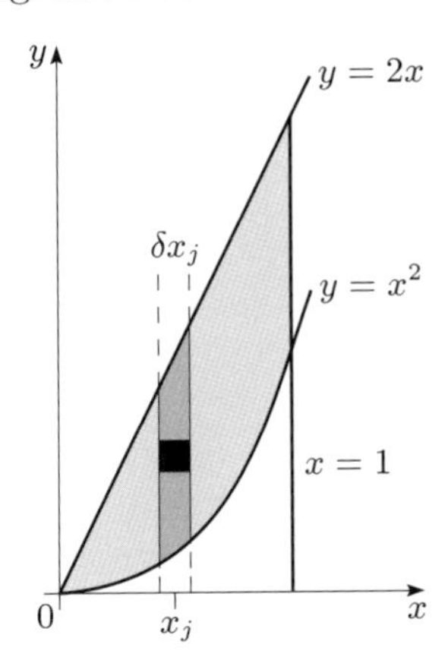

Figure 1.11

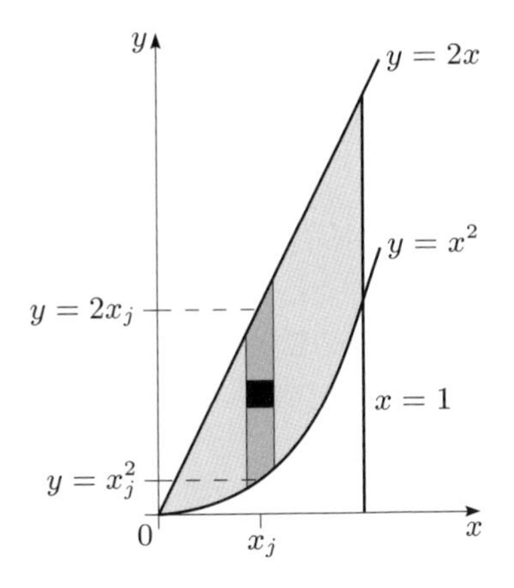

Figure 1.12

The x-integration sums over all the strips (see Figure 1.13). The first strip is at $x = 0$ and the last strip is at $x = 1$. Hence the lower and upper limits for the x-integration are $x = 0$ and $x = 1$ respectively, and in the limit Equation (1.2) becomes

$$\int_S xy\,dA = \int_{x=0}^{x=1} \left(\int_{y=x^2}^{y=2x} xy\,dy \right) dx. \qquad (1.5)$$

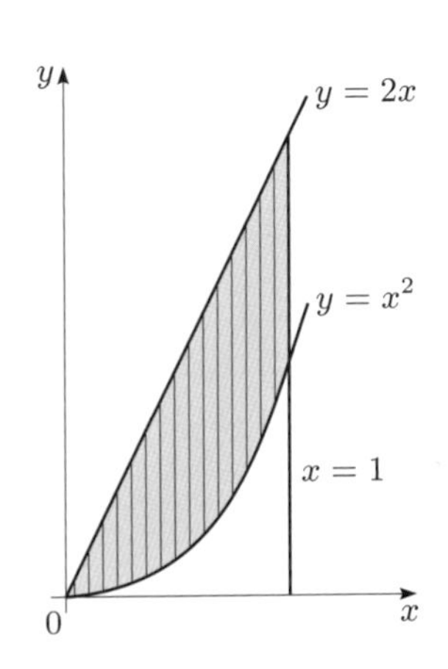

Figure 1.13

The inner integral, in the brackets, is an integral with respect to y and can be evaluated by treating x as a constant, to give

$$\int_{y=x^2}^{y=2x} xy\,dy = x\left[\tfrac{1}{2}y^2\right]_{y=x^2}^{y=2x} = x\left(\tfrac{1}{2}(2x)^2 - \tfrac{1}{2}(x^2)^2\right) = 2x^3 - \tfrac{1}{2}x^5.$$

Notice that the result of evaluating this integral is a function of x so the area integral in Equation (1.5) is reduced to a single integral over x, and

$$\int_S xy\,dA = \int_{x=0}^{x=1} \left(2x^3 - \tfrac{1}{2}x^5\right) dx = \left[\tfrac{2}{4}x^4 - \tfrac{1}{12}x^6\right]_0^1 = \tfrac{5}{12}. \quad \blacksquare$$

In Example 1.3 the limits on the integral over y depend on the variable x. Drawing a diagram of the region of integration is very helpful in getting the limits correct and the method of solution given works for all area integrals. We shall now generalize the procedure for evaluating area integrals.

Consider a non-rectangular region S like the ones shown in Figure 1.14. Suppose that a and b are the minimum and maximum values of x for the points on the boundary of S. Let $y = \alpha(x)$ and $y = \beta(x)$ be the equations of the boundary curves AB and CD respectively, as shown in Figure 1.14. Then

The minimum and maximum values can be straight lines, as shown in Figure 1.14(a) or points. One such point is shown in Figure 1.14(b).

$$\int_S f(x,y)\,dA = \int_{x=a}^{x=b} \left(\int_{y=\alpha(x)}^{y=\beta(x)} f(x,y)\,dy \right) dx.$$

The area integral can be written as two single definite integrals but we must be careful with the limits. The limits on the inner integral are functions of x rather than constants.

We can summarize the steps for evaluating an area integral $\int_S f(x,y)\,dA$, using vertical strips, as follows.

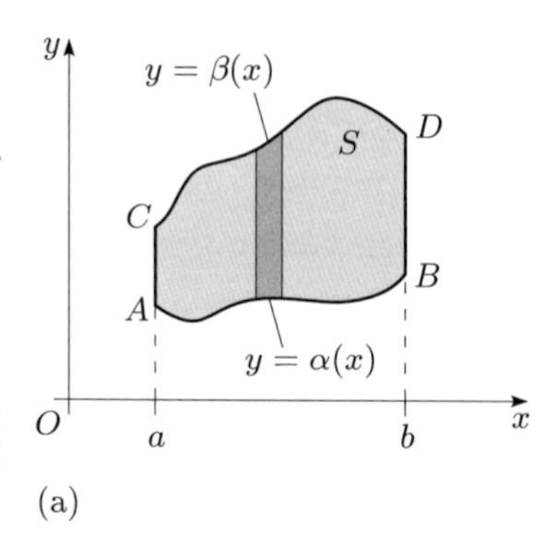

(a)

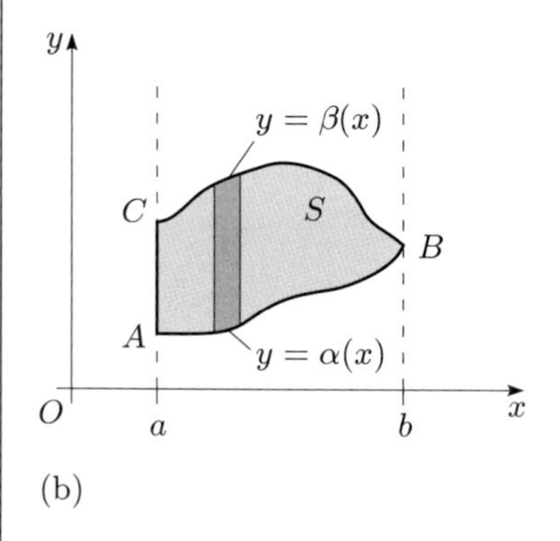

(b)

Figure 1.14

Procedure 1.1 Evaluating an area integral

To evaluate an area integral

$$\int_S f(x,y)\,dA,$$

proceed as follows.

(a) Draw a diagram showing the region of integration, S.

(b) Draw on the diagram a strip parallel to the y-axis and show the lower limit $y = \alpha(x)$ and the upper limit $y = \beta(x)$ of this strip. These are the limits of the y-integration, i.e. for the 'inner' integral.

(c) Determine the minimum value a and maximum value b of x for points on the boundary of S. These are the limits of the x-integration, i.e. for the 'outer' integral.

(d) Write the area integral as two single integrals, making sure that the outer limits are constants. The integral becomes

$$\int_S f(x,y)\,dA = \int_{x=a}^{x=b} \left(\int_{y=\alpha(x)}^{y=\beta(x)} f(x,y)\,dy \right) dx.$$

(e) Evaluate the inner integral, holding x constant, to give

$$g(x) = \int_{y=\alpha(x)}^{y=\beta(x)} f(x,y)\,dy.$$

(f) Evaluate the outer integral to give

$$\int_S f(x,y)\,dA = \int_{x=a}^{x=b} g(x)\,dx.$$

Exercise 1.3

Use Procedure 1.1 to find the value of the area integral of the function $f(x,y) = y$ over the region bounded by the curves $y = x^2$ and $y = x + 2$.

Exercise 1.4

Find the value of the area integral of the function $f(x,y) = x - y$ over the triangle bounded by the lines $y = x - 1$, $x = 3$ and $y = 0$.

So far we have chosen to organize the area elements into vertical strips and integrate over y first and then x. We can reverse the order of integration, carrying out the x-integration first and then the y-integration by imagining the area divided into horizontal strips. The following example illustrates how this is done.

Procedure 1.1 is easily adapted for this reversed order of integration by interchanging x and y.

Example 1.4

Find the value of the area integral of the function xy^2 over the region bounded by the curve $y = x^2$ and the line $y = x$.

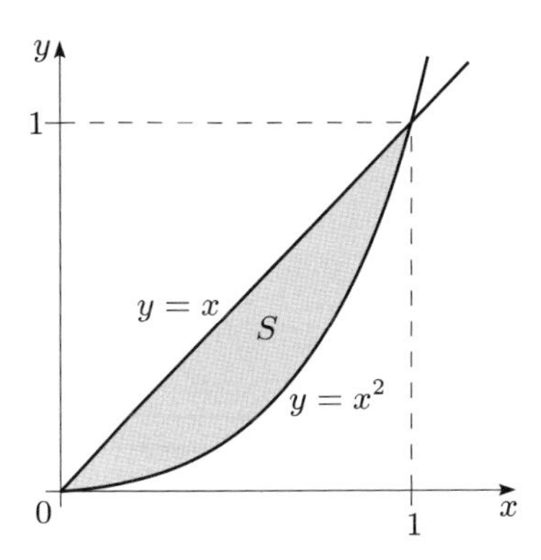

Figure 1.15

Solution

The region of integration is shown in Figure 1.15, and one horizontal strip is shown in Figure 1.16. The x-integral effectively sums area elements along each horizontal strip. To decide on the limits for the x-integral, look at the left-hand and right-hand endpoints of the strip. These endpoints lie on the graphs of $x = y$ and $x = \sqrt{y}$, and so the lower and upper limits of the x-integral are the functions $x = y$ and $x = \sqrt{y}$ respectively. Hence the area integral is

$$\int_S f(x,y)\,dA = \int_{y=0}^{y=1} \left(\int_{x=y}^{x=\sqrt{y}} xy^2\,dx \right) dy.$$

The limits for y are the values where the graphs intersect, where $y = x = x^2$, i.e. where $x^2 - x = 0$. These points of intersection are therefore (0, 0) and (1, 1) as can be seen in Figure 1.15.

The x-integral can be evaluated, treating y as a constant, to give

$$\int_{x=y}^{x=\sqrt{y}} xy^2 dx = y^2 \left[\tfrac{1}{2}x^2\right]_{x=y}^{x=\sqrt{y}} = \tfrac{1}{2}\left(y^3 - y^4\right),$$

and so evaluation of the area integral is reduced to a single integral in y giving

$$\int_S f(x,y)\,dA = \int_{y=0}^{y=1} \tfrac{1}{2}\left(y^3 - y^4\right)dy = \tfrac{1}{40}. \quad ■$$

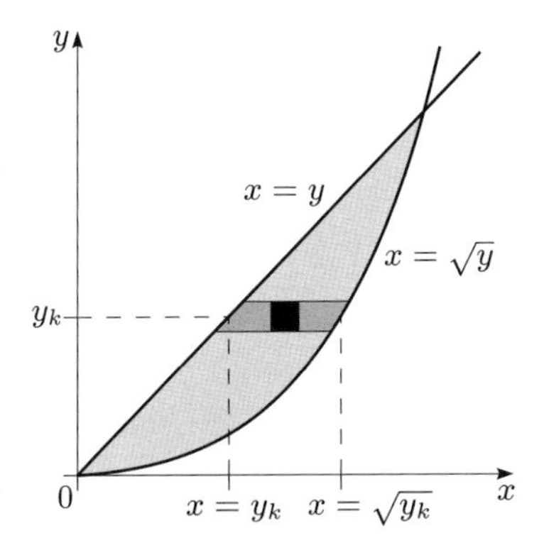

Figure 1.16

*Exercise 1.5

Evaluate $\int_S (x^2 + y^2)dA$ where S is the triangle formed by the lines $y = 0$, $y = x - 1$ and $x = 2$, by:

(a) integrating over y first and then over x;

(b) integrating over x first and then over y.

Either order of integration is acceptable although the calculations are often easier for one particular order. It is important to be careful with the limits on the two single integrals. The limits on the outer integral are constants whereas the limits on the inner integral will, in general, be non-constant functions. Only for rectangular regions of integration will all four limits be constants.

End-of-section Exercises

*Exercise 1.6

Find the value of the area integral of the function $f(x,y) = x + y$ over the triangle bounded by the lines $y = 1 - x$, $x = 0$ and $y = 0$.

Exercise 1.7

Find the value of the area integral of the function $f(x,y) = x$ over the quarter disc $x^2 + y^2 \leq 1$ $(x \geqslant 0, y \geqslant 0)$.

Exercise 1.8

Determine the region of integration for, and evaluate, $\displaystyle\int_{x=1}^{x=2} \left(\int_{y=x^2}^{y=x+2} 1dy \right) dx.$

---

2 Applications of area integrals

In Section 1 we have been concerned with the mathematical problem of evaluating area integrals. In this section we consider applications of area integrals to a variety of problems involving surface density functions, beginning in Subsection 2.1. Some of the applications involve integrating over a circular region of the (x, y)-plane and in such cases it is usually easier to evaluate these area integrals using plane polar coordinates, as we shall demonstrate in Subsection 2.2. In Subsection 2.3 we shall see how area integrals can be used to obtain centres of mass of laminae. We shall also, in Subsection 2.4, introduce the idea of the *moment of inertia* of a body, a subject of great importance for *Unit 27*, and show how the moments of inertia of laminae can be calculated as area integrals.

Surface density functions were mentioned at the beginning of Section 1.

2.1 Integrating surface density functions

Surface density functions can describe surface distributions of mass, populations and many other scalar quantities. The area integral of a surface density function then gives the total mass, population or whatever of the surface.

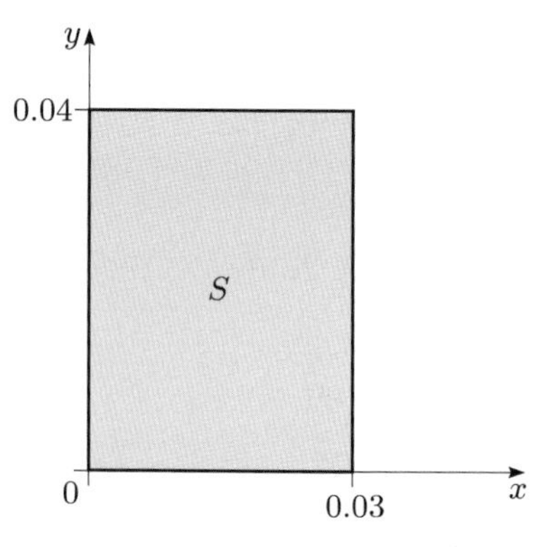

Figure 2.1

Example 2.1

A population of bacteria is grown on a rectangular glass plate. The plate is placed in the (x, y)-plane with its edges on the lines $y = 0$, $y = 0.04\,\text{m}$ and $x = 0$, $x = 0.03\,\text{m}$ (see Figure 2.1). Determine the total number P of bacteria on the plate given that the distribution of the population (in bacteria per square metre) is described by the surface density function $f(x, y) = (1 - 1000x^2) \times 10^{11}$.

Solution

We integrate the surface density function over the rectangular region occupied by the plate, choosing, arbitrarily, to integrate over x first. Thus

$$P = \int_{\text{plate}} f\,dA = 10^{11} \int_{y=0}^{y=0.04} \left(\int_{x=0}^{x=0.03} (1 - 1000x^2)\,dx \right) dy$$

$$= 10^{11} \int_{y=0}^{y=0.04} \left[x - \tfrac{1000}{3}x^3\right]_{x=0}^{x=0.03} dy$$

$$= 10^{11} \int_0^{0.04} 0.021\,dy = 8.4 \times 10^7. \quad \blacksquare$$

Exercise 2.1

The density of bacteria on the surface of a glass plate in the (x, y)-plane is given by $f(x, y) = A(2 - x^2/a^2 - y^2/a^2)$ where A and a are positive constants. How many bacteria are there on a triangular region of the plate bounded by the x- and y-axes and the line $y = a - x$, when $A = 10^{12}\,\text{m}^{-2}$ and $a = 0.01\,\text{m}$?

In this exercise the constants are represented by symbols which can be used throughout the calculation. You are advised to do this, only putting in the numbers at the end in order to answer the question. The symbolic answer gives a more general result, which could be used with other values of the constants.

Suppose in Exercise 2.1 we want to know the number of bacteria within a circle of radius a centred on the origin. The circular region is shown in Figure 2.2 (overleaf). Let's choose to integrate with respect to y first. The lower and upper ends of a vertical strip lie on the lower and upper semicircles

$$y = -\sqrt{a^2 - x^2} \quad \text{and} \quad y = \sqrt{a^2 - x^2}.$$

These functions are the limits of the y-integration. The x-integral represents the addition of vertical strips starting at $x = -a$ and ending at $x = a$. Hence the total number of bacteria within the circle (over the disc) is

$$\int_{\text{disc}} f\,dA = A\int_{x=-a}^{x=a}\left(\int_{y=-\sqrt{a^2-x^2}}^{y=\sqrt{a^2-x^2}}\left(2-\frac{x^2}{a^2}-\frac{y^2}{a^2}\right)dy\right)dx. \qquad (2.1)$$

Evaluating the integral in Equation (2.1) is not particularly difficult, but it is more difficult than it need be. You will see in the next subsection that this double integral, and many other area integrals over circular regions, become much easier when we use plane polar coordinates.

Figure 2.2

2.2 Changing to plane polar coordinates

In order to see how to set up an area integral in plane polar coordinates, recall first how a rectangular region was divided up in Cartesian coordinates by a rectangular grid of lines, $x =$ constant and $y =$ constant. A small rectangular element, the **Cartesian area element**, has area $\delta A = \delta y \delta x$. This element is represented symbolically as $dy\,dx$ in the area integral

$$\int_a^b\left(\int_c^d f(x,y)\,dy\right)dx.$$

Now consider the case of plane polar coordinates r and θ. Figure 2.3 shows the subdivision of a circular region (disc) by a grid of circles $r =$ constant and 'spokes' $\theta =$ constant. Each *area element* is nearly a rectangle of area $\delta A \simeq r\delta\theta \times \delta r$ and this approximation improves as δr and $\delta\theta$ tend to zero. The value of a function f at a point of this element is $f(r,\theta)$, and so the contribution of this area element to the area integral is approximately $f(r,\theta)r\delta r\,\delta\theta$. Summing over all area elements and taking the limit in Equation (1.1) we have the following definition.

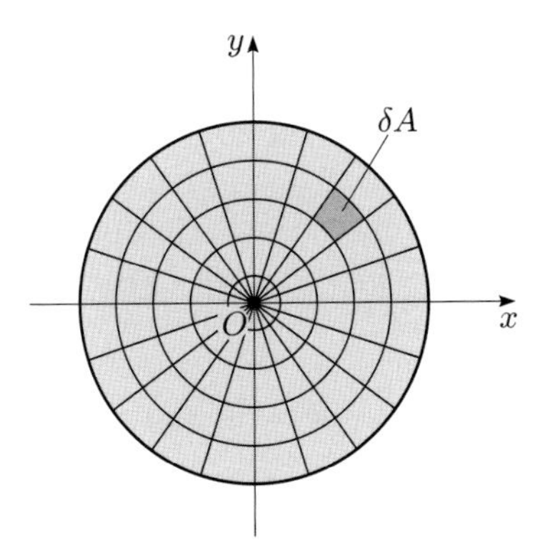

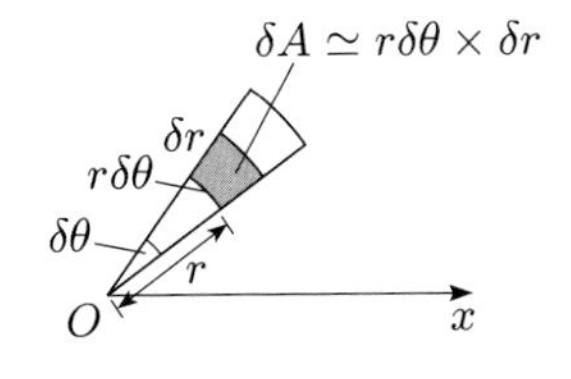

Figure 2.3

Area integral in plane polar coordinates

The area integral of a function $f(r,\theta)$ over a disc D of radius a is

$$\int_D f\,dA = \int_{\theta=-\pi}^{\theta=\pi}\left(\int_{r=0}^{r=a} f(r,\theta)r\,dr\right)d\theta. \qquad (2.2)$$

The factor r comes from the approximation $r\delta r\,\delta\theta$ of the area of the area element. It's very easy to forget this factor!

We can choose to integrate with respect to r first and then θ as in Equation (2.2), or we can reverse the order of integration, as is convenient. Because the limits are constants, they will not change when the order of integration is reversed.

Example 2.2

Evaluate the number of bacteria on the circular region of the (x,y)-plane of radius a centred at the origin when the surface density of bacteria is given by $f(x,y) = A(2 - x^2/a^2 - y^2/a^2)$. What is the number P of bacteria in the circle when $A = 10^{12}\,\text{m}^{-2}$ and $a = 0.01\,\text{m}$?

Solution

We first express the surface density function in plane polar coordinates. Thus, recognizing $x^2 + y^2 = r^2$, we have $f(r,\theta) = A(2 - r^2/a^2)$. The region of integration is a disc of radius a centred on the origin. Using Equation (2.2), we can express the number of bacteria as

$$P = A\int_{\theta=-\pi}^{\theta=\pi}\left(\int_{r=0}^{r=a}\left(2-\frac{r^2}{a^2}\right)r\,dr\right)d\theta. \qquad (2.3)$$

The inner integral, the integral with respect to r with θ constant, represents summing elements of length δr along the narrow sector shown in Figure 2.3. The θ-integral then represents the summing of all sectors of the circle.

The r-integral gives

$$\int_{r=0}^{r=a} \left(2 - \frac{r^2}{a^2}\right) r\,dr = \left[r^2 - \frac{r^4}{4a^2}\right]_0^a = \tfrac{3}{4}a^2.$$

The area integral in Equation (2.3) is now reduced to a single integral so

$$P = \tfrac{3}{4}Aa^2 \int_{-\pi}^{\pi} d\theta = \tfrac{3}{4}Aa^2[\theta]_{-\pi}^{\pi} = \tfrac{3}{2}\pi Aa^2.$$

For the given values of A and a, the total number P of bacteria in the circular region is 4.7×10^8. ■

There are two points to notice about Example 2.2. First, the area integral has constant limits and is very easy to evaluate compared with the Cartesian equivalent, Equation (2.1). Secondly, the function $f(r, \theta)$ has circular symmetry. It is independent of the angular coordinate θ and depends on r only and consequently the integration over θ in the area integral yields the factor

$$\int_{-\pi}^{\pi} d\theta = [\theta]_{-\pi}^{\pi} = 2\pi.$$

Thus for any function $f(r, \theta)$ that varies with r only, the area integral over a disc D of radius a centred on the origin is

$$\int_D f\,dA = 2\pi \int_0^a f(r) r\,dr \qquad (2.4)$$

in which we have written $f(r)$ for $f(r, \theta)$ since f depends on r only.

Exercise 2.2

A thin circular magnifying glass of radius a can be modelled as a thin disc with a surface mass density given by $f(r, \theta) = k(1 - r^2/a^2)$, where the constant k is the surface density at the centre. Determine the total mass of the lens when $a = 2.5 \times 10^{-2}$ m and $k = 3\,\text{kg}\,\text{m}^{-2}$.

2.3 Centres of mass

We now turn to the calculation of centres of mass using area integrals. How can we find the centre of mass of a lamina such as a semicircular plate which is bounded by curved lines? We need to return to the definition of centre of mass. The position vector $\mathbf{r}_G$ of the centre of mass of a system of N particles each with mass m_i and position vector $\mathbf{r}_i$ is

You saw in *Unit 19* how the centre of mass of a uniform lamina made up of squares, rectangles and triangles can be found by exploiting the geometries of these figures, especially any symmetries.

You met this definition in *Unit 19*.

$$\mathbf{r}_G = \frac{\sum_{i=1}^{N} m_i \mathbf{r}_i}{M}, \qquad (2.5)$$

where M is the total mass. If the particles lie in the (x, y)-plane we can project Equation (2.5) onto the unit vectors $\mathbf{i}$ and $\mathbf{j}$ to obtain the coordinates of the centre of mass

$$\mathbf{r}_G \cdot \mathbf{i} = x_G = \frac{\sum_{i=1}^{N} m_i x_i}{M} \quad \text{and} \quad \mathbf{r}_G \cdot \mathbf{j} = y_G = \frac{\sum_{i=1}^{N} m_i y_i}{M}. \qquad (2.6)$$

Now expressions (2.6) are for the centre of mass of a system of N discrete particles lying in the (x, y)-plane. Suppose the number of particles N increases indefinitely. Then, in the limit, the particles will coalesce to form a lamina and the summations in (2.6) will become integrals and give the centre of mass of the lamina.

Let's look at the expression for x_G in detail. First, consider the denominator. This is the total mass of the lamina and can be considered as either the limit of the sum of N particles each of mass m_i or as the limit of the sum of area elements $\delta x_j \delta y_k$ each of surface density $f(x_j, y_k)$. So

$$M = \lim_{N\to\infty} \sum_{i=1}^{N} m_i = \lim_{n\to\infty} \left(\sum_{j=1}^{n} \left(\lim_{m\to\infty} \sum_{k=1}^{m} f(x_j, y_k)\delta y_k \right) \delta x_j \right) = \int_S f(x, y)\, dA,$$

where S is the region of the (x, y)-plane occupied by the lamina. In a similar way, the numerator can be considered as the limit as $N \to \infty$ for the particle model and as both $m \to \infty$ and $n \to \infty$ for the area element model. So we have

$$\lim_{N\to\infty} \sum_{i=1}^{N} m_i x_i = \lim_{n\to\infty} \left(\sum_{j=1}^{n} \left(\lim_{m\to\infty} \sum_{k=1}^{m} f(x_j, y_k)\delta y_k \right) x_j \delta x_j \right) = \int_S x f(x, y)\, dA.$$

Thus the coordinates (x_G, y_G) of the **centre of mass of a lamina** are

$$x_G = \frac{\int_S x f\, dA}{M} = \frac{\int_S x f\, dA}{\int_S f\, dA} \quad \text{and} \quad y_G = \frac{\int_S y f\, dA}{M} = \frac{\int_S y f\, dA}{\int_S f\, dA}.$$

For a uniform lamina, the surface density f is a constant and can be taken outside the integral.

Example 2.3

Determine the position of the centre of mass of the uniform semicircular plate in Figure 2.4.

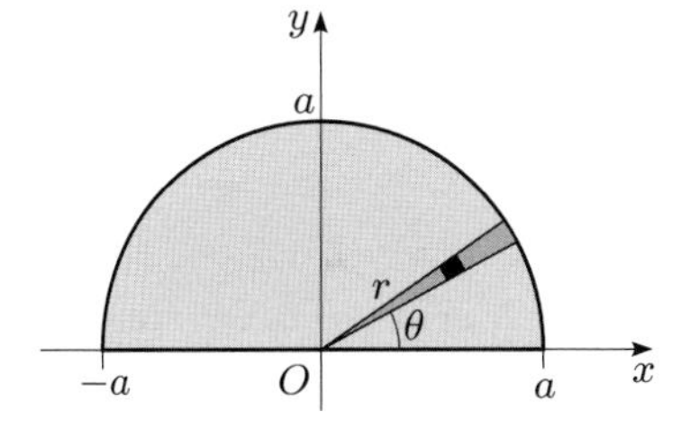

Figure 2.4

Solution

The y-axis is a symmetry axis of the semicircle and so we must have $x_G = 0$. To find the y-coordinate we must evaluate $\int_S y f\, dA$. We can use plane polar coordinates with $y = r\sin\theta$ and surface density $f =$ constant. Then the area integral is

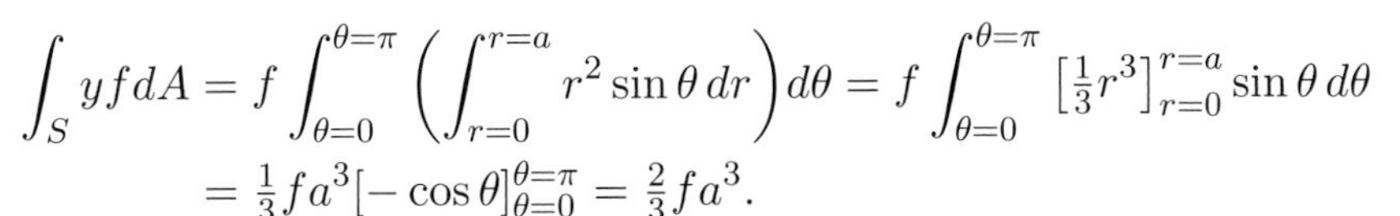

$$\int_S y f\, dA = f \int_{\theta=0}^{\theta=\pi} \left(\int_{r=0}^{r=a} r^2 \sin\theta\, dr \right) d\theta = f \int_{\theta=0}^{\theta=\pi} \left[\tfrac{1}{3} r^3\right]_{r=0}^{r=a} \sin\theta\, d\theta$$
$$= \tfrac{1}{3} f a^3 [-\cos\theta]_{\theta=0}^{\theta=\pi} = \tfrac{2}{3} f a^3.$$

Remember $\delta A = r\delta r\, \delta\theta$.

The mass M of the semicircle is $\frac{1}{2}\pi a^2 f$, and so we have $y_G = \frac{4a}{3\pi}$. Hence the centre of mass of the semicircular plate is $\mathbf{r} = \frac{4a}{3\pi}\mathbf{j}$. ■

The mass is the area $\frac{1}{2}\pi a^2$ times the (constant) surface density f.

Exercise 2.3

Confirm the answer for the coordinate y_G in Example 2.3 by working in Cartesian coordinates (see Figure 2.5).

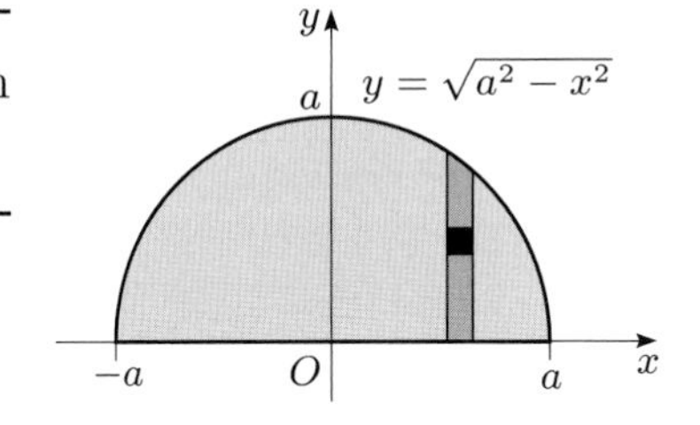

Figure 2.5

2.4 Moments of inertia

We now turn to an important application of area integrals, the calculation of *moments of inertia* for laminae. The central role played by moments of inertia in the dynamics of rotating bodies is fully described in *Unit 27*. Here, and in the next section, we are concerned only with calculations of moments of inertia using multiple integrals, and so we give only a minimal introduction to the topic.

Figure 2.6 shows a particle of mass m moving in a plane with constant speed v along a circular path of radius d centred on a point O. If O is the origin of the (x, y)-plane, then such a motion can be thought of as rotation about the z-axis. You know that the kinetic energy of the particle is $\frac{1}{2}mv^2$. We can write this as $\frac{1}{2}m\omega^2 d^2$, where $\omega = v/d$ is the *angular speed* of the particle.

Angular speed was discussed in *Unit 20*.

> ***Definition***
>
> The quantity $I = md^2$, the product of a particle's mass m and the square of its distance d from a fixed axis is called the **moment of inertia of the particle about the axis.**

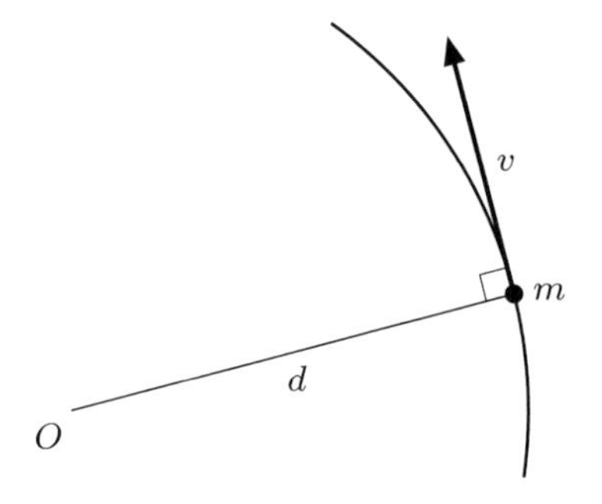

Figure 2.6

The kinetic energy of the particle is $\frac{1}{2}mv^2 = \frac{1}{2}I\omega^2$. Comparing this with the more familiar $\frac{1}{2}mv^2$, you can see that when the motion of the particle is described by an angular speed ω rather than a speed v, then I replaces m as the parameter describing the inertia of the particle.

Consider now an N-particle system rotating about an axis. Each particle rotates in a circle of radius given by its distance from the axis (see Figure 2.7). The ith particle of the system has moment of inertia $m_i d_i^2$, where m_i is the mass of the particle and d_i is its distance from the axis. So the moment of inertia of the N-particle system about the axis is

$$I = \sum_{i=1}^{N} m_i d_i^2. \tag{2.7}$$

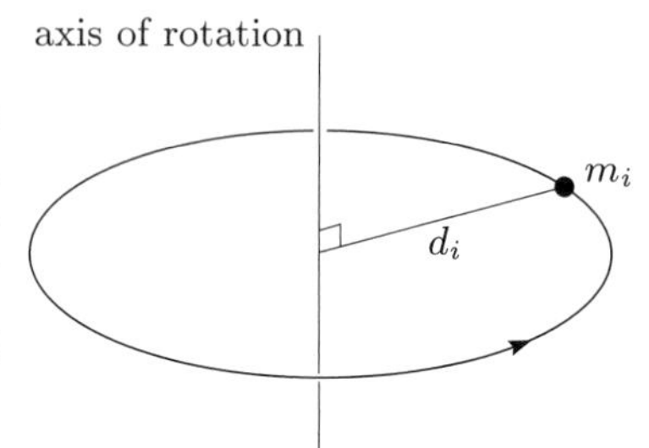

Figure 2.7

In *Unit 27* we shall be interested in the motion of rigid bodies that can rotate about fixed axes and we shall need to consider, for each rigid body, its moment of inertia. We can define the *moment of inertia* of a rigid body about an axis to be the limit of the sum of the moments of inertia of its N constituent particles when $N \to \infty$. Thus, using Equation (2.7), the moment of inertia I of the rigid body about the fixed axis is

$$I = \lim_{N\to\infty} \sum_{i=1}^{N} m_i d_i^2. \tag{2.8}$$

If the rigid body is a lamina in the (x, y)-plane which can rotate about the z-axis, see Figure 2.8, then any variation of composition can be described by a surface density function $f(x, y)$. We subdivide the lamina into a large number N of small area elements δA_i, modelled as particles. Each element has a mass $\delta m_i = f_i \delta A_i$, where f_i is the surface density at a point in the area element δA_i. The moment of inertia of this element about the z-axis is $\delta m_i d_i^2 = f_i \delta A_i d_i^2$, where d_i is the distance of the element from the origin. The moment of inertia I of the whole lamina about the z-axis is, from Equation (2.8), $\lim\limits_{N\to\infty} \sum_{i=1}^{N} f_i \delta A_i d_i^2$, the area integral of fd^2, where $d(x, y)$ is a function giving the distance of the point (x, y) from the axis of rotation. Thus if a lamina occupies a region S of the (x, y)-plane and has surface density function f, then its moment of inertia about the z-axis is given as follows.

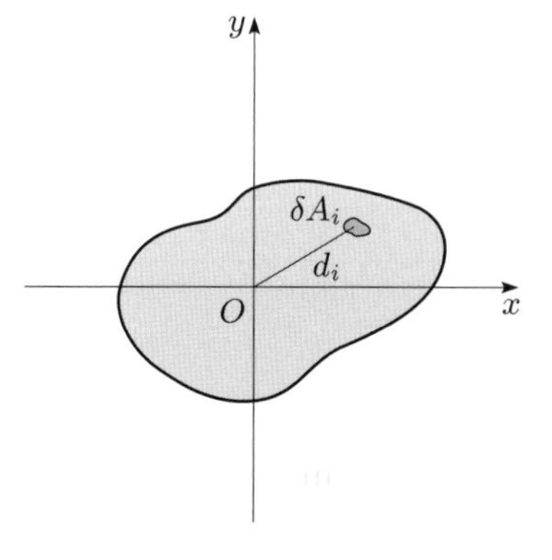

Figure 2.8

Moment of inertia of a lamina

The moment of inertia about the z-axis of a lamina with surface density function f occupying a region S of the (x, y)-plane is

$$I = \int_S f d^2 dA, \qquad (2.9)$$

where d is the distance from the z-axis so that

$$fd^2 = \begin{cases} f(x,y)(x^2+y^2) & \text{in Cartesian coordinates,} \\ f(r,\theta)r^2 & \text{in plane polar coordinates.} \end{cases}$$

Example 2.4

Determine the moment of inertia of a square plate of side length a, constant surface density f and negligible thickness about an axis passing perpendicular to the plane of the plate through its centre.

Solution

Figure 2.9 shows the plate or lamina in the (x, y)-plane with its centre at the origin. Since the region of integration is a square we use Cartesian coordinates. The surface density function f is constant, so we can take it outside the area integral of Equation (2.9), and we have

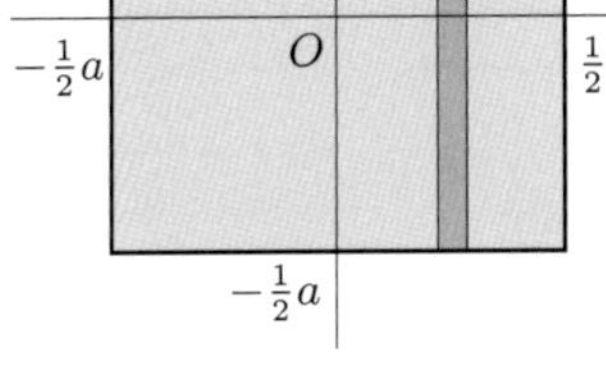

Figure 2.9

$$I = f \int_{x=-\frac{1}{2}a}^{x=\frac{1}{2}a} \left(\int_{y=-\frac{1}{2}a}^{y=\frac{1}{2}a} (x^2+y^2)\, dy \right) dx = f \int_{x=-\frac{1}{2}a}^{x=\frac{1}{2}a} \left[x^2 y + \tfrac{1}{3}y^3\right]_{y=-\frac{1}{2}a}^{y=\frac{1}{2}a} dx$$

$$= 2f \int_{-\frac{1}{2}a}^{\frac{1}{2}a} \left(\tfrac{1}{2}x^2 a + \tfrac{1}{24}a^3\right) dx = \tfrac{1}{6} f a^4.$$

The mass of the plate is $M = fa^2$, and so we can express the moment of inertia of the plate as $I = \frac{1}{6}Ma^2$. ■

**Exercise 2.4*

Determine the moment of inertia of a flat ruler of length $a = 0.30\,\text{m}$ and width $b = 0.04\,\text{m}$ about an axis passing perpendicular to the plane of the ruler through its centre. Assume the mass of the ruler can be modelled by a constant surface density function $f = 10^{-2}\,\text{kg}\,\text{m}^{-2}$.

The ruler is considered as a lamina in that its thickness is assumed negligible.

(*Hint*: Evaluate the area integral using the symbols a, b and f and then substitute the numbers into the answer.)

It is usual to quote the moment of inertia of a body in terms of its total mass M and its dimensions. For a square of side length a, the moment of inertia about an axis through its centre and perpendicular to the plane of the square is

We did this in Example 2.4 and in the solution to Exercise 2.4. Note that the SI units of moment of inertia are $\text{kg}\,\text{m}^2$.

$$I_{\text{square}} = \tfrac{1}{6}Ma^2,$$

and for a rectangle of length a and width b, the moment of inertia about an axis through its centre and perpendicular to the plane of the rectangle is

$$I_{\text{rectangle}} = \tfrac{1}{12}M(a^2+b^2). \qquad (2.10)$$

This last result can be used to find the moment of inertia of a thin rod of mass M and length a about an axis through its centre at right angles to its length. We take the limit as $b \to 0$ in Equation (2.10) to obtain

$$I_{\text{rod}} = \tfrac{1}{12}Ma^2.$$

We used Cartesian coordinates in Example 2.4 and Exercise 2.4 because the regions of integration were rectangular. To find the moment of inertia of a disc, it is simpler to use plane polar coordinates.

Example 2.5

Express the moment of inertia of a disc of radius a with surface density function f about an axis perpendicular to its plane and passing through its centre as an area integral in plane polar coordinates.

Solution

Using plane polar coordinates in Equation (2.9), the moment of inertia of the disc about its centre is given by the area integral

$$I_{\text{disc}} = \int fr^2 dA = \int_{\theta=-\pi}^{\theta=\pi} \left(\int_{r=0}^{r=a} fr^3 dr \right) d\theta. \quad \blacksquare$$

Here we have left the surface density function f inside the integral in case it is not a constant.

*Exercise 2.5

Evaluate the area integral in Example 2.5 for the case of a uniform disc of radius a and hence show that the moment of inertia of the disc about an axis perpendicular to its plane and passing through its centre is $\frac{1}{2}Ma^2$ where M is the mass of the disc.

In the above examples we have modelled plates and discs as laminae with variations of composition described by surface density functions. In an improved model of a plate we recognize that the thickness cannot be ignored and model the plate as a solid body, forming a *volume integral* by summing over small *volume elements* of the body. We do this in Section 3.

Laminae, by definition, have negligible thicknesses.

End-of-section Exercises

Exercise 2.6

A drop of coloured chemical falls onto a plane sheet of blotting paper and spreads to form a stain. The density of the chemical in the stain is described by $f(r, \theta) = A\exp(-r^2/a^2)$, where $A = 10^{-5}\,\text{kg}\,\text{m}^{-2}$ and $a = 1.5 \times 10^{-2}\,\text{m}$. Find the mass of chemical within a radius of $b = 0.01\,\text{m}$ from the centre.

*Exercise 2.7

Find the moment of inertia of a flat circular washer of uniform material, negligible thickness and total mass M in the shape of an annulus of internal radius a and external radius b, about an axis perpendicular to the plane of the washer through its centre.

*Exercise 2.8

Determine the moment of inertia about the z-axis of the magnifying glass in Exercise 2.2.

Exercise 2.9

Confirm the result that the centre of mass of an isosceles triangle is one third of the way up a median from its base, by evaluating an area integral.

This result was given in *Unit 19*.

---

3 Volume integrals

In Section 2 you saw how to calculate the masses and moments of inertia of laminae where the distribution of mass was modelled by a surface density function defined on a region of the (x, y)-plane. A more fundamental approach is to recognize at the outset that a real body is a three-dimensional object. Masses and moments of inertia are then expressed as *volume integrals*. In this section we define the volume integral and show how volume integrals are evaluated and used to find masses and moments of inertia.

The ideas here can also be used to extend straightforwardly the ideas on centres of mass from Subsection 2.3 to three-dimensional objects, but we do not do so here for reasons of space.

3.1 Defining and evaluating volume integrals

You know that the mass of an object of uniform density is simply the product of its volume times its density, where the *density* here is the *mass per unit volume*, measured in kg m^{-3}. To find the mass of an object of non-uniform density, we subdivide the object into very small **volume elements**, estimate the mass of an element as the product of its volume times the local value of the density, form the sum over all elements, and then go to the limit of an infinitely large number of small elements. The summation then becomes an integral called the *volume integral*, which we can evaluate.

Consider a scalar field $f(x, y, z)$ defined in a three-dimensional region B and subdivide B into N elements, where element i has volume δV_i. We make the following definition.

Definition

The **volume integral** of $f(x, y, z)$ over a **region of integration** B, subdivided into N elements where element i contains the point (x_i, y_i, z_i) and is of volume δV_i, is

$$\int_B f(x, y, z)dV = \lim_{N\to\infty} \sum_{i=1}^{N} f(x_i, y_i, z_i)\delta V_i, \quad (3.1)$$

where $\delta V_i \to 0$ as $N \to \infty$.

Before we can evaluate a volume integral we must choose a shape for the volume elements. The shape we choose depends on whether it is best to work in the Cartesian, cylindrical polar or spherical polar coordinate system. We begin with the Cartesian system.

Volume integral over a cuboid

The volume integral of a function $f(x, y, z)$ over a cuboid B whose faces lie in coordinate planes $x = a, x = b$ and $y = c, y = d$ and $z = p, z = q$ is obtained as three successive integrals as follows:

$$\int_B f(x, y, z)dV = \int_{x=a}^{x=b} \left(\int_{y=c}^{y=d} \left(\int_{z=p}^{z=q} f(x, y, z)dz \right) dy \right) dx. \quad (3.2)$$

A *cuboid* is just a rectangular block.

The method of evaluating the volume integral is similar to that of evaluating surface integrals over rectangular regions in the (x, y)-plane except that now we have to integrate over three variables. The method is best illustrated by an example.

For this reason volume integrals are sometimes referred to as *triple integrals*.

Example 3.1

The density inside a cube whose faces are the planes $x = 0$, $x = 1$ and $y = 0$, $y = 1$ and $z = 0$, $z = 1$ is given by the density function $f(x, y, z) = c(x^2 + y^2 + z^2)$ where c is a constant. Determine the mass of the cube.

Solution

The mass of the cube is given by the volume integral

$$\int_B f dV = \int_B c(x^2 + y^2 + z^2) dV.$$

The region of integration is shown in Figure 3.1. To evaluate this volume integral, we form three single integrals. The method of finding the limits for these single integrals is similar to the approach we used for area integrals. The volume element in Cartesian coordinates is a small block with volume $\delta V = \delta x\, \delta y\, \delta z$. If we draw within the region a vertical column of rectangular cross-section then the volume of the column is found by summing the volume elements along this column. This column intersects the bottom and top faces of the region at the lower and upper limits of the z-integration. In this case, the limits are $z = 0$ and $z = 1$ (see Figure 3.2).

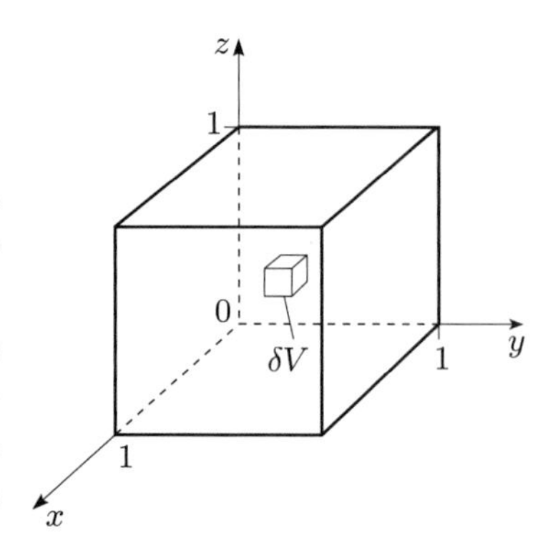

Figure 3.1

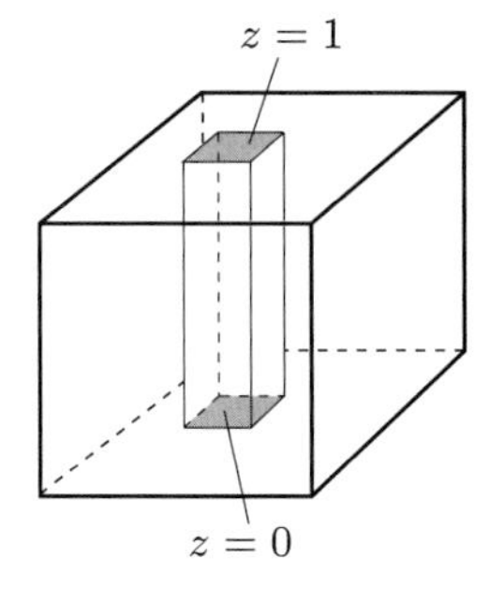

Figure 3.2

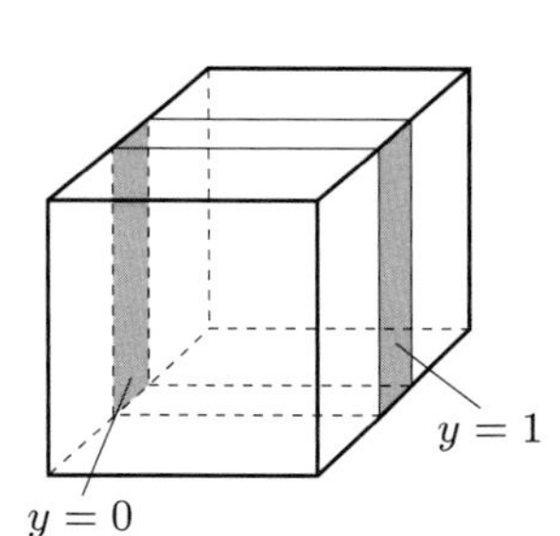

Figure 3.3

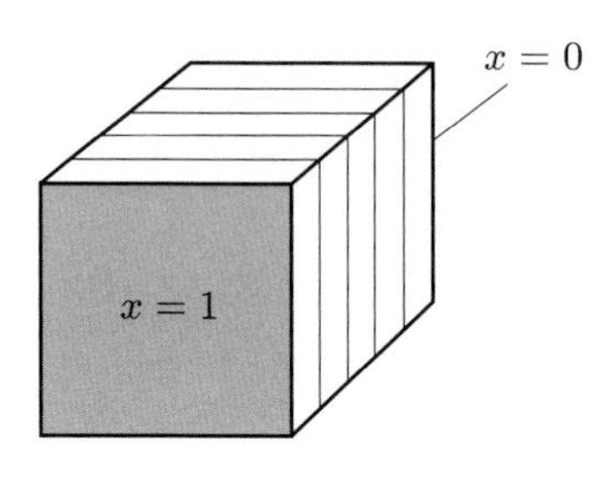

Figure 3.4

Now we form the y-integral by summing all the columns in a 'slice' parallel to the (y, z)-plane. The limits of the y-integration are therefore $y = 0$ and $y = 1$ (see Figure 3.3). Finally, we complete the volume by adding together all possible slices so that the limits of the x-integration are $x = 0$ and $x = 1$ (see Figure 3.4).

Hence the mass M of the cube can be found from three successive integrals and

$$M = \int_{x=0}^{x=1} \left(\int_{y=0}^{y=1} \left(\int_{z=0}^{z=1} c(x^2 + y^2 + z^2)\, dz \right) dy \right) dx.$$

The inner integral is evaluated first. This is an integral over z with x and y treated as constants. Hence

$$M = \int_{x=0}^{x=1} \left(\int_{y=0}^{y=1} c(x^2 + y^2 + \tfrac{1}{3})\, dy \right) dx.$$

Now we are left with an area integral which we know how to evaluate. Thus

$$M = \int_{x=0}^{x=1} c(\tfrac{2}{3} + x^2)\, dx = c. \quad \blacksquare$$

The main point to notice is that after each integration the number of variables is reduced by one.

*Exercise 3.1

The density of the material in a block with faces $x = 0$, $x = 2$, $y = 1$, $y = 2$, $z = 2$ and $z = 5$ is given by $f(x, y, z) = x + y + z$. Find the mass of the block.

Sometimes it is more appropriate to evaluate a volume integral using cylindrical polar coordinates. We must then divide the region of integration into volume elements with surfaces $\rho =$ constant, $\theta =$ constant and $z =$ constant. A typical volume element is shown in Figure 3.5. It is approximately a cuboid of sides δz, $\rho\delta\theta$ and $\delta\rho$, and so its volume is $\delta V \simeq \rho\,\delta z\,\delta\theta\,\delta\rho$ and this approximation improves as δz, $\delta\theta$ and $\delta\rho$ tend to zero. If the region of integration is a cylinder of radius a and height h, with the base of the cylinder on the (x, y)-plane, then in cylindrical polar coordinates the limits of integration are: $z = 0$ and $z = h$; $\theta = -\pi$ and $\theta = \pi$; $\rho = 0$ and $\rho = a$. So the volume integral of a scalar field f over the cylinder is as follows.

Cylindrical polar coordinates were introduced in Subsection 4.1 of *Unit 23*.

Note the factor ρ again.

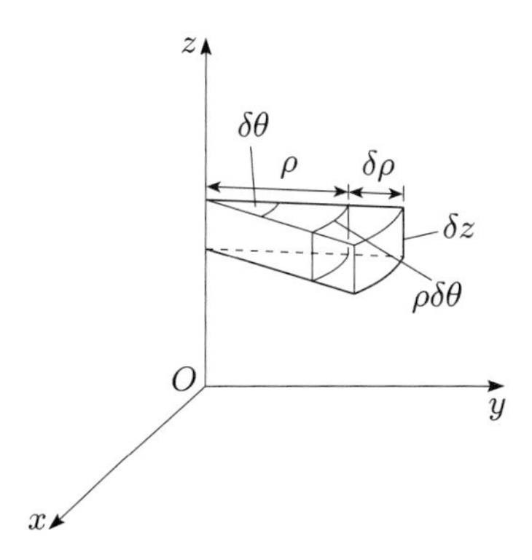

Figure 3.5

Volume integral in cylindrical polar coordinates

$$\int_B f\,dV = \int_B f(\rho, \theta, z)\rho\,dz\,d\theta\,d\rho$$
$$= \int_{\rho=0}^{\rho=a} \left(\int_{\theta=-\pi}^{\theta=\pi} \left(\int_{z=0}^{z=h} f\rho\,dz \right) d\theta \right) d\rho. \quad (3.3)$$

In most applications that you will meet in this course, the scalar field f is independent of the azimuthal angle θ, and so the θ-integration simply gives a factor $\int_{-\pi}^{\pi} d\theta = 2\pi$ and Equation (3.3) becomes

$$\int_B f\,dV = 2\pi \int_{\rho=0}^{\rho=a} \left(\int_{z=0}^{z=h} f\rho\,dz \right) d\rho, \quad (3.4)$$

which is an area integral.

Example 3.2

The density of a cylinder of height h and radius a is given by $f = k\rho^2$, where k is a positive constant and ρ is the perpendicular distance from the axis of the cylinder. Find the total mass of the cylinder when $h = 2\,\text{m}$ and $a = 0.5\,\text{m}$.

Solution

Use cylindrical polar coordinates with the axis of the cylinder aligned along the z-axis and its base on the (x, y)-plane. The total mass of the cylinder is given by

$$M = \int_B f\,dV = \int_B f\rho\,dz\,d\theta\,d\rho = \int_B k\rho^3\,dz\,d\theta\,d\rho.$$

Using Equation (3.4),

$$M = 2\pi \int_{\rho=0}^{\rho=a} \left(\int_{z=0}^{z=h} k\rho^3 dz \right) d\rho,$$
$$= 2\pi k \int_0^a \rho^3 h d\rho = \tfrac{1}{2}\pi k a^4 h.$$

When $h = 2\,\text{m}$ and $a = 0.5\,\text{m}$, the mass of the cylinder is $\frac{1}{16}\pi k\,\text{kg}$. ■

Now we turn our attention to spherical polar coordinates. In order to evaluate volume integrals in this system, we need to find the volume δV of the volume element that is shown in Figure 3.6.

Spherical polar coordinates were introduced in Subsection 4.3 of *Unit 23*.

This volume is approximately a cuboid with sides PQ, PR and PS. Hence the volume of the element is

$$\delta V \simeq PQ \times PR \times PS.$$

From Figure 3.6 we see that $PQ = \delta r$, $PR = r\delta\theta$, and $PS = AP\delta\phi = (OP\sin\theta)\delta\phi = r\sin\theta\,\delta\phi$. So the volume element is

$$\delta V \simeq r^2 \sin\theta\,\delta\phi\,\delta\theta\,\delta r,$$

and this approximation improves as $\delta\phi$, $\delta\theta$ and δr tend to zero. Hence the volume integral of a scalar field f, over a region B, is given by the following

.

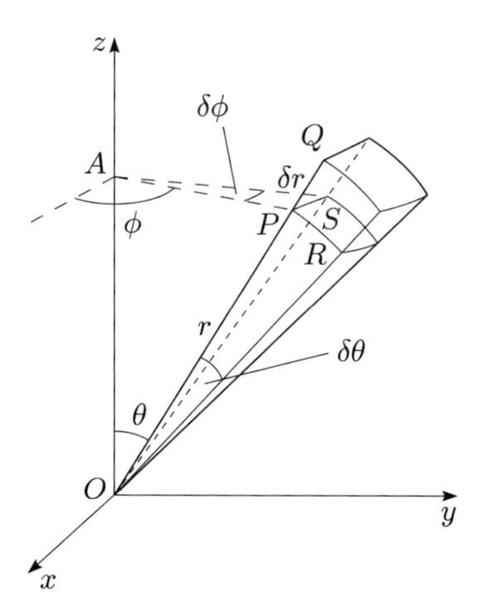

Figure 3.6

Volume integral in spherical polar coordinates

$$\int_B f\,dV = \int_B f(r,\theta,\phi)r^2 \sin\theta\,d\phi\,d\theta\,dr. \qquad (3.5)$$

Once the function $f(r,\theta,\phi)$ is given, Equation (3.5) can be evaluated as three successive integrals over ϕ, θ and r.

In many cases, the scalar field f is spherically symmetric so that f depends on r only, not on θ or ϕ. In such cases, and for a region contained between spherical shells of radii R_1 and R_2 ($R_1 < R_2$), Equation (3.5) takes the form

$$\int_B f\,dV = \int_{r=R_1}^{r=R_2} \left(\int_{\theta=0}^{\theta=\pi} \left(\int_{\phi=-\pi}^{\phi=\pi} f(r)r^2 \sin\theta\,d\phi \right) d\theta \right) dr.$$

The ϕ-integral gives a factor 2π, and the θ-integral gives $[-\cos\theta]_0^\pi = 2$. Thus in such cases,

$$\int_B f\,dV = 4\pi \int_{R_1}^{R_2} f(r)r^2\,dr. \qquad (3.6)$$

***Exercise 3.2**

By evaluating a volume integral, find the mass of a sphere of radius R which is centred at the origin and whose density is given by $f = c + \alpha r$, where c and α are positive constants, and r is the distance from the origin.

In the examples we have considered in this subsection the regions of integration have been cuboids, cylinders and spheres. The boundaries of these regions coincide with coordinate surfaces in the appropriate coordinate system and so the limits of integration are all constants. In Subsection 3.3 we shall look at examples where the regions of integration cut across coordinate planes and as a result some of the limits of integration are functions. Meanwhile, in the next subsection, we show an application of volume integrals to the calculation of moments of inertia of rigid bodies.

3.2 Moments of inertia of rigid bodies

In Subsection 2.4 we calculated the moments of inertia of laminae in the (x, y)-plane, with mass distributions described by surface density functions $f(x, y)$. We now consider a rigid body that can rotate about the z-axis.

The mass distribution in a rigid body is modelled by a density function $f(x, y, z)$ with units of kg m^{-3}. As in Subsection 2.4, our starting point is Equation (2.8) giving the moment of inertia of a rigid body as the limit of a summation.

Suppose a rigid body is divided into a very large number N of volume elements, modelled as particles. The mass of an element is approximately $f_i \delta V_i$, where δV_i is the volume of the element and f_i is the density at a point inside the element, and so the moment of inertia of the element about the z-axis is approximately $(f_i \delta V_i) d_i^2 = f_i d_i^2 \delta V_i$ where d_i is the perpendicular distance of the ith element from the z-axis. The moment of inertia of the whole body about the z-axis is found by summing over all elements and taking the limit as $N \to \infty$. The moment of inertia about the z-axis (see Figure 3.7) is then the volume integral of the function fd^2 over the region of space B occupied by the body.

The function $d(x, y, z)$ gives the distance of the point (x, y, z) from the point z on the z-axis.

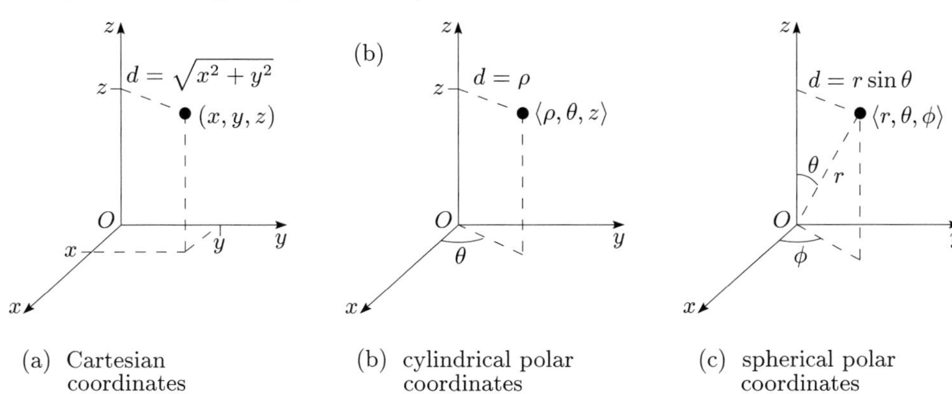

(a) Cartesian coordinates (b) cylindrical polar coordinates (c) spherical polar coordinates

Figure 3.7

> **Moment of inertia of a rigid body**
>
> The moment of inertia about the z-axis of a rigid body with density function f occupying a region B of space is
>
> $$I = \int_B f d^2 dV, \qquad (3.7)$$
>
> where d is the distance from the z-axis so that
>
> $$fd^2 = \begin{cases} f(x, y, z)(x^2 + y^2) & \text{in Cartesian coordinates,} \\ f(\rho, \theta, z)\rho^2 & \text{in cylindrical polar coordinates,} \\ f(r, \theta, \phi)(r \sin\theta)^2 & \text{in spherical polar coordinates.} \end{cases}$$

Example 3.3

Starting from Equation (3.7), evaluate the moment of inertia I of a uniform sphere of radius R and constant density D about an axis through its centre.

Solution

Let the centre of the sphere be at the origin and we shall calculate the moment of inertia about the z-axis. The density function $f = D$ is constant, and the distance d from the z-axis in spherical polar coordinates is $d = r \sin\theta$, see Figure 3.7(c). The moment of inertia of the sphere is

Since the region of integration B is a sphere we use spherical polar coordinates (and Equation (3.7)).

$$I = \int_{\text{sphere}} D(r\sin\theta)^2 dV = D \int_{\text{sphere}} (r\sin\theta)^2 r^2 \sin\theta \, dr \, d\theta \, d\phi$$

$$= D \int_{r=0}^{r=R} \left(\int_{\theta=0}^{\theta=\pi} \left(\int_{\phi=-\pi}^{\phi=\pi} r^4 \sin^3\theta \, d\phi \right) d\theta \right) dr.$$

The ϕ-integral yields the factor $\int_{-\pi}^{\pi} d\phi = 2\pi$. The θ-integral yields the factor

$$\int_0^{\pi} \sin^3\theta\, d\theta = \int_0^{\pi} \sin\theta(1-\cos^2\theta)d\theta = \left[-\cos\theta + \tfrac{1}{3}\cos^3\theta\right]_0^{\pi} = \tfrac{4}{3}$$

and the r-integral gives $\int_0^R r^4 dr = \frac{1}{5}R^5$. Hence the volume integral yields the moment of inertia $I = \frac{8}{15}\pi D R^5$. ■

Note that in Example 3.3 the limits are all constant and so the three integrals can be carried out in any order without changing the limits.

Exercise 3.3

Determine the mass M of a uniform sphere of radius R and density D by evaluating a volume integral and hence show that the moment of inertia of the sphere about an axis through its centre is $I = \frac{2}{5}MR^2$.

*Exercise 3.4

Show that the moment of inertia of a uniform solid cylinder of mass M, height h and radius a about its axis is $I = \frac{1}{2}Ma^2$.

Exercise 3.5

Find the moment of inertia of a uniform spherical shell of mass M, outer radius b and inner radius a about an axis through its centre.

The answer to Exercise 3.5 can be used to find the moment of inertia of a very thin spherical shell, such as a ping-pong ball, about an axis through its centre. We put $b = a + h$ where h, the thickness of the shell, is very small compared with a. Then you have

$$I_{\text{shell}} = \frac{2M(b^5 - a^5)}{5(b^3 - a^3)} = \frac{2M((a+h)^5 - a^5)}{5((a+h)^3 - a^3)} = \frac{2Ma^5\left(\left(1+\frac{h}{a}\right)^5 - 1\right)}{5a^3\left(\left(1+\frac{h}{a}\right)^3 - 1\right)}.$$

We can expand $\left(1+\frac{h}{a}\right)^5 \simeq 1 + 5h/a$ and $\left(1+\frac{h}{a}\right)^3 \simeq 1 + 3h/a$ by using a Taylor polynomial, keeping only the first-degree (i.e. linear) terms in h, since h/a is very much less than 1. Thus

See *Unit 12*.

$$I_{\text{thin shell}} \simeq \frac{2Ma^5(5h/a)}{5a^3(3h/a)} = \tfrac{2}{3}Ma^2.$$

You may have noticed that the moment of inertia of the uniform cylinder in Exercise 3.4 is the same as the moment of inertia of the uniform disc in Exercise 2.5. This is not surprising since the moment of inertia is the sum over all elements of the quantity (mass) × (distance from z-axis)^2 which is independent of the distribution of mass in the z-direction. It follows that the moment of inertia of a uniform body is unchanged by projecting the mass distribution of the body onto the (x, y)-plane, provided distances from the z-axis do not change. The moment of inertia of any solid body about the z-axis can always, in principle, be evaluated as an area integral over a region of the (x, y)-plane, *provided* the equivalent projected surface density in the (x, y)-plane is known.

The disc was assumed to be a lamina in the (x, y)-plane.

The z-integration of the volume integral in the solution to Exercise 3.4 yields a factor Dh, the mass per unit volume times the height. This is equivalent to a mass per unit area, a surface density, in the (x, y)-plane. The integrals over ρ and θ that are left after the z-integral is evaluated are the same as those you evaluated in Exercise 2.5 to get the moment of inertia of a disc in the (x, y)-plane.

Exercise 3.6

Find the moment of inertia of a uniform cylindrical shell of mass M, outer radius b and inner radius a about its axis.

3.3 Further volume integrals

Here we evaluate volume integrals where the boundaries of the region of integration do not coincide with coordinate surfaces. The limits on some of the integrals are then functions which have to be determined. Thus the first stage in the evaluation of a volume integral is to decide on a coordinate system and the limits of integration. The second stage is to evaluate the single integrals and this latter task is one that can most easily be carried out by computer. Selecting the coordinate system and deciding on the limits of integration is a task that you have to carry out yourself. In this subsection we shall illustrate how limits are decided upon in cases where we use Cartesian coordinate systems for non-rectangular regions of integration. The procedure is to carry out the z-integration first. When this is done we are left with an area integral in the (x, y)-plane which you can evaluate as in Subsection 1.3.

So instead of the volume integral with constant limits as in Equation (3.2) we have variable limits in the z- (and possibly y-) direction.

Volume integral over a general volume

$$\int_B f(x,y,z)dV = \int_{x=a}^{x=b}\left(\int_{y=\alpha(x)}^{y=\beta(x)}\left(\int_{z=\gamma(x,y)}^{z=\psi(x,y)} f(x,y,z)\,dz\right)dy\right)dx. \tag{3.8}$$

To illustrate the method we consider a volume integral of a function f over the cylindrical region of radius a shown in Figure 3.8(a). Note that this cylinder has its axis on the y-axis, not the z-axis, and the curved boundary does not coincide with any Cartesian coordinate surface. Recall that the volume elements in Cartesian coordinates are small blocks of volume $\delta V = \delta z\, \delta y\, \delta x$. We choose to integrate first over z. The z-integration then represents summing up the volume elements in the vertical column in Figure 3.8(a). Where this column intersects the bottom and top curved boundaries of the cylinder are the lower and upper limits of the z-integration. In this case the limits are $z = -\sqrt{a^2 - x^2}$ and $z = \sqrt{a^2 - x^2}$. Hence the z-integral is

The curved boundary has the equation $x^2 + z^2 = a^2$ so is made up of $z = \sqrt{a^2 - x^2}$ $(z \geqslant 0)$ and $z = -\sqrt{a^2 - x^2}$ $(z < 0)$.

$$\int_{z=-\sqrt{a^2-x^2}}^{z=\sqrt{a^2-x^2}} f(x,y,z)\,dz = h(x,y).$$

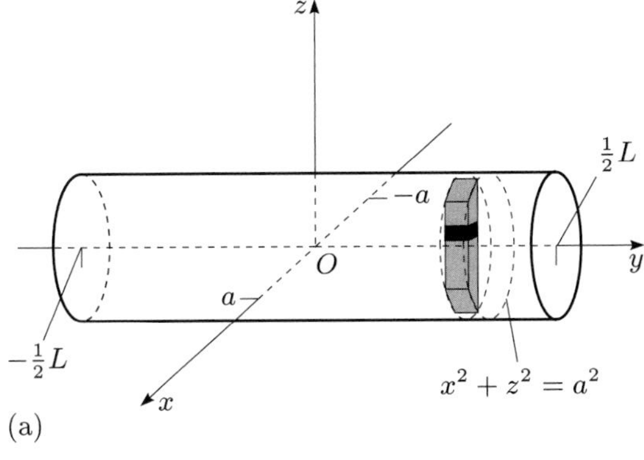

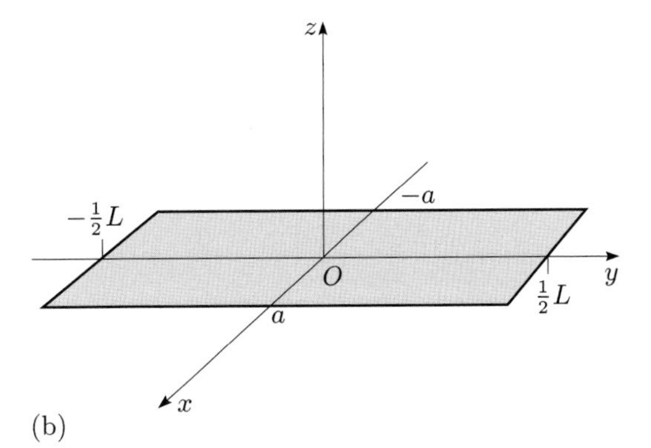

Figure 3.8

The result of the integration over z is $h(x, y)$, some function of x and y only. To complete the volume integral we have to evaluate the area integral

$$\int_S h(x, y)\, dy\, dx$$

where the region S is the projection of the cylinder onto the (x, y)-plane. This projection is just the rectangle shown in Figure 3.8(b). To illustrate the method, we now evaluate the moment of inertia of the cylinder in Figure 3.8(a) about the z-axis.

Example 3.4

Find the moment of inertia of a uniform solid cylinder of mass M, radius a, and length L about an axis through its centre at right angles to the cylinder's axis, using Cartesian coordinates.

Solution

Figure 3.8(a) shows the cylinder lying with its centre at the origin and its axis on the y-axis. We require the moment of inertia of the cylinder about the z-axis. Using Equation (3.7) this is given by

$$I = \int_{\text{cylinder}} f d^2 dV = f \int_{\text{cylinder}} (x^2 + y^2)\, dz\, dy\, dx.$$

So we must calculate the volume integral of the function $(x^2 + y^2)$ over the cylinder. The limits of the z-integral are chosen as described above, and so the z-integral gives

$$h(x, y) = f \int_{z=-\sqrt{a^2-x^2}}^{z=\sqrt{a^2-x^2}} (x^2 + y^2)\, dz = 2f\sqrt{a^2 - x^2}(x^2 + y^2).$$

We are now left with the x- and y-integrations in Equation (3.8). We have to evaluate the area integral of $h(x, y)$ over the projection of the cylinder on the (x, y)-plane, which is the rectangle shown in Figure 3.8(b). Following Procedure 1.1 for evaluating area integrals, we first note that the limits of the x-integral are $-a$ and a and the limits on the y-integral are $-\frac{1}{2}L$ and $\frac{1}{2}L$. Thus Equation (3.7) becomes

$$\begin{aligned} I &= \int_{\text{rectangle}} h(x, y)\, dy\, dx \\ &= 2f \int_{x=-a}^{x=a} \left(\int_{y=-\frac{1}{2}L}^{y=\frac{1}{2}L} \sqrt{a^2 - x^2}(x^2 + y^2)\, dy \right) dx \\ &= 2f \int_{x=-a}^{x=a} \left[\sqrt{a^2 - x^2}\left(x^2 y + \tfrac{1}{3}y^3\right) \right]_{y=-\frac{1}{2}L}^{y=\frac{1}{2}L} dx \\ &= 2fL \int_{-a}^{a} \sqrt{a^2 - x^2}\left(x^2 + \tfrac{1}{12}L^2\right) dx = \tfrac{1}{12}\pi f a^2 L(3a^2 + L^2). \end{aligned}$$

You can use the computer algebra package to calculate these integrals.

The mass of the cylinder is $M = f\pi a^2 L$ and so the moment of inertia is

$$I = \tfrac{1}{12}M(3a^2 + L^2). \quad \blacksquare$$

Note that in the limit as $a \to 0$ this becomes $\frac{1}{12}ML^2$, the moment of inertia of a thin rod of length L about an axis through its centre perpendicular to its length, as found in Subsection 2.4.

The steps we have used to evaluate a volume integral $\int_B f(x, y, z)\, dV$ are summarized in the following box.

Procedure 3.1 Evaluating volume integrals

To evaluate a volume integral

$$\int_B f(x, y, z)\, dV$$

proceed as follows.

(a) Draw two diagrams showing the region of integration, B, with the equations of the upper and lower boundaries marked, and the projection S of this region onto the (x, y)-plane.

(b) Within the region B draw a column perpendicular to the (x, y)-plane and determine the limits of the z-integration, $z = \gamma(x, y)$ and $z = \psi(x, y)$, say.

(c) Evaluate the single integral of $f(x, y, z)$ over z between $z = \gamma(x, y)$ and $z = \psi(x, y)$, keeping x and y constant, to find the function $h(x, y)$ defined by

$$h(x, y) = \int_{z=\gamma(x,y)}^{z=\psi(x,y)} f(x, y, z)\, dz.$$

(d) Evaluate the area integral of $h(x, y)$ over the region S using Procedure 1.1.

In Example 3.4 we had $\gamma(x, y) = -\sqrt{a^2 - x^2}$ and $\psi(x, y) = \sqrt{a^2 - x^2}$.

***Exercise 3.7**

Find the value of the volume integral of the function $f(x, y, z) = x^2yz$ over the wedge-shaped region bounded by the planes $z = 0$, $y = 0$, $x = 0$, $x = 1$ and $y + z = 1$ (as shown in Figure 3.9).

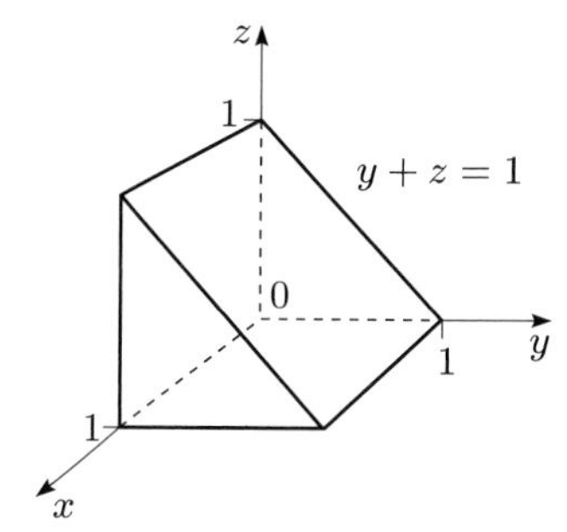

Figure 3.9

Exercise 3.8

Find the value of the volume integral of the function $f(x, y, z) = z + 3x - 2$ over the region inside the circular cylinder $x^2 + y^2 = 1$ lying between the planes $z = 0$ and $z = 1$.

End-of-section Exercises

Exercise 3.9

The density of a rectangular block B bounded by the planes $x = 1$, $x = 2$, $y = 0$, $y = 3$, $z = -1$ and $z = 0$ is given by $f(x, y, z) = x(y + 1) - z$. Find the mass of the block.

Exercise 3.10

The density of a sphere of radius R varies as $f(\mathbf{r}) = c|\mathbf{r}|^2$, where c is a constant and $\mathbf{r}$ is measured from the sphere's centre. Determine (a) the mass of the sphere and (b) the moment of inertia of the sphere about an axis through its centre.

***Exercise 3.11**

The volume of a region B of space is $V = \int_B 1 dV$. Find the volume of the region B bounded by the surface $z = \frac{1}{9}(x^2 + y^2)$ and the plane $z = 1$. (You may assume that $\int_{x=-3}^{x=3} (9 - x^2)^{\frac{3}{2}}\, dx = \frac{243}{8}\pi$.)

Exercise 3.12

Find the moment of inertia of a cone of mass M, height h and base radius a about its axis (see Figure 3.10).

(*Hint*: Use cylindrical polar coordinates and integrate first over z; express the height z of the vertical column in terms of a and h.)

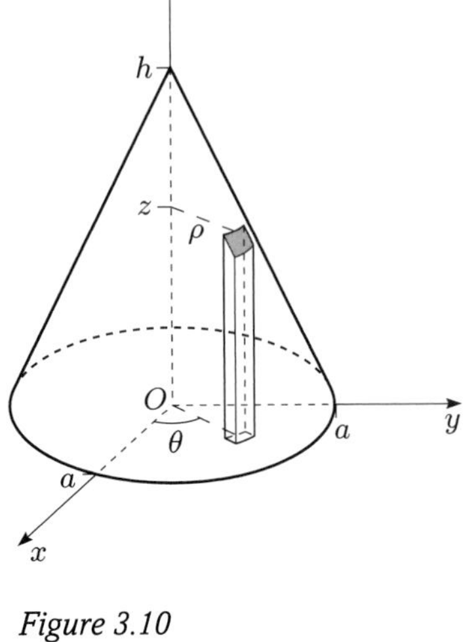

Figure 3.10

4 The area of a surface

In *Unit 24* we studied the scalar line integral, and showed that as a particular application we can find the length of a curve. In this section we find a corresponding application of the ideas from Section 1; this enables us to calculate the area of a curved surface.

In Section 1 we defined and calculated many area integrals. However the areas we considered were always in a plane. Sometimes it is useful to be able to calculate areas of surfaces in three-dimensional space — for example we may need to know the area of a curved surface like part of a sphere. Fortunately there is a way to find such an area in terms of area integrals.

Consider a surface in space defined by the equation $z = f(x, y)$, a portion of which is shown in Figure 4.1.

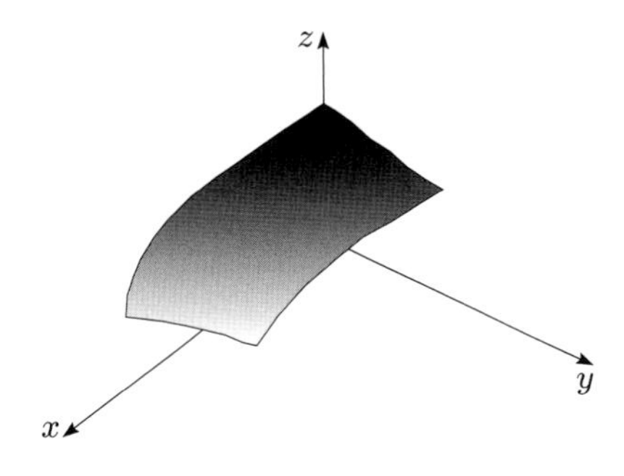

Figure 4.1

Suppose that we wish to calculate the area A of that part of the surface that lies above the rectangle defined by $a \le x \le b$ and $c \le y \le d$. Take a small element of the area above the point (x_0, y_0) as shown below.

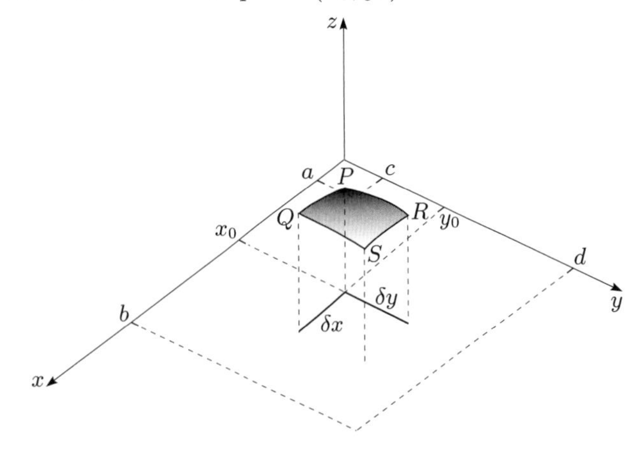

Figure 4.2

If small enough, the element will be approximately rectangular with vertices

$$P = (x_0, y_0, f(x_0, y_0)), \quad Q = (x_0 + \delta x, y_0, f(x_0 + \delta x, y_0)),$$
$$R = (x_0, y_0 + \delta y, f(x_0, y_0 + \delta y)), \quad S = (x_0 + \delta x, y_0 + \delta y, f(x_0 + \delta x, y_0 + \delta y)).$$

Now recall that a point (x, y, z) in space can be represented as a position vector

$$x\,\mathbf{i}+y\,\mathbf{j}+z\,\mathbf{k}.$$

We can, therefore, think of the edges PQ and PR as forming two vectors, $\mathbf{v}_1$ and $\mathbf{v}_2$, as follows

$$\begin{aligned}
\mathbf{v}_1 &= \overrightarrow{PQ} \\
&= ((x_0+\delta x)\,\mathbf{i}+y_0\,\mathbf{j}+f(x_0+\delta x,y_0)\,\mathbf{k})-(x_0\,\mathbf{i}+y_0\,\mathbf{j}+f(x_0,y_0)\,\mathbf{k}) \\
&= \delta x\,\mathbf{i}+(f(x_0+\delta x,y_0)-f(x_0,y_0))\,\mathbf{k} \\
&\simeq \delta x\,\mathbf{i}+\delta x\,\frac{\partial f}{\partial x}\,\mathbf{k},
\end{aligned}$$

Here we use the approximation
$$\frac{\partial f}{\partial x}\simeq\frac{f(x_0+\delta x,y_0)-f(x_0,y_0)}{\delta x}.$$

and

$$\begin{aligned}
\mathbf{v}_2 &= \overrightarrow{PR} \\
&= (x_0\,\mathbf{i}+(y_0+\delta y)\,\mathbf{j}+f(x_0,y_0+\delta y)\,\mathbf{k})-(x_0\,\mathbf{i}+y_0\,\mathbf{j}+f(x_0,y_0)\,\mathbf{k}) \\
&= \delta y\,\mathbf{j}+(f(x_0,y_0+\delta y)-f(x_0,y_0))\,\mathbf{k} \\
&\simeq \delta y\,\mathbf{j}+\delta y\,\frac{\partial f}{\partial y}\,\mathbf{k}.
\end{aligned}$$

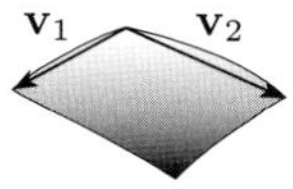

$\mathbf{v}_1$ $\mathbf{v}_2$

Figure 4.3

Now the area of the parallelogram formed by two vectors is given by the magnitude of their vector cross product. In our context this becomes

See *Unit 4*.

$$\begin{aligned}
\delta A &= |\mathbf{v}_1\times\mathbf{v}_2| \\
&= \left|\left(\delta x\,\mathbf{i}+\delta x\,\frac{\partial f}{\partial x}\,\mathbf{k}\right)\times\left(\delta y\,\mathbf{j}+\delta y\,\frac{\partial f}{\partial y}\,\mathbf{k}\right)\right| \\
&= \left|-\delta x\,\delta y\,\frac{\partial f}{\partial x}\,\mathbf{i}-\delta x\,\delta y\,\frac{\partial f}{\partial y}\,\mathbf{j}+\delta x\,\delta y\,\mathbf{k}\right| \\
&= \delta x\delta y\sqrt{1+\left(\frac{\partial f}{\partial x}\right)^2+\left(\frac{\partial f}{\partial y}\right)^2}, \qquad (4.1)
\end{aligned}$$

where δA is the area of the small element. The area A of the whole surface is given approximately by adding up the areas of all the small elements, so that

$$A\simeq\sum\sqrt{1+\left(\frac{\partial f}{\partial x}\right)^2+\left(\frac{\partial f}{\partial y}\right)^2}\,\delta y\,\delta x.$$

As the size of the elements tends to zero we can pass to the limit, and the sum becomes an area integral in the sense of Section 1;

$$A=\int_{x=a}^{x=b}\left(\int_{y=c}^{y=d}\sqrt{1+\left(\frac{\partial f}{\partial x}\right)^2+\left(\frac{\partial f}{\partial y}\right)^2}\,dy\right)dx.$$

As in Section 1 the integrations can be performed in either order. We have dealt with a portion of surface lying over a rectangular region of the plane, but as in Section 1 this can be extended to more general regions (see Example 4.2). The limits of the two integrals are then determined by the context, but often, as we found in Section 1, the limits of the inner integral will be functions rather than constants.

Procedure 4.1 Finding the area of a surface

Suppose that a surface is described in the form $z = f(x, y)$. To find the area of a portion of the surface lying over the region S in the (x, y)-plane proceed as follows.

(a) Form the function

$$g(x, y) = \sqrt{1 + \left(\frac{\partial f}{\partial x}\right)^2 + \left(\frac{\partial f}{\partial y}\right)^2}.$$

(b) Calculate the area integral

$$A = \int_S g(x, y)\, dA,$$

as in Procedure 1.1.

The idea is simple enough, although the integrals can be extremely messy — even for fairly simple surfaces.

Example 4.1

Express the area of the surface $z = \frac{1}{2}x^2 + \frac{1}{2}y^2$ lying over the square defined by $-1 \leq x,\ y \leq 1$ as an area integral. (Do *not* attempt to evaluate the integral.)

Solution

Following Procedure 4.1 we write

$$g(x, y) = \sqrt{1 + x^2 + y^2},$$

and obtain the integral

$$A = \int_S g(x, y)\, dA.$$

With the appropriate limits this becomes

$$A = \int_{-1}^{1} \left(\int_{-1}^{1} \sqrt{1 + x^2 + y^2}\, dy \right) dx.$$

This integral can be computed (by hand, or by using a computer algebra package) but the details are beyond the scope of this course. ■

As in Section 2, the evaluation of a surface integral may sometimes be dramatically simplified by using polar coordinates.

Example 4.2

Find the area of the portion of a sphere of radius a, centred at the origin and lying above the (x, y)-plane defined by the angle ψ as shown in Figure 4.4 (where $0 \leq \psi \leq \pi/2$).

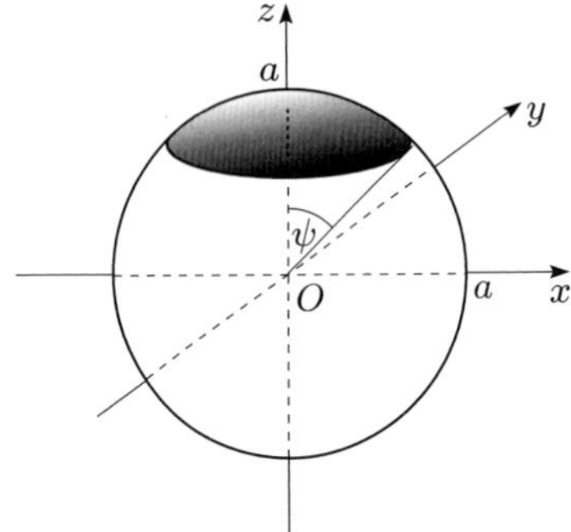

Figure 4.4

Solution

This is a surface given by the equation

$$f(x,y) = \sqrt{a^2 - x^2 - y^2},$$

(Since $x^2 + y^2 + z^2 = a^2$.)

and the corresponding region in the (x, y)-plane is a circular disc of radius $a \sin \psi$. Now

$$\frac{\partial f}{\partial x} = \frac{-x}{\sqrt{a^2 - x^2 - y^2}} \quad \text{and} \quad \frac{\partial f}{\partial y} = \frac{-y}{\sqrt{a^2 - x^2 - y^2}},$$

and we have to compute

$$A = \int_{x=a}^{x=b} \left(\int_{y=\alpha(x)}^{y=\beta(x)} \sqrt{1 + \left(\frac{\partial f}{\partial x}\right)^2 + \left(\frac{\partial f}{\partial y}\right)^2}\, dy \right) dx$$

over the disc in the (x, y)-plane given by

$$x^2 + y^2 \leq a^2 \sin^2 \psi.$$

Following the discussion after Exercise 2.1, we see that the limits are

Compare with Figure 2.2.

$$-a \sin \psi \leq x \leq a \sin \psi, \qquad -\sqrt{a^2 \sin^2 \psi - x^2} \leq y \leq \sqrt{a^2 \sin^2 \psi - x^2},$$

and we must evaluate

$$\begin{aligned} A &= \int_{x=-a\sin\psi}^{x=a\sin\psi} \left(\int_{y=-\sqrt{a^2\sin^2\psi - x^2}}^{y=\sqrt{a^2\sin^2\psi - x^2}} \sqrt{1 + \left(\tfrac{\partial f}{\partial x}\right)^2 + \left(\tfrac{\partial f}{\partial y}\right)^2}\, dy \right) dx \\ &= \int_{x=-a\sin\psi}^{x=a\sin\psi} \left(\int_{y=-\sqrt{a^2\sin^2\psi - x^2}}^{y=\sqrt{a^2\sin^2\psi - x^2}} \frac{a}{\sqrt{a^2 - x^2 - y^2}}\, dy \right) dx. \end{aligned}$$

It is clear that this will be considerably easier to deal with if we use polar coordinates, so we proceed as in Section 2. The function to be integrated is simply

$$f(r, \theta) = \frac{a}{\sqrt{a^2 - r^2}}.$$

The limits for the r-integration are 0 and $a \sin \psi$, whilst for θ the limits are simply $-\pi$ and π. Therefore the required integral is

$$\begin{aligned} A &= \int_{r=0}^{r=a\sin\psi} \left(\int_{\theta=-\pi}^{\theta=\pi} \frac{a}{\sqrt{a^2 - r^2}}\, r\, d\theta \right) dr \\ &= 2\pi a \int_{r=0}^{r=a\sin\psi} \frac{r}{\sqrt{a^2 - r^2}}\, dr \\ &= 2\pi a \left[-\sqrt{a^2 - r^2} \right]_0^{a\sin\psi} \\ &= 2\pi a \left(-a\cos\psi - (-a) \right) \\ &= 2\pi a^2 (1 - \cos\psi). \end{aligned}$$

We can confirm that this is a plausible answer by considering some specific values of ψ. When $\psi = 0$ we obtain 0, and when $\psi = \pi/2$ we obtain $2\pi a^2$ (which is the correct formula for the area of a hemisphere of radius a). ■

End-of-section Exercise

Exercise 4.1

Find the surface area of a cone of height h and base radius a.

5 Integrals on the computer

In this section you will use the computer algebra package to consolidate your work in this unit by means of a variety of activities involving area and volume integrals. Some of the activities are based on exercises and examples from the unit, and some ask you to compute results that will be needed in *Unit 27*.

Use your computer to complete the following activities.

PC

Activity 5.1

(a) Find the value of the area integral of the function $f(x, y) = y$ over the region bounded by the curves $y = x^2$ and $y = x + 2$.

(b) Find the value of the area integral of the function $f(x, y) = x$ over the quarter disc $x^2 + y^2 \leq 1\,(x \geq 0, y \geq 0)$.

This is Exercise 1.3. Note that the two curves intersect when $x = -1$ and when $x = 2$.

Activity 5.2

In Subsection 2.1, the number of bacteria in a circular region was given as

$$A \int_{x=-a}^{x=a} \left(\int_{y=-\sqrt{a^2-x^2}}^{y=\sqrt{a^2-x^2}} \left(2 - \frac{x^2}{a^2} - \frac{y^2}{a^2} \right) dy \right) dx.$$

Determine a formula for the number of bacteria in the region and hence calculate the number of bacteria when $A = 10^{12}\,\mathrm{m}^{-2}$ and $a = 0.01\,\mathrm{m}$.

Activity 5.3

Determine the moment of inertia of a square plate of side length $a = 0.25\,\mathrm{m}$, uniform density $k = 2\,\mathrm{kg\,m}^{-2}$ and negligible thickness about an axis passing perpendicular to the plane of the plate through its centre.

Compare with Example 2.4.

Activity 5.4

In Example 2.2, the number of bacteria in a circular region was given in plane polar coordinates as

$$A \int_{\theta=-\pi}^{\theta=\pi} \left(\int_{r=0}^{r=a} \left(2 - \frac{r^2}{a^2} \right) r dr \right) d\theta.$$

Evaluate this integral for $A = 10^{12}\,\mathrm{m}^{-2}$ and $a = 0.01\,\mathrm{m}$, and compare your solution with the results of Activity 5.2 (which used Cartesian coordinates).

Activity 5.5

Determine the mass and moment of inertia of a cog-wheel of uniform density k and negligible thickness, whose boundary in plane polar coordinates is given by $r = 2 + \frac{1}{2}\sin(12\theta)$, about an axis perpendicular to the plane of the cog-wheel through its centre.

Activity 5.6

Find the value of the volume integral of the function $f(x, y, z) = x^2yz$ over the wedge-shaped region bounded by the planes $x = 0$, $x = 1$, $y = 0$, $z = 0$, and $y + z = 1$.

This is Exercise 3.7.

Activity 5.7

(a) Find the mass M and the moment of inertia I about the z-axis of an object of uniform density k that is bounded by the surface $z = \frac{1}{9}(x^2 + y^2)$ and the plane $z = 1$.

This is similar to Exercise 3.11 where $k = 1$.

(b) Find the mass M and the moment of inertia I about the z-axis of an object of uniform density k that is bounded by the surface $z = \frac{1}{a^2}(x^2 + y^2)$ and the plane $z = 1$.

Activity 5.8

(a) Find the mass M and the moment of inertia I about the z-axis of a solid cylinder of radius a, height h and uniform density k.

Compare with Exercise 3.4.

(b) Find the mass M and the moment of inertia I about the z-axis of a hollow cylinder of external radius a, height h, thickness t and uniform density k. Write down the moment of inertia in terms of M and a as t becomes small.

Compare with Exercise 3.6.

(c) Find the mass M and the moment of inertia I about the z-axis of a solid cone of base radius a, height h and uniform density k.

Compare with Exercise 3.12.

Activity 5.9

(a) Find the mass M and the moment of inertia I about the z-axis of a solid sphere of radius a and uniform density k.

Compare with Example 3.3 and Exercise 3.3.

(b) Find the mass M and the moment of inertia I about the z-axis of a hollow sphere of inner radius a, thickness t and uniform density k. Write down the moment of inertia in terms of M and a as t becomes small.

Compare with Exercise 3.5.

Outcomes

After studying this unit you should be able to:

- evaluate area integrals over regions of the (x, y)-plane using Cartesian or plane polar coordinate systems;
- use area integrals for evaluating population models in the (x, y)-plane, and for obtaining the masses, centres of mass and moments of inertia of laminae;
- evaluate volume integrals over regions of space using Cartesian, cylindrical polar or spherical polar coordinate systems;
- use volume integrals to evaluate the masses and moments of inertia of solids;
- use area integrals to find surface areas.

Solutions to the exercises

Section 1

1.1 $$\int_S x^2y^3\,dA = \int_{x=0}^{x=2}\left(\int_{y=1}^{y=3} x^2y^3\,dy\right)dx$$
$$= \int_{x=0}^{x=2}\left(\left[x^2\left(\tfrac{1}{4}y^4\right)\right]_{y=1}^{y=3}\right)dx$$
$$= \int_{x=0}^{x=2}(20x^2)\,dx = \left[\tfrac{20}{3}x^3\right]_{x=0}^{x=2} = \tfrac{160}{3}.$$

1.2 We have to evaluate the expression
$$\int_{y=1}^{y=2}\left(\int_{x=0}^{x=3} xy\,dx\right)dy.$$
Taking the integral over x first, $\int_{x=0}^{x=3} xy\,dx$, treating y as a constant, we have
$$\int_{x=0}^{x=3} xy\,dx = y\left[\tfrac{1}{2}x^2\right]_{x=0}^{x=3} = \tfrac{9}{2}y.$$
Now the y-integration gives
$$\int_{y=1}^{y=2}\tfrac{9}{2}y\,dy = \tfrac{9}{2}\left[\tfrac{1}{2}y^2\right]_{y=1}^{y=2} = \tfrac{27}{4}.$$

1.3 Step (a):

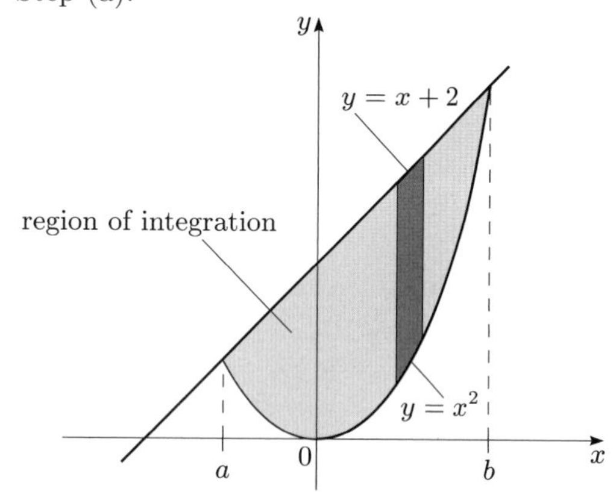

Step (b): To find the y-limits we draw in a vertical strip at some general position in the region as shown in the figure above. The lower point of this strip is then $y = x^2$ and the upper limit is $y = x + 2$.

Step (c): The limits of the x-integration are $x = a$ and $x = b$, and these values of x are solutions to the simultaneous equations $y = x^2$ and $y = x + 2$, i.e. of $x^2 - x - 2 = 0$, giving $x = 2$ and $x = -1$, so that $a = -1$ and $b = 2$.

Step (d): $\displaystyle\int_S y\,dA = \int_{x=-1}^{x=2}\left(\int_{y=x^2}^{y=x+2} y\,dy\right)dx.$

Step (e): $\displaystyle\int_{y=x^2}^{y=x+2} y\,dy = \left[\tfrac{1}{2}y^2\right]_{y=x^2}^{y=x+2}$
$$= \tfrac{1}{2}(x+2)^2 - \tfrac{1}{2}x^4.$$

Step (f): $\displaystyle\int_{x=-1}^{x=2}\left(\tfrac{1}{2}(x+2)^2 - \tfrac{1}{2}x^4\right)dx$
$$= \left[\tfrac{1}{6}(x+2)^3 - \tfrac{1}{10}x^5\right]_{x=-1}^{x=2} = \tfrac{36}{5}.$$

1.4 Step (a):

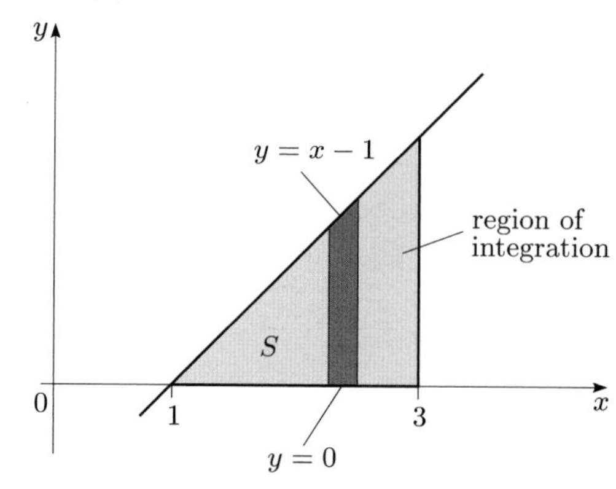

Step (b): The y-limits are $y = 0$ and $y = x - 1$.

Step (c): The x-limits are $x = 1$ and $x = 3$.

Step (d): $\displaystyle\int_S (x-y)\,dA = \int_{x=1}^{x=3}\left(\int_{y=0}^{y=x-1}(x-y)\,dy\right)dx.$

Step (e): $\displaystyle\int_{y=0}^{y=x-1}(x-y)\,dy = \left[xy - \tfrac{1}{2}y^2\right]_{y=0}^{y=x-1}$
$$= x(x-1) - \tfrac{1}{2}(x-1)^2$$
$$= \tfrac{1}{2}x^2 - \tfrac{1}{2}.$$

Step (f): $\displaystyle\int_{x=1}^{x=3}\left(\tfrac{1}{2}x^2 - \tfrac{1}{2}\right)dx = \left[\tfrac{1}{6}x^3 - \tfrac{1}{2}x\right]_{x=1}^{x=3} = \tfrac{10}{3}.$

1.5 **(a)** If we integrate over y first then we *fix* x and draw in a *vertical* strip as shown.

Step (a):

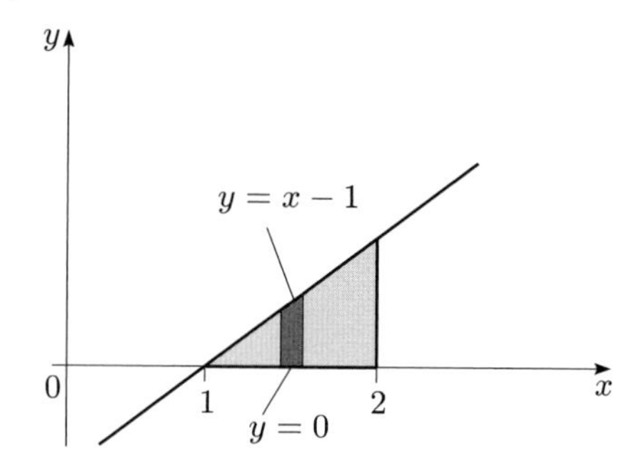

Step (b): The y-limits are $y = 0$ and $y = x - 1$.

Step (c): The x-limits are $x = 1$ and $x = 2$.

Step (d): $\displaystyle\int_S (x^2+y^2)\,dA$
$$= \int_{x=1}^{x=2}\left(\int_{y=0}^{y=x-1}(x^2+y^2)\,dy\right)dx.$$

Step (e): $\displaystyle\int_{y=0}^{y=x-1}(x^2+y^2)\,dy = \left[x^2y + \tfrac{1}{3}y^3\right]_{y=0}^{y=x-1}$
$$= x^2(x-1) + \tfrac{1}{3}(x-1)^3.$$

Step (f): $\displaystyle\int_{x=1}^{x=2}\left(x^3 - x^2 + \tfrac{1}{3}(x-1)^3\right)dx$
$$= \left[\tfrac{1}{4}x^4 - \tfrac{1}{3}x^3 + \tfrac{1}{12}(x-1)^4\right]_{x=1}^{x=2} = \tfrac{3}{2}.$$

(b) If we integrate over x first (and then over y) we *fix* y and draw in a *horizontal* strip.

Step (a):

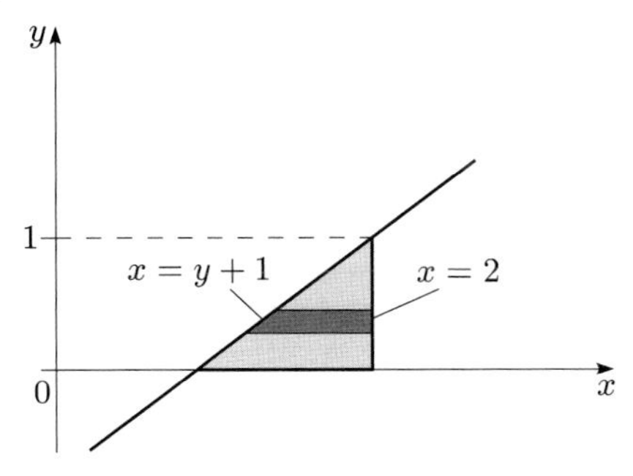

Step (b): The x-limits are $x = y + 1$ and $x = 2$.

Step (c): The y-limits are $y = 0$ and $y = 1$.

Step (d): $\int_S (x^2 + y^2)dA$

$$= \int_{y=0}^{y=1} \left(\int_{x=y+1}^{x=2} (x^2 + y^2)\, dx \right) dy.$$

Step (e): $\int_{x=y+1}^{x=2} (x^2 + y^2)\, dx = \left[\frac{1}{3}x^3 + xy^2\right]_{x=y+1}^{x=2}$

$$= \tfrac{8}{3} + 2y^2 - \tfrac{1}{3}(y+1)^3 - (y+1)y^2.$$

Step (f): $\int_{y=0}^{y=1} \left(\frac{8}{3} - \frac{1}{3}(y+1)^3 + y^2 - y^3\right)dy$

$$= \left[\tfrac{8}{3}y - \tfrac{1}{12}(y+1)^4 + \tfrac{1}{3}y^3 - \tfrac{1}{4}y^4\right]_{y=0}^{y=1} = \tfrac{3}{2}.$$

1.6
$$\int_{\text{triangle}} f dA = \int_{x=0}^{x=1} \left(\int_{y=0}^{y=1-x} (x+y)\, dy \right) dx$$
$$= \int_{x=0}^{x=1} \left[xy + \tfrac{1}{2}y^2\right]_{y=0}^{y=1-x} dx$$
$$= \int_0^1 \left(x(1-x) + \tfrac{1}{2}(1-x)^2\right) dx$$
$$= \tfrac{1}{3}.$$

1.7
$$\int_{\text{quadrant}} f dA = \int_{x=0}^{x=1} \left(\int_{y=0}^{y=\sqrt{1-x^2}} x\, dy \right) dx$$
$$= \int_{x=0}^{x=1} [xy]_{y=0}^{y=\sqrt{1-x^2}}\, dx$$
$$= \int_0^1 x\sqrt{1-x^2}\, dx$$
$$= \left[-\tfrac{1}{3}(1-x^2)^{\frac{3}{2}}\right]_0^1 = \tfrac{1}{3}.$$

1.8 The region is enclosed by the straight lines $x = 1$, $x = 2$, $y = x + 2$ and the parabola $y = x^2$.

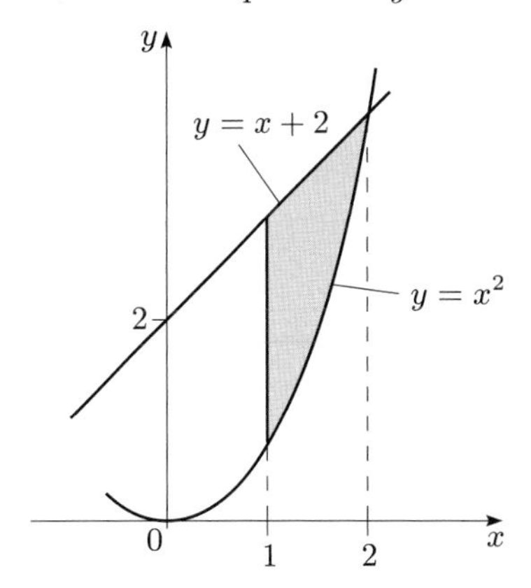

$$\int_{x=1}^{x=2} \left(\int_{y=x^2}^{y=x+2} 1 dy \right) dx$$
$$= \int_{x=1}^{x=2} [y]_{y=x^2}^{y=x+2}\, dx = \int_1^2 (x + 2 - x^2)\, dx = \tfrac{7}{6}.$$

Section 2

2.1 The total population is the area integral of the surface density function over the triangular region of the plate shown in the figure.

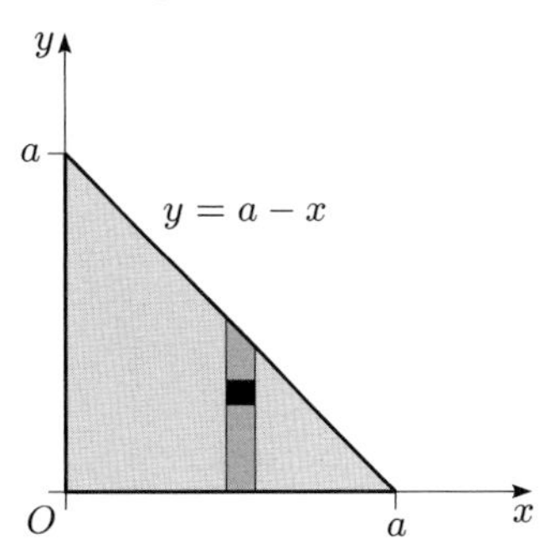

Integrating first over y, i.e. using vertical strips, the lower and upper limits of the y-integral are $y = 0$ and $y = a - x$. The strips begin at $x = 0$ and end at $x = a$. Hence the total number of bacteria is given by the area integral

$$A \int_{x=0}^{x=a} \left(\int_{y=0}^{y=a-x} \left(2 - \frac{x^2}{a^2} - \frac{y^2}{a^2}\right) dy \right) dx$$
$$= A \int_{x=0}^{x=a} \left[2y - \frac{x^2 y}{a^2} - \frac{1}{3}\frac{y^3}{a^2}\right]_{y=0}^{y=a-x} dx$$
$$= A \int_0^a \left(2(a-x) - \frac{x^2(a-x)}{a^2} - \frac{1}{3}\frac{(a-x)^3}{a^2}\right) dx$$
$$= \tfrac{5}{6}Aa^2.$$

When $A = 10^{12}\,\text{m}^{-2}$ and $a = 0.01\,\text{m}$ the number of bacteria is 8.3×10^7.

2.2 The mass of the lens is

$$\int_{\text{disc}} f\,dA = 2\pi k \int_{r=0}^{r=a} \left(1 - \frac{r^2}{a^2}\right) r\,dr$$
$$= 2\pi k \left[\tfrac{1}{2}r^2 - \tfrac{1}{4}\frac{r^4}{a^2}\right]_0^a = \tfrac{1}{2}\pi k a^2$$
$$= 2.9 \times 10^{-3}\,\text{kg},$$

for $a = 2.5 \times 10^{-2}$ m and $k = 3\,\text{kg}\,\text{m}^{-2}$.

2.3 The area integral is

$$\int_S y f\,dA = f \int_{x=-a}^{x=a} \left(\int_{y=0}^{y=\sqrt{a^2-x^2}} y\,dy\right) dx$$
$$= f \int_{x=-a}^{x=a} \left[\tfrac{1}{2}y^2\right]_{y=0}^{y=\sqrt{a^2-x^2}} dx$$
$$= \tfrac{1}{2} f \int_{-a}^{a} (a^2 - x^2)\,dx$$
$$= \tfrac{1}{2} f \left[a^2 x - \tfrac{1}{3}x^3\right]_{-a}^{a} = \tfrac{2}{3} f a^3,$$

and so $y_G = \frac{4a}{3\pi}$ as in Example 2.3.

2.4 The ruler is modelled as a lamina in the (x, y)-plane with its centre at the origin. The region of integration is shown in the figure.

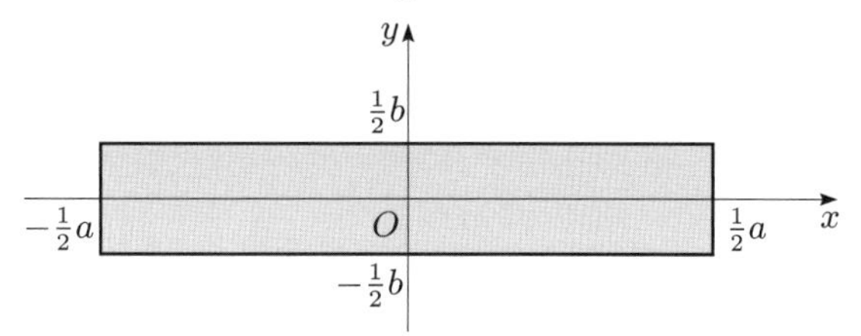

Using Cartesian coordinates we have

$$I = f \int_{x=-\frac{1}{2}a}^{x=\frac{1}{2}a} \left(\int_{y=-\frac{1}{2}b}^{y=\frac{1}{2}b} (x^2 + y^2)\,dy\right) dx$$
$$= 2f \int_{-\frac{1}{2}a}^{\frac{1}{2}a} \left(\tfrac{1}{2}x^2 b + \tfrac{1}{24}b^3\right) dx = \tfrac{1}{12} f ab(a^2 + b^2),$$

where fab is the total mass M of the ruler. Hence $I = \frac{1}{12}M(a^2 + b^2)$, and the moment of inertia of the ruler is

$$I = 10^{-2} \times \frac{0.30 \times 0.04}{12}(0.30^2 + 0.04^2)$$
$$= 9.16 \times 10^{-7}\,\text{kg}\,\text{m}^2.$$

2.5 Taking the constant surface density f outside the area integral we have

$$I_{\text{disc}} = f \int_{\theta=-\pi}^{\theta=\pi} \left(\int_{r=0}^{r=a} r^3\,dr\right) d\theta = 2\pi f \int_0^a r^3 dr$$
$$= \tfrac{1}{2}\pi f a^4.$$

The mass of the disc is $M = f\pi a^2$, and so we have $I_{\text{disc}} = \frac{1}{2}Ma^2$, as required.

2.6 The required mass is the area integral of f on a disc of radius b. Noting that f depends on r only, we have

$$\int_S f\,dA = 2\pi A \int_0^b \exp(-r^2/a^2) r\,dr$$
$$= -\pi A a^2 [\exp(-r^2/a^2)]_0^b = \pi a^2 A(1 - \exp(-b^2/a^2))$$
$$= \pi \times (1.5 \times 10^{-2})^2 \times 10^{-5}(1 - \exp(-1/1.5^2))$$
$$= 2.5 \times 10^{-9}\,\text{kg},$$

for $A = 10^{-5}\,\text{kg}\,\text{m}^{-2}$, $a = 1.5 \times 10^{-2}$ m and $b = 0.01$ m.

2.7 Let f be the density of the washer. Then

$$I_{\text{washer}} = 2\pi f \int_a^b r^3 dr = 2\pi f \left[\tfrac{1}{4}r^4\right]_a^b$$
$$= \tfrac{1}{2}\pi f(b^4 - a^4).$$

The mass of the washer is $M = f\pi(b^2 - a^2)$, and so $I_{\text{washer}} = \frac{1}{2}M(b^2 + a^2)$.

2.8 The moment of inertia of the magnifying glass is

$$I = 2\pi k \int_0^a \left(1 - \frac{r^2}{a^2}\right) r^3 dr = 2\pi k \left[\frac{r^4}{4} - \frac{r^6}{6a^2}\right]_0^a$$
$$= \tfrac{1}{6}\pi k a^4 = 6.1 \times 10^{-7}\,\text{kg}\,\text{m}^2,$$

for the given values of k and a.

2.9

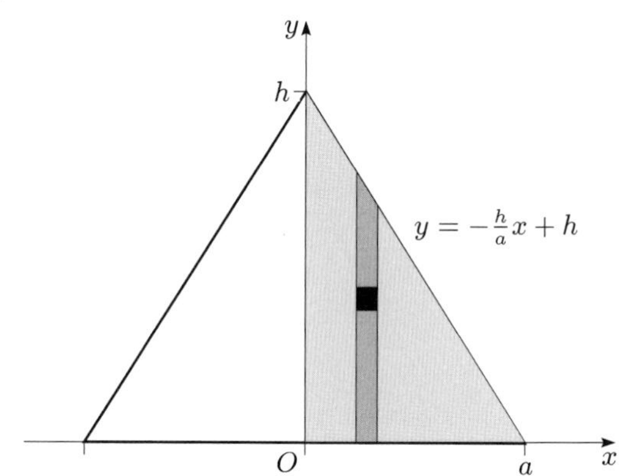

We have $x_G = 0$ by symmetry. Also by symmetry the y-coordinates of the centres of mass of the two triangles in the positive and negative x-regions are the same and are given by

$$y_G = \frac{1}{M} f \int_{x=0}^{x=a} \left(\int_{y=0}^{y=-\frac{h}{a}x+h} y\,dy\right) dx,$$

where the mass M of the half-triangle is $\frac{1}{2}ahf$. Thus

$$y_G = \frac{2}{ah} \int_{x=0}^{x=a} \tfrac{1}{2}\left(-\frac{h}{a}x + h\right)^2 dx = \tfrac{1}{3}h.$$

Section 3

3.1 The mass of the block is the volume integral

$$M = \int_V f dV = \int_V (x + y + z)\, dV.$$

The region of integration is shown in the figure.

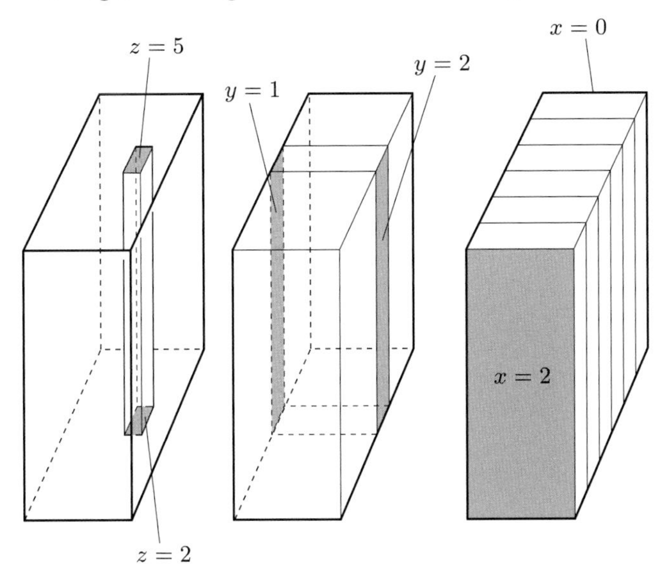

$$M = \int_{x=0}^{x=2} \left(\int_{y=1}^{y=2} \left(\int_{z=2}^{z=5} (x + y + z)\, dz \right) dy \right) dx$$
$$= \int_{x=0}^{x=2} \left(\int_{y=1}^{y=2} (3x + 3y + \tfrac{21}{2})\, dy \right) dx$$
$$= \int_{x=0}^{x=2} (3x + 15)\, dx = 36.$$

3.2 The scalar function $f = c + \alpha r$ is spherically symmetric so, using Equation (3.6),

$$M = 4\pi \int_{r=0}^{r=R} (c + \alpha r) r^2\, dr = 4\pi \left[\tfrac{1}{3} c r^3 + \tfrac{1}{4} \alpha r^4\right]_0^R$$
$$= \tfrac{1}{3}\pi R^3 (4c + 3\alpha R)\,.$$

(The case $c = 1$ and $\alpha = 0$ gives the volume of a sphere.)

3.3 The mass of the sphere of density D is

$$M = D \int_{r=0}^{r=R} \left(\int_{\theta=0}^{\theta=\pi} \left(\int_{\phi=-\pi}^{\phi=\pi} r^2 \sin\theta\, d\phi \right) d\theta \right) dr.$$

Using Equation (3.6), $M = \frac{4}{3}\pi D R^3$, and using this result in the solution to Example 3.3, we find $I = \frac{2}{5} M R^2$.

3.4 Let the constant density of the cylinder be D. The volume integral in cylindrical polar coordinates can be carried out in any order so Equation (3.4) becomes

$$I = 2\pi \int_{\rho=0}^{\rho=a} \left(\int_{z=0}^{z=h} D\, dz \right) \rho^3 d\rho.$$

The z-integral yields a factor Dh and the ρ-integral yields $\frac{1}{4}a^4$. Hence $I = \frac{1}{2}\pi D h a^4$. The mass M of the cylinder is given by a similar volume integral but with ρ replacing ρ^3 in the integrand. Hence $M = \pi D h a^2$ and so $I = \frac{1}{2} M a^2$.

3.5 We use spherical polar coordinates.

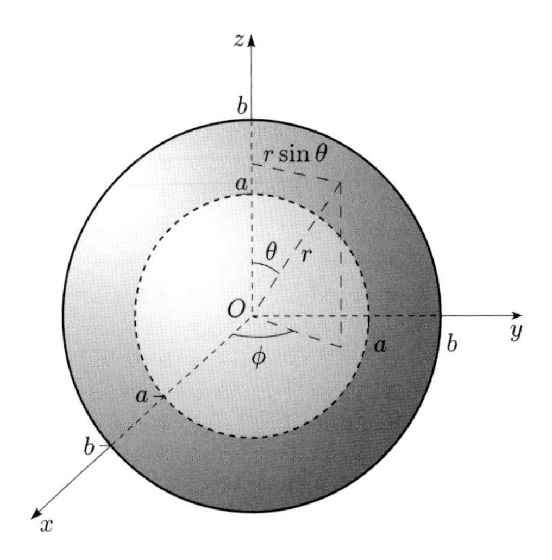

Using Equation (3.7) we have, with $f = D$,

$$I = D \int_{\text{shell}} (r \sin\theta)^2 r^2 \sin\theta\, d\phi\, d\theta\, dr.$$

The function to be integrated does not depend on azimuthal angle ϕ and so the ϕ-integral yields a factor 2π. This leaves the area integral $2\pi D \int_{r=a}^{r=b} \left(\int_{\theta=0}^{\theta=\pi} r^4 \sin^3\theta d\theta \right) dr$. We can write $\sin^3\theta = \sin\theta\left(1 - \cos^2\theta\right)$ and so the θ-integral yields $\left[-\cos\theta + \frac{1}{3}\cos^3\theta\right]_0^\pi = \frac{4}{3}$. Hence

$$I = \tfrac{8}{3}\pi D \int_a^b r^4\, dr = \tfrac{8}{15}\pi D (b^5 - a^5).$$

The mass of the shell is $M = \frac{4}{3}\pi D (b^3 - a^3)$ and so we have

$$I = \frac{2M(b^5 - a^5)}{5(b^3 - a^3)}.$$

(Note that this answer gives $\frac{2}{5} M b^2$ in the limit $a \to 0$, which is the moment of inertia of a uniform solid sphere of radius b as found in Exercise 3.3.)

3.6 With the axis of the cylinder on the z-axis, and since the cylinder is uniform, the moment of inertia must be the same as the moment of inertia of the (uniform) washer, see Exercise 2.7, since the projection of the cylindrical shell onto the (x, y)-plane occupies the same region as the washer. Thus we have

$$I_{\text{shell}} = I_{\text{washer}} = \tfrac{1}{2} M (b^2 + a^2).$$

3.7 The region and the projection onto the (x, y)-plane are shown below.

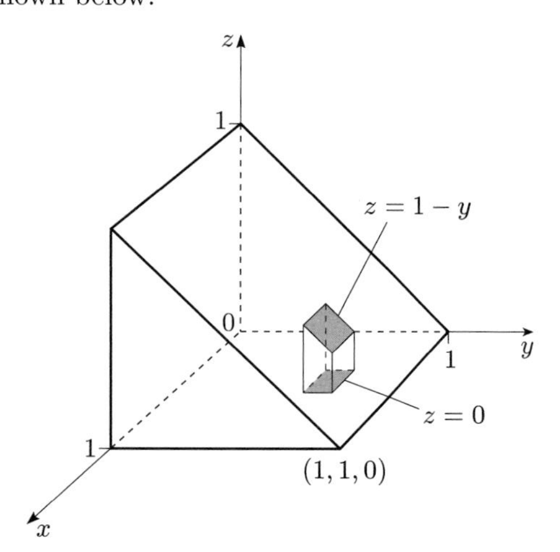

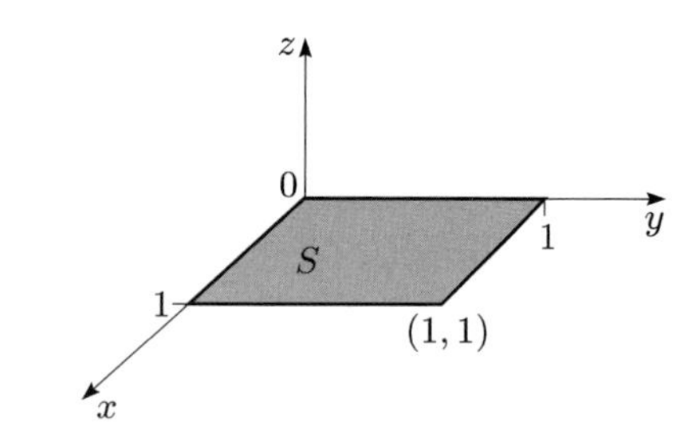

The integral over z gives

$$h(x,y) = \int_{z=0}^{z=1-y} x^2yz\,dz = \left[\tfrac{1}{2}x^2yz^2\right]_{z=0}^{z=1-y}$$
$$= \tfrac{1}{2}x^2y(1-y)^2.$$

Now following the steps in Procedure 1.1 for evaluating the area integral of $h(x, y)$ over S,

$$\int_S h(x,y)dA = \int_{x=0}^{x=1}\left(\int_{y=0}^{y=1} \tfrac{1}{2}x^2y(1-y)^2\,dy\right)dx$$
$$= \int_{x=0}^{x=1} \left[\tfrac{1}{2}x^2\left(\tfrac{1}{2}y^2 - \tfrac{2}{3}y^3 + \tfrac{1}{4}y^4\right)\right]_{y=0}^{y=1} dx$$
$$= \int_0^1 \tfrac{1}{24}x^2\,dx = \tfrac{1}{72}.$$

3.8 The region B is illustrated below.

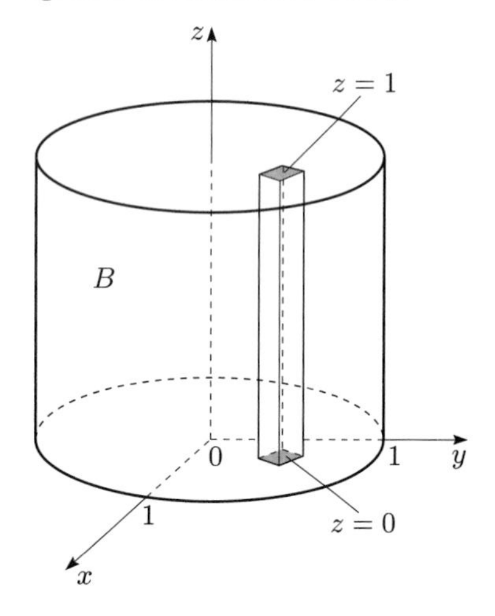

The projection of B onto the (x, y)-plane is the disc $x^2 + y^2 \leq 1$.

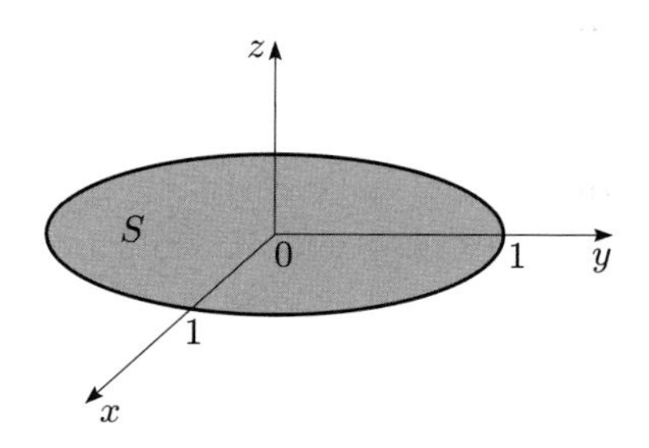

The column is shown in the first figure above. The z-limits are $z = 0$ and $z = 1$. The integral over z is

$$h(x,y) = \int_{z=0}^{z=1} (z + 3x - 2)\,dz$$
$$= \left[\tfrac{1}{2}z^2 + (3x-2)z\right]_{z=0}^{z=1}$$
$$= \tfrac{1}{2} + 3x - 2 = 3x - \tfrac{3}{2}.$$

We now evaluate the area integral.

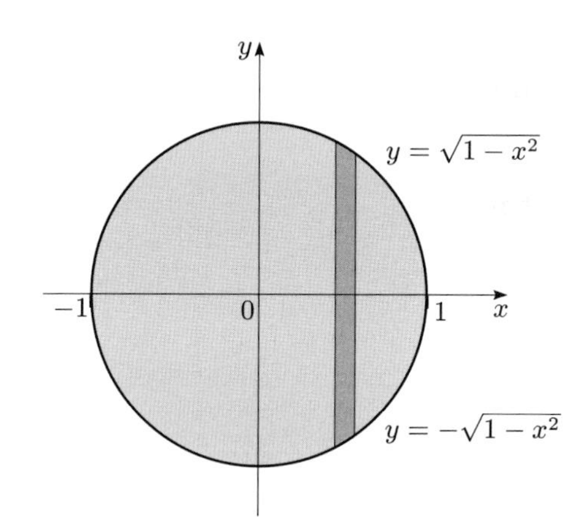

$$\int_S h(x,y)dA = \int_{x=-1}^{x=1}\left(\int_{y=-\sqrt{1-x^2}}^{y=\sqrt{1-x^2}} \left(3x - \tfrac{3}{2}\right)dy\right)dx$$
$$= \int_{-1}^{1}\left(\left(3x - \tfrac{3}{2}\right)2\sqrt{1-x^2}\right)dx = -\tfrac{3\pi}{2}.$$

3.9 The mass of the block is

$$\int_B (x(y+1) - z)dV$$
$$= \int_{x=1}^{x=2}\left(\int_{y=0}^{y=3}\left(\int_{z=-1}^{z=0} (x(y+1) - z)\,dz\right)dy\right)dx$$
$$= \int_{x=1}^{x=2}\left(\int_{y=0}^{y=3} \left(x(y+1) + \tfrac{1}{2}\right)dy\right)dx$$
$$= \int_1^2 \left(\tfrac{9}{2}x + 3x + \tfrac{3}{2}\right)dx = \tfrac{51}{4}.$$

3.10 **(a)** Use spherical polar coordinates. The density function is $f(\mathbf{r}) = cr^2$, so using Equation (3.6) the mass of the sphere is

$$M = 4\pi \int_0^R (cr^2)r^2\,dr = \tfrac{4}{5}\pi c R^5.$$

(b) The moment of inertia I is the volume integral of the function $g(r,\theta,\phi) = f(r)d^2 = (cr^2)(r\sin\theta)^2$ (which is *not* spherically symmetric). Hence

$$\begin{aligned} I &= \int_{\text{sphere}} cr^2(r\sin\theta)^2 dV \\ &= c\int_{\text{sphere}} r^2(r\sin\theta)^2 r^2\sin\theta\,d\phi\,d\theta\,dr \\ &= c\int_{r=0}^{r=R}\int_{\theta=0}^{\theta=\pi}\int_{\phi=-\pi}^{\phi=\pi} r^6\sin^3\theta\,d\phi\,d\theta\,dr \\ &= \tfrac{8}{21}c\pi R^7 = \tfrac{10}{21}MR^2, \end{aligned}$$

using $\int_0^\pi \sin^3\theta\,d\theta = \frac{4}{3}$ from Solution 3.5 or Example 3.3.

3.11 The volume is the integral $\int_B 1dV$.
The region B is illustrated below.

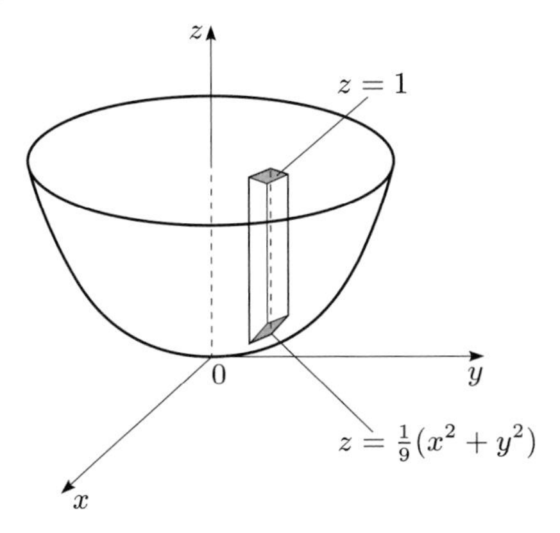

The projection of B onto the (x,y)-plane is the disc $x^2 + y^2 \le 9$.

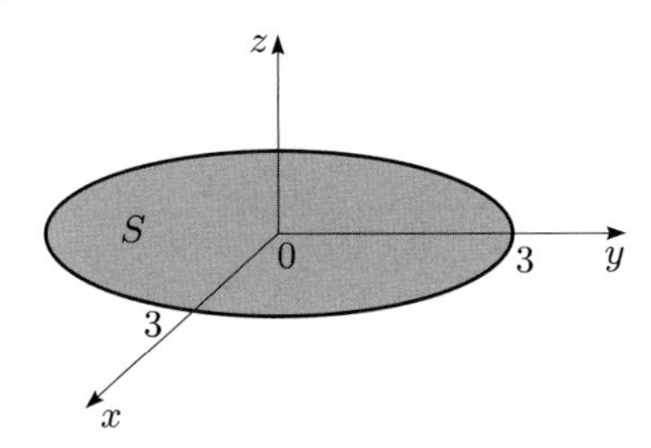

A vertical column is shown in the first figure above. The z-limits are $z = \frac{1}{9}(x^2+y^2)$ and $z = 1$. The z-integral is

$$\int_{z=(x^2+y^2)/9}^{z=1} 1dz = 1 - \tfrac{1}{9}(x^2+y^2) = h(x,y).$$

Next evaluate $\int_S \left(1 - \frac{1}{9}(x^2+y^2)\right) dA$ on the region S below.

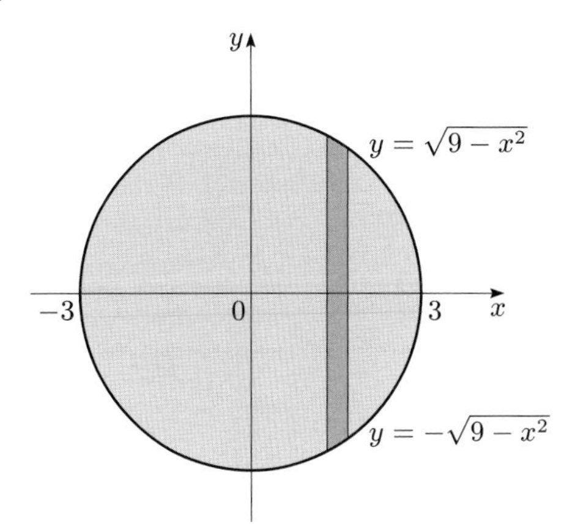

$$\begin{aligned} &\int_{x=-3}^{x=3}\left(\int_{y=-\sqrt{9-x^2}}^{y=\sqrt{9-x^2}} \left(1 - \tfrac{1}{9}x^2 - \tfrac{1}{9}y^2\right)dy\right)dx \\ &\quad = \int_{x=-3}^{x=3}\left(\left(1-\tfrac{1}{9}x^2\right)2\sqrt{9-x^2} - \tfrac{2}{27}(9-x^2)^{\frac{3}{2}}\right)dx \\ &\quad = \int_{-3}^{3} \tfrac{4}{27}(9-x^2)^{\frac{3}{2}}\,dx = \tfrac{9\pi}{2}. \end{aligned}$$

3.12 Let the base of the cone lie in the (x,y)-plane with the axis of the cone on the z-axis, as shown in Figure 3.10. Use cylindrical polar coordinates and integrate over z first. This represents first summing elements in the column starting at the base, $z = 0$, and ending at $z = h(1-\rho/a)$, the top of the column where h is the height of the cone. Thus taking the uniform density to be D, the moment of inertia of the cone is

$$\begin{aligned} I_{\text{cone}} &= \int_{\text{cone}} D\rho^2 dV \\ &= D\int_{\rho=0}^{\rho=a}\left(\int_{\theta=-\pi}^{\theta=\pi}\left(\int_{z=0}^{z=h(1-\rho/a)} \rho^3\,dz\right)d\theta\right)d\rho \end{aligned}$$

Integrating over z leaves the area integral over the circular base in the (x,y)-plane, which, using Equation (2.4) gives

$$I_{\text{cone}} = 2\pi D\int_0^a \rho^3 h(1-\rho/a)\,d\rho = \tfrac{1}{10}\pi D h a^4.$$

The mass of the cone is simply the volume integral of D over the region occupied by the cone, which is

$$\begin{aligned} M_{\text{cone}} &= D\int_{\rho=0}^{\rho=a}\left(\int_{\theta=-\pi}^{\theta=\pi}\left(\int_{z=0}^{z=h(1-\rho/a)} \rho\,dz\right)d\theta\right)d\rho \\ &= 2\pi D\int_0^a \rho h(1-\rho/a)\,d\rho = \tfrac{1}{3}D\pi a^2 h. \end{aligned}$$

Hence $I_{\text{cone}} = \frac{3}{10}Ma^2$.

Section 4

4.1

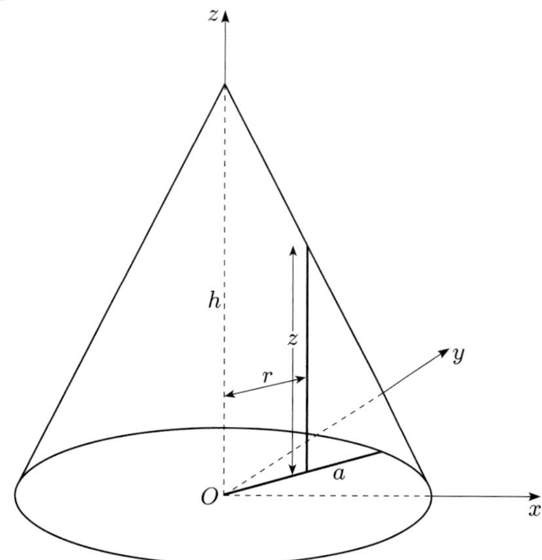

The equation of the cone can easily be found by using similar triangles. Specifically, since $r = \sqrt{x^2 + y^2}$, then

$$\frac{z}{a - r} = \frac{h}{a}.$$

Thus $z = h - hr/a$, or (replacing r by x and y)

$$z = h - \frac{h}{a}\sqrt{x^2 + y^2}.$$

The partial derivatives are therefore

$$\frac{\partial z}{\partial x} = \frac{-hx}{a\sqrt{x^2 + y^2}} \quad \text{and} \quad \frac{\partial z}{\partial y} = \frac{-hy}{a\sqrt{x^2 + y^2}}$$

and the area of the cone is given by the double integral

$$\begin{aligned} A &= \int_S \sqrt{1 + \frac{h^2x^2}{a^2(x^2 + y^2)} + \frac{h^2y^2}{a^2(x^2 + y^2)}}\, dA \\ &= \int_S \sqrt{\frac{a^2 + h^2}{a^2}}\, dA. \end{aligned}$$

The limits for both integrals can be found as in Example 4.2. However the surface area is much easier to compute using polar coordinates, and the integral becomes simply

$$\begin{aligned} A &= \frac{\sqrt{a^2 + h^2}}{a} \int_0^a \left(\int_0^{2\pi} r\, d\theta \right) dr \\ &= \frac{2\pi\sqrt{a^2 + h^2}}{a} \int_0^a r\, dr \\ &= \frac{2\pi\sqrt{a^2 + h^2}}{a} \frac{a^2}{2} \\ &= \pi a\sqrt{a^2 + h^2}. \end{aligned}$$

UNIT 26 Numerical methods for differential equations

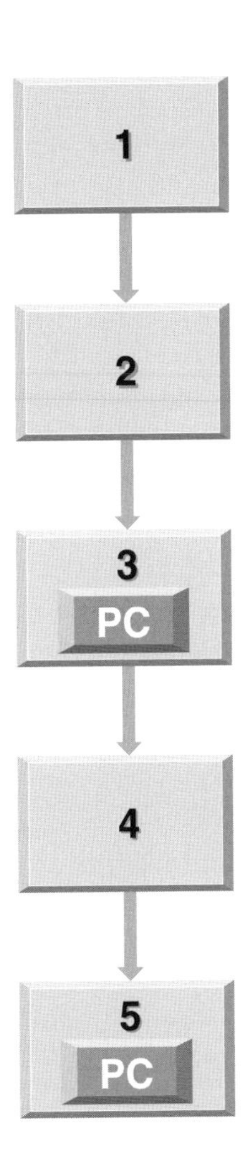

Study guide for Unit 26

Unit 2 included an introduction to Euler's method, which is the simplest numerical method for solving initial-value problems for differential equations. Most of this unit is concerned with more advanced numerical methods, which may be used to obtain accurate solutions more efficiently.

Section 1 contains some material on Taylor polynomials, which were discussed in *Unit 12* of this course.

Section 2 develops some further numerical methods for differential equations which require an understanding of Taylor approximations for functions of more than one variable, which were introduced in *Unit 12*.

Section 3 involves use of the computer to experiment with these methods. It is desirable to carry out this experimentation before studying Section 4.

Section 4 introduces you to some methods of analysing when the methods described earlier in the unit work (and when they do not).

Section 5 requires further use of the computer, to put the analysis of Section 4 into practice.

In this unit, numbers will normally be quoted to six-figure accuracy (unless circumstances require extra places), but the underlying calculations will have been done to the full accuracy of the calculator or computer.

Introduction

The early units of this course provided an introduction to differential equations, and also to systems of differential equations. This unit introduces the study of differential equations once again, from a different point of view, by considering a fairly general form of first-order differential equation:

See *Units 2, 3, 11, 13.*

$$\frac{dy}{dx} = f(x, y).$$

Some methods have been given for finding analytic solutions of differential equations of this form. In particular, it is possible to write down an analytic expression for the general solution in the cases where:

(a) $f(x, y) = g(x)h(y)$, using the method of separation of variables,

(b) $f(x, y) = h(x) - g(x)y$, using the integrating factor method.

Analytic methods exist for solving a few other special forms of differential equations, but there are many differential equations for which it is not possible to obtain an analytic solution. For example, a differential equation as simple as

$$\frac{dy}{dx} = x^2 + y^2$$

has no analytic expression for the solution. Even where the method of separation of variables, or the integrating factor method, can be used, the resulting analytic solution may involve integrals which cannot be evaluated in terms of expressions involving familiar functions. Such is the case for the differential equation

$$\frac{dy}{dx} = 1 - xy,$$

where the solution involves the integral

$$\int \exp(\tfrac{1}{2}x^2)\, dx.$$

In such cases, we must use numerical methods, of which the simplest, Euler's method, has already been introduced. The main aim of this unit is to introduce you to a variety of numerical methods.

Euler's method was discussed in *Unit 2.*

Euler's method provides a means of solving an *initial-value problem*, and so obtaining a *particular solution* of a differential equation which satisfies some given initial condition; it does not provide a general solution. The same is true of all numerical methods: they provide particular solutions to initial-value problems, not general solutions.

Before we go on to look at numerical methods, we begin in Section 1 by recalling how $f(x)$ may be approximated by an nth-order Taylor polynomial. We then go on to look at the accuracy of the nth-order Taylor approximation, and introduce some new ideas that will be useful throughout the unit.

Such Taylor polynomials are discussed in *Unit 12.*

Section 2 recaps Euler's method for solving initial-value problems involving first-order differential equations and goes on to explain that more efficient methods exist, in that they can achieve the same or better accuracy for less work. Three new methods, known as Runge–Kutta methods, are derived. Section 3 provides an opportunity to use the computer algebra package to apply the methods introduced in Section 2.

Section 4 establishes a way of determining how small the step size h would need to be in order to achieve a given accuracy for a given initial-value problem. A numerical method, such as Euler's method, gives rise to approximations to the exact solution at a discrete set of points throughout the interval in question. It is often, though not always, the case that the largest error occurs at the end of that interval. Thus the analysis will concentrate on achieving a given accuracy at the end of the interval in question. It will be seen that, in order to obtain an accurate solution, it is sometimes necessary to reduce the step size h to a size which is impractical, either because it increases the amount of computation to an unacceptable level, or because the arithmetic is not done to a sufficient number of decimal places, and the resulting rounding errors accumulate to dominate the numerical solution. It is for these reasons that numerical methods other than Euler's method need to be considered, so as to obtain a desired accuracy more efficiently. These other numerical methods are based on Taylor polynomials, and their derivations make use of Taylor approximations for functions of more than one variable.

These were introduced in *Unit 12*.

In Section 5 you will be given the opportunity to use the course's computer algebra package, to investigate the solution of an initial-value problem to a given accuracy using the ideas in Section 4.

The discussions in this unit are based upon three initial-value problems:

$$\frac{dy}{dx} = 3(x-1)^2 + 20(y-(x-1)^3), \qquad y(0) = -1, \tag{0.1}$$

$$\frac{dy}{dx} = 20x(2-x) - 20y, \qquad y(0) = 0, \tag{0.2}$$

$$\frac{dy}{dx} = y(20-y), \qquad y(0) = 12, \tag{0.3}$$

The first two of these are linear, with analytic solutions that may be obtained by the integrating factor method, and the third involves a logistic equation, with an analytic solution that can be found by separation of variables. It is useful to consider problems for which analytic solutions are available, as it enables us to understand how numerical methods work, and in particular to observe how errors propagate. In practice, of course, numerical methods would be used mainly to find solutions when no analytic solution is available.

Logistic equations and their solutions were considered in *Units 2* and *13*.

1 Taylor's Theorem

You know that a function $f(x)$ can be approximated by *Taylor polynomials*, provided that the values of the function and of the first few of its derivatives are known at some point $x = a$. If the first n derivatives exist and are continuous at a, then the *nth-order Taylor polynomial about* $x = a$ is given by

$$p_n(x) = f(a) + f'(a)(x-a) + \tfrac{1}{2!}f''(a)(x-a)^2 + \cdots + \tfrac{1}{n!}f^{(n)}(a)(x-a)^n.$$

Exercise 1.1

Let $f(x) = e^{2x}$. Calculate the Taylor polynomials $p_1(x)$, $p_2(x)$, $p_3(x)$ and $p_4(x)$ for $f(x)$ about $x = 0$.

In *Unit 12* we stated that 'successively higher-order Taylor polynomials will give successively better approximations, at least for values of x that are reasonably close to a'. This is illustrated in Figure 1.1, which shows the graphs of the function $f(x) = e^{2x}$, together with those of its first four Taylor polynomials about $x = 0$.

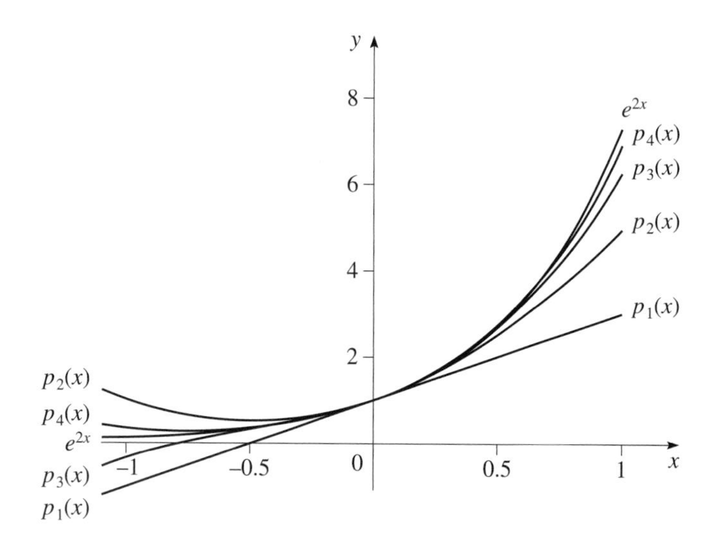

Figure 1.1 Taylor polynomial approximations to e^{2x}

You should be able to see that, at any point close to $x = 0$, as the order of the polynomial increases, the approximation improves. Each polynomial is obtained by adding one more term to the previous polynomial, and each provides a good approximation around $x = 0$ over a larger interval than the previous polynomial.

In *Unit 12* you should have worked through several exercises concerning Taylor polynomials about $x = 0$; but it is important to be confident with calculating Taylor polynomials at other points.

*Exercise 1.2

Determine the second-order and third-order Taylor polynomials for $f(x) = x^{\frac{1}{2}}$ about $x = 1$. Evaluate these polynomials at $x = 1.44$, and compare the answers with the value of $f(x)$ at $x = 1.44$.

Exercise 1.3

(a) Show that the Taylor polynomial of degree n for $f(x) = \ln x$ about $x = 1$ is

$$p_n(x) = (x-1) - \tfrac{1}{2}(x-1)^2 + \tfrac{1}{3}(x-1)^3 - \cdots + (-1)^{n+1}\tfrac{1}{n}(x-1)^n.$$

(b) Evaluate the third- and fourth-order Taylor polynomials at $x = 1.6$, and compare the answers with $\ln 1.6$.

When using a Taylor polynomial $p_n(x)$ to approximate a function $f(x)$, it is often important to know the accuracy of the approximation. The error associated with Taylor polynomial approximation usually arises through limiting the degree of the polynomial or the number of derivatives which are used. Such an error is called a *truncation error*, and an indication of accuracy is given either as an estimate of that error, or as an upper bound on its magnitude. For Taylor polynomial approximation, the **truncation error** $\varepsilon(x)$ is defined by

You will see the reason for the word *truncation* on page 47.

$$\varepsilon(x) = p_n(x) - f(x).$$

By way of example, the truncation error for the third-order Taylor polynomial approximating e^{2x} about $x = 0$ is

$$\varepsilon(x) = 1 + 2x + 2x^2 + \tfrac{4}{3}x^3 - e^{2x}.$$

This is plotted in Figure 1.2.

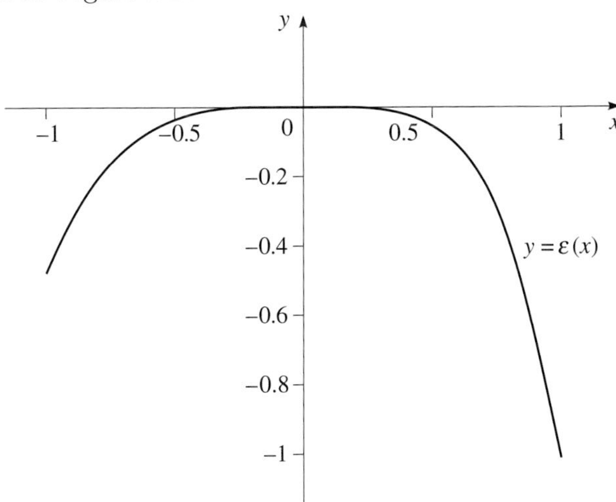

Figure 1.2

The very flat behaviour of $\varepsilon(x)$ near $x = 0$ in the above figure should be expected, and illustrates that the graph of the Taylor polynomial is indistinguishable from that of $f(x) = e^{2x}$ over an interval around $x = 0$.

Suppose now that we have obtained $p_n(x)$, the Taylor polynomial approximating some given function $f(x)$ about $x = a$, and we wish to use this polynomial p_n to approximate f at a particular value of x. We need some idea of what the magnitude of the truncation error is at this value of x. Taylor's Theorem gives a method of doing this: it will not be proved here, but may be stated as follows.

Theorem 1.1 Taylor's Theorem

Let f and its first $n + 1$ derivatives exist and be continuous at all points between a and x, including a and x themselves. Then, writing $x = a + h$, $f(x)$ can be expressed as

$$f(x) = f(a + h) = f(a) + hf'(a) + \tfrac{1}{2!}h^2 f''(a) + \cdots + \tfrac{1}{n!}h^n f^{(n)}(a) - \varepsilon(x), \qquad (1.1)$$

where the truncation error, or **remainder**, $\varepsilon(x)$, takes the form

$$\varepsilon(x) = -\tfrac{1}{(n+1)!}h^{n+1} f^{(n+1)}(c_x)$$

for some number c_x between a and x.

The requirement that the $n + 1$ derivatives of $f(x)$ should exist excludes functions such as $|x|$ or $x^{\frac{1}{3}}$ over an interval which includes 0.

Notice how writing $x = a + h$ (or equivalently, $h = x - a$) allows us to write the expression more compactly, using powers of h rather than powers of the expression $(x - a)$.

The expression (1.1) is often called the ***n*th Taylor expansion** of $f(x)$ about $x = a$ **with remainder**.

The expression

$$f(x) = f(a + h) = f(a) + hf'(a) + \tfrac{1}{2!}h^2 f''(a) + \cdots + \tfrac{1}{n!}h^n f^{(n)}(a) + \cdots$$

is called the **Taylor expansion** (or **Taylor series**) of $f(x)$ about a. This expression takes the form of an 'infinite sum'. You should think of it as a recipe for producing the Taylor polynomials: to obtain the nth-order polynomial you simply add the first n terms and chop the rest off (or *truncate* them).

You met infinite sums in *Unit 21* in the context of Fourier series.

Hence, when using the nth-order polynomial to approximate $f(x)$, you have a *truncation error*.

The essence of Taylor's Theorem is that the truncation error term, $-\varepsilon(x)$, in the nth-order approximation is equal to an expression that is very like the last term in the $(n+1)$th-order approximation! The latter term is $\frac{1}{(n+1)!}h^{n+1}f^{(n+1)}(a)$, whereas the truncation error term is $-\varepsilon(x) = \frac{1}{(n+1)!}h^{n+1}f^{(n+1)}(c_x)$.

To obtain an exact expression for c_x would be hoping for too much: that would mean that we had an exact expression for the error, and thus we could find an exact value for $f(a+h)$, so that there would be no need for approximation! But the theorem *does* say that c_x must lie between a and x, and so if $f^{(n+1)}(x)$ is a reasonably slowly-varying function, then the negative of the $(n+1)$th term, $-\frac{1}{(n+1)!}h^{n+1}f^{(n+1)}(a)$, is often a very good *estimate* of the truncation error.

The next term in the Taylor series is a good approximation to the error when the subsequent terms are much smaller. However care is needed, for example, for even functions about $x = 0$, where the odd terms in the expansion are all zero.

In the next example we use the formula for the truncation error to obtain an upper bound for the error in approximating a function using a Taylor polynomial.

Example 1.1

(a) Give an estimate of the truncation error for the third-order Taylor polynomial approximating e^{2x} about $x = 0$.

(b) Verify that for all c satisfying $0 \leq c \leq 0.75$ we have $|e^{2c}| \leq e^{1.5}$.

(c) Deduce that, for all x satisfying $0 \leq x \leq 0.75$, the truncation error of the third-order Taylor polynomial approximating e^{2x} about $x = 0$ satisfies $|\varepsilon(x)| \leq Ax^4$, where $A = \frac{2}{3}e^{1.5}$.

In this case, since the expansion is about $x = 0$, then $h = x$.

Solution

(a) An estimate of the truncation error is provided by the next term of the Taylor expansion. From the solution to Exercise 1.1, this is seen to be

$$\varepsilon(x) \simeq -\tfrac{2}{3}x^4.$$

(b) Since e^{2x} is always positive we have $|e^{2c}| = e^{2c}$, and since $c \leq 0.75$ and the function is increasing we have $e^{2c} \leq e^{1.5}$. It follows that $|e^{2c}| \leq e^{1.5}$ as required.

(c) Taylor's Theorem, with $f(x) = e^{2x}$, gives

$$e^{2x} = 1 + 2x + 2x^2 + \tfrac{4}{3}x^3 - \varepsilon(x),$$

where

$$\varepsilon(x) = -\tfrac{1}{24}x^4 f^{(4)}(c_x) = -\tfrac{2}{3}x^4 \exp(2c_x). \qquad (1.2)$$

The estimate in part (a) was obtained by evaluating $f^{(4)}$ at 0 instead of at c_x. However, since $0 \leq x \leq 0.75$, it follows that $0 \leq c_x \leq 0.75$ and hence, by part (b), that $|\exp(2c_x)| \leq e^{1.5}$.

Using Equation (1.2) we deduce that, for $0 \leq x \leq 0.75$,

$$|\varepsilon(x)| \leq |-\tfrac{2}{3}x^4e^{1.5}| = \tfrac{2}{3}x^4e^{1.5} = Ax^4,$$

where $A = \frac{2}{3}e^{1.5} \simeq 2.9878$. ■

It may seem rather unsatisfactory that the estimate of the truncation error in approximating an exponential function is itself given in terms of the exponential expression $e^{1.5}$, but as long as you are prepared to accept that $e < 3$, then it follows that $e^{1.5} < 3\sqrt{3} < 3 \times 2 = 6$, so that $A < 4$. Therefore, even without any detailed knowledge of the values of the exponential function, we know that in the range $0 \leq x \leq 0.75$, the function $4x^4$ is an upper bound for the magnitude of the truncation error.

More generally, for the nth-order Taylor approximation, we know that the magnitude of the truncation error, $-\frac{1}{(n+1)!}h^{n+1}f^{(n+1)}(c_x)$, cannot rise above some definite multiple of h^{n+1}, so that if h is small then the error is much smaller. In other words, the truncation error in the nth-order approximation behaves like h^{n+1} as h approaches 0.

The O notation

This insight that the error in the nth-order approximation 'behaves like' h^{n+1} for small h is an important one that has many applications in the study of numerical (approximate) methods of solution of mathematical problems. There is a notation for this: for $x = a + h$, we write

$$\varepsilon(x) = O(h^{n+1}) \text{ as } h \to 0$$

to mean that

$$|\varepsilon(x)| \leq |Ah^{n+1}|$$

for some constant A and sufficiently small h. Note that the 'O' is a capital 'Oh', *not* zero. We read $O(\ldots)$ as 'of order ... ,' so '$O(h^{n+1})$' is read as 'of order h^{n+1}'.

This notation will be used on several occasions in the following sections to describe the truncation errors arising from approximate methods of solving differential equations. As we shall always be concerned with the error in some interval about some point, we shall not usually state the qualification 'as $h \to 0$'.

You are encouraged to practise using the O notation in the next two exercises.

*Exercise 1.4

(a) Verify that $|\cos c| \leq 1$ for all c.

(b) Determine the sixth-order Taylor polynomial approximating $\sin x$ about $x = 0$. Give an estimate of the truncation error for this approximation.

(c) Compute an upper bound on the magnitude of the truncation error for this approximation for all x satisfying $0 \leq x \leq 1$.

Exercise 1.5

(a) Give an estimate of the truncation error for the third-order Taylor polynomial approximating $f(x) = x^5$ about $x = 1$.

(b) Compute an upper bound on the magnitude of the truncation error for this approximation, valid for all x satisfying $1 \leq x \leq 1.5$. (Note that you are *not* asked to compute the third-order Taylor polynomial itself.)

As you have seen, the *truncation error* that appears in Taylor's Theorem arises through limiting the degree of the polynomial approximation. The theorem is based on the assumption that all calculations are carried out exactly. In practice, numerical calculations, such as those involved in evaluating a Taylor polynomial, are only carried out to a fixed number of significant figures, and thereby involve some *rounding error*, quite independent of any truncation error. When large amounts of calculation are required, rounding errors can accumulate in such a way as to dominate a numerical solution. This can occur when solving differential equations by numerical methods, such as Euler's method or the methods to be introduced in the next section, and so care is sometimes needed in choosing an appropriate numerical method.

End-of-section Exercises

Exercise 1.6

Give an estimate of the truncation error for the approximation $\sin x \simeq x$ for small x. What is the magnitude of the error if this approximation is used to evaluate $\sin \frac{\pi}{180}$?

$\frac{\pi}{180}$ radians is equivalent to $1°$.

Exercise 1.7

(a) Determine the third-order Taylor polynomial approximating $f(x) = x^{-2}$ about $x = 1$. Give an estimate of the truncation error for this approximation.

(b) Use this polynomial to approximate $f(1.05)$, and compute an upper bound on the magnitude of the error for this approximation.

2 Numerical solution of differential equations

This section begins with a reminder of Euler's method for solving initial-value problems involving first-order differential equations, of the form

$$\frac{dy}{dx} = f(x, y), \qquad y(x_0) = y_0. \tag{2.1}$$

Although simple, Euler's method can be effective and, by making the step size h small enough, it is possible to achieve any predetermined accuracy, provided that the arithmetic is done to a sufficient number of decimal places. However, it is often necessary to make the step size so small that the amount of computation reaches an unacceptable level, and, furthermore, rounding errors may accumulate to dominate the numerical solution. It is important to realize the crucial dilemma involved here. If arithmetic operations could be performed exactly, then decreasing the step size would guarantee an increase in accuracy, since each individual step could be made as accurate as desired. But in practice arithmetic always involves rounding, which is a source of errors that are quite separate from those that arise from the mathematics of the method itself. There is usually a trade-off between these two sources of error.

There are various ways of alleviating this difficulty, only some of which are considered in this unit. Basically, the idea is to approximate the solution using polynomials of higher degree, so as to reduce the size of the errors for any given step size, and thus to achieve the required accuracy while using larger step sizes than those that would be needed using Euler's method.

Euler's method uses an approximating polynomial of first degree.

The main approach considered here is to evaluate the slope function $f(x, y)$ more than once in each step, in order to accumulate enough information to approximate a Taylor polynomial of higher degree. This approach leads to a class of *Runge–Kutta methods*.

Runge–Kutta methods were first introduced by Carle Runge in 1895, and developed by Karl Heun in 1900 and Wilhelm Kutta in 1901.

2.1 Euler's method

As stated above, this section begins with a reminder of Euler's method. Definitions are then given for the forms of *truncation error* which are relevant to numerical methods for solving initial-value problems. These definitions provide the motivation for studying further numerical methods for such problems.

It is worth recalling Euler's method from *Unit 2*.

Euler's method

To apply Euler's method to the initial-value problem

$$\frac{dy}{dx} = f(x, y), \qquad y(x_0) = y_0, \tag{2.1}$$

proceed as follows.

(a) Take x_0 and $Y_0 = y_0$ as starting values, choose a step size h, and set $r = 0$.

(b) Set

$$x_{r+1} = x_r + h. \tag{2.2}$$

(c) Calculate an approximation Y_{r+1} to $y(x_{r+1})$, using the iteration formula

$$Y_{r+1} = Y_r + hf(x_r, Y_r). \tag{2.3}$$

(d) If further approximate values are required, increase r by 1, and return to sub-step (b).

We refer to (a), (b),(c) and (d) as sub-steps here, because the whole process of going from (x_r, Y_r) to (x_{r+1}, Y_{r+1}) is best thought of as a *single* step in the method.

The exact solution value $y(x_r)$ is sometimes denoted by the contracted form y_r. To distinguish it from the exact value, the numerical approximation is denoted by Y_r.

Example 2.1

Consider the initial-value problem (0.1):

$$\frac{dy}{dx} = 3(x-1)^2 + 20(y - (x-1)^3), \qquad y(0) = -1.$$

Use Euler's method, with step size $h = 0.01$, to obtain an approximation to $y(0.02)$.

Solution

From the question, $x_0 = 0$ and $Y_0 = y_0 = -1$. The step size is given as $h = 0.01$ and so Equation (2.2) with $r = 0$ gives $x_1 = 0.01$. Since

$$f(x, y) = 3(x-1)^2 + 20(y - (x-1)^3),$$

Equation (2.3), again with $r = 0$, gives

$$\begin{aligned} Y_1 &= Y_0 + hf(x_0, Y_0) \\ &= -1 + 0.01(3 \times (-1)^2 + 20(-1 - (-1)^3)) = -0.97. \end{aligned}$$

For the second step, from Equations (2.2) and (2.3) with $r = 1$,

$$\begin{aligned} x_2 &= x_1 + 0.01 = 0.02, \\ Y_2 &= Y_1 + hf(x_1, Y_1) \\ &= -0.97 + 0.01(3 \times (-0.99)^2 + 20(-0.97 - (-0.99)^3)) = -0.940\,537. \end{aligned}$$

So, at $x = 0.02$, Euler's method, with step size $h = 0.01$, gives the approximation $y(0.02) \simeq Y_2 = -0.940\,537$. ■

The situation at $r = 0$ may be represented graphically by Figure 2.1.

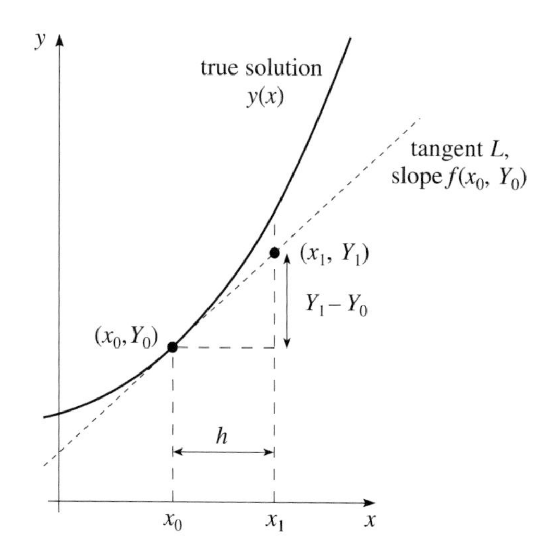

Figure 2.1

The value of the slope function $f(x_0, Y_0)$ is the slope at x_0 of the solution of Equation (2.1) that we are trying to find, namely the solution with $y(x_0) = y_0 = Y_0$. This is also the slope of the line L in Figure 2.1, drawn through the points (x_0, Y_0) and (x_1, Y_1). Now L has the equation

$$p_1(x) = Y_0 + (x - x_0)f(x_0, Y_0), \qquad (2.4)$$

and this is just the Taylor polynomial of first order about x_0, approximating the required solution $y(x)$ of Equation (2.1). (You can check this by noting that $p_1(x_0) = Y_0$ and $p_1'(x_0) = f(x_0, Y_0)$.) The Taylor polynomial of first order is also called the *tangent approximation*, and indeed L in Figure 2.1 is a tangent at x_0 to the solution $y(x)$.

As you saw in *Unit 12*.

According to Taylor's Theorem, the error in approximating $y(x_1)$ by $Y_1 = p_1(x_1) = Y_0 + hf(x_0, Y_0)$ can be expressed as

$$\varepsilon(x_1) = Y_1 - y(x_1) = -\tfrac{1}{2}h^2 y''(c_0), \qquad (2.5)$$

where $x_1 = x_0 + h$ and $y''(c_0)$ is the second derivative of the true solution at some point c_0 between x_0 and x_1.

Thus, although we do not usually know the exact value of $y''(c_0)$, we see that $\varepsilon(x_1) = O(h^2)$, so that the approximation improves quite rapidly as we decrease the step size h. The error is a *truncation* error, since (as we have seen) it involves truncating the higher-order terms in a Taylor expansion; it is also *local*, as it occurs in performing just one step.

More generally, at the $(r + 1)$th step, we are starting from a value Y_r that is already approximate, and trying to solve the initial-value problem

$$\frac{dy}{dx} = f(x, y), \qquad y(x_r) = Y_r.$$

This is a *different* initial-value problem from the one we started with at step 1, as we are now starting from a value Y_r that is not quite the true value of $y(x_r)$. Let us represent by $\hat{y}_r(x)$ the (true) solution of this (new) initial-value problem.

We represent this function by $\hat{y}_r$ rather than just $\hat{y}$ because, at each step, there is a new initial-value problem to solve, and we need a notation that distinguishes them.

We now perform the $(r+1)$th step of Euler's method, by setting $Y_{r+1} = Y_r + hf(x_r, Y_r)$, and we have introduced another error, as Y_{r+1} is not exactly $\hat{y}_r(x_{r+1})$. We may use Taylor's Theorem exactly as we did for step 1, to obtain

$$\varepsilon(x_{r+1}) = Y_{r+1} - \hat{y}_r(x_{r+1}) = -\tfrac{1}{2}h^2\hat{y}_r''(c_r),$$

where $x_{r+1} = x_r + h$ and c_r lies somewhere between x_r and x_{r+1}.

After several steps of the calculation, using Euler's method, we have used a tangent approximation to calculate each step in the solution, making a local truncation error each time. However, it is not the local truncation errors, $Y_r - \hat{y}_{r-1}(x_r)$, that are really important from a practical point of view: we really need an estimate for the *global error*, $Y_r - y(x_r)$, the difference between the approximate solution and the exact solution after r steps.

To see the difference between local (truncation) errors and global errors, consider Figure 2.2, which shows the steps in the solution of a typical initial-value problem by Euler's method.

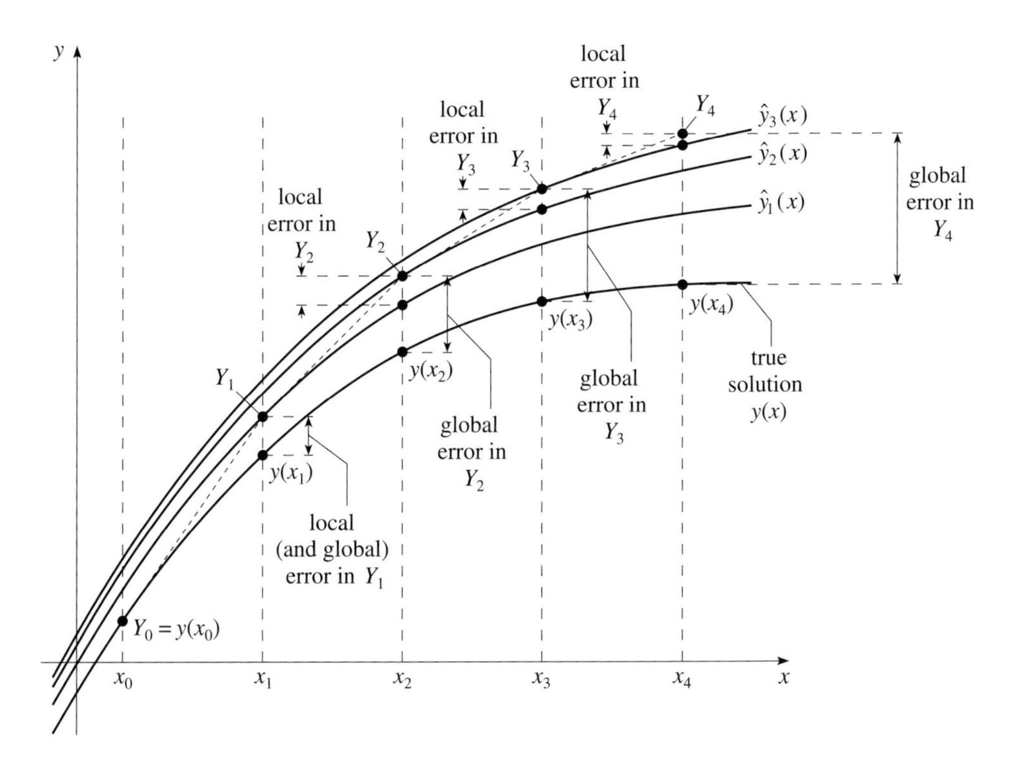

Figure 2.2

You can see the family of curves $\hat{y}_1$, $\hat{y}_2$ and $\hat{y}_3$ and the tangent approximations used in the method. The point to emphasize here is that the global error is *not* the sum of the local errors.

Now Euler's method is an example of a **one-step method**, where the approximation Y_{r+1} is calculated using just the approximation at the previous step Y_r rather than, for example, using Y_r and Y_{r-1}. For one-step methods, the following definition of the local truncation error is applicable.

Definition

Given a one-step numerical method for solving an initial-value problem, $dy/dx = f(x, y,), \ y(x_0) = y_0$, the **local truncation error**, in the step from x_r to x_{r+1}, is the difference between the numerical approximation Y_{r+1} and the value at x_{r+1} of the solution $\hat{y}_r(x)$ of the initial-value problem

$$\frac{dy}{dx} = f(x, y), \qquad y(x_r) = Y_r.$$

For Euler's method, the local truncation error is $\varepsilon(x_{r+1}) = -\frac{1}{2}h^2\hat{y}_r''(c_r)$, where $\hat{y}_r''(c_r)$ is the second derivative, at some point c_r between x_r and x_{r+1}, of the solution of the initial-value problem

$$\frac{dy}{dx} = f(x, y), \qquad y(x_r) = Y_r.$$

Local truncation errors, in themselves, are of little *practical* importance, but they are worth analysing as they are the theoretical key to understanding how global errors behave.

Definition

For a numerical method for solving an initial-value problem of the form $dy/dx = f(x, y), \ y(x_0) = y_0$, the **global error**, at the point $x = x_N$, is the difference, $Y_N - y(x_N)$, between the numerical approximation Y_N and the value of the exact solution $y(x_N)$ of the initial-value problem at that point.

We have seen that the local truncation error in Euler's method is $\varepsilon(x_{r+1}) = -\frac{1}{2}h^2\hat{y}_r''(c_r) = O(h^2)$. We are interested in determining how the global error behaves at some fixed point $b = x_N$ as the step size is reduced, where

$$N = \frac{b - x_0}{h}.$$

In *Unit 2*, we observed that for Euler's method the global error at b is proportional to h as the step size tends to zero, so that

$$Y_N - y(b) \simeq Ch = O(h)$$

for some constant C. In Section 4 we shall state a theorem that the global errors in a numerical method will always be of order one less than the order of the local truncation error, for any differential equation in which the solution is sufficiently differentiable. The result should not be that surprising (although it is devilishly difficult to prove), since the accumulation of N local truncation errors of $O(h^2)$, where N is proportional to $1/h$, suggests that the order of the global error will be one lower. If we know how the global errors vary with the step size h, then we can use this information to control the growth of global errors.

For this reason we analyse numerical methods by using Taylor series expansions to determine the local truncation error for the method. If the local truncation error is $O(h^{p+1})$, then we define the **method** to be **of order** $\boldsymbol{p}$ since it is our expectation that the global errors will be $O(h^p)$.

Hence Euler's method is a **first-order method** since its local truncation errors are $O(h^2)$, and we therefore expect the global errors to be $O(h)$.

***Exercise 2.1**

Consider the differential equation

$$\frac{dy}{dx} = (2x + 1)y.$$

(a) Verify that the general solution of this differential equation is $y = Ae^{x(x+1)}$, where A is an arbitrary constant.

(b) Use Euler's method, with step size $h = 0.05$, to obtain approximations to $y(0.05)$ and $y(0.1)$, given that $y(x)$ satisfies the initial condition $y(0) = 1$.

(c) Determine the global error at $x = 0.1$, to six decimal places.

When the exact solution of the differential equation (2.1) is not known, it may still be possible to estimate the local truncation error, but it is much more difficult to estimate the *global error*, though this will be discussed in Section 4. However, it has been seen that the global error results from accumulation of local errors, and so, if local errors can be controlled, then the global error will also be kept under control.

As may be seen from Equation (2.4), Euler's method is based upon the *first-order* Taylor polynomial about x_r of a local solution of the differential equation (2.1). Its local truncation error is $O(h^2)$, corresponding to the truncation error of the first-order Taylor polynomial approximation. It is natural to consider whether an improvement can be obtained based upon Taylor polynomials of higher degree. This is the subject of the next subsection.

2.2 Improvements on Euler's method

Euler-midpoint method

Euler's method involves using Equation (2.3), which would have zero local truncation error if only the slope $f(x, y)$ remained constant at the value $f(x_r, Y_r)$ throughout the interval $[x_r, x_{r+1}]$. It does not do so, of course; but it seems natural to assume that the slope at a point halfway between x_r and x_{r+1} would be a better approximation to the average slope than $f(x_r, Y_r)$, the slope at the left-hand end of the interval. However, to calculate the slope at the halfway point, we need a value for y as well as the value $\frac{1}{2}(x_r + x_{r+1}) = x_r + \frac{1}{2}h$ (which we shall call $x_{r+\frac{1}{2}}$) for x; and we cannot have an exact value for y, as that requires a knowledge of the function we are trying to approximate! The best we can do is to find the value of y taken by the tangent approximation to $\hat{y}_r$ at the point $x_{r+\frac{1}{2}}$. Let us call this y-value $Y_{r+\frac{1}{2}}$. It is found by incrementing Y_r by $\frac{1}{2}hf(x_r, Y_r)$ (instead of $hf(x_r, Y_r)$), to obtain

$$Y_{r+\frac{1}{2}} = Y_r + \tfrac{1}{2}hf(x_r, Y_r).$$

Using this value means that we evaluate the slope at the point $(x_{r+\frac{1}{2}}, Y_{r+\frac{1}{2}})$, to obtain $f(x_{r+\frac{1}{2}}, Y_{r+\frac{1}{2}})$. Finally, we calculate Y_{r+1} using this slope value:

$$Y_{r+1} = Y_r + hf(x_{r+\frac{1}{2}}, Y_{r+\frac{1}{2}}).$$

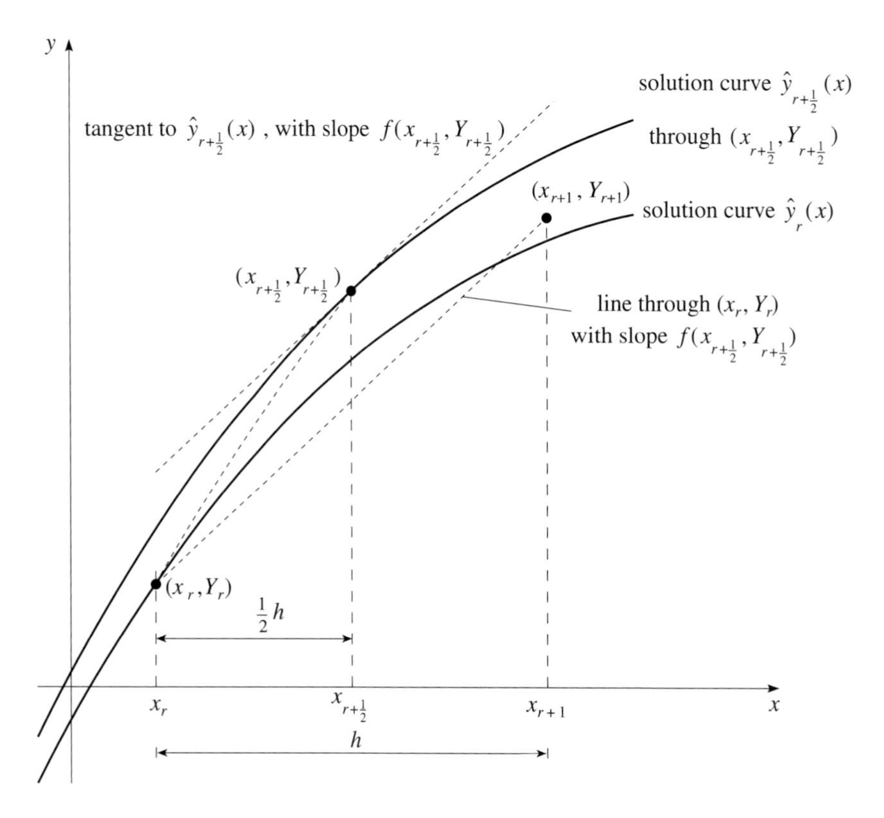

Figure 2.3

This method, illustrated in Figure 2.3, is the *Euler-midpoint method.* It involves two evaluations of f: first, $f(x_r, Y_r)$ is evaluated, then this information is used in order to calculate $Y_{r+\frac{1}{2}}$, then $f(x_{r+\frac{1}{2}}, Y_{r+\frac{1}{2}})$ is evaluated. It is useful to denote these two function evaluations by $F_{1,r}$ and $F_{2,r}$, and we then have the following procedure.

Euler-midpoint method

To apply the Euler-midpoint method to the initial-value problem

$$\frac{dy}{dx} = f(x, y), \qquad y(x_0) = y_0,$$

proceed as follows.

(a) Take x_0 and $Y_0 = y_0$ as starting values, choose a step size h, and set $r = 0$.

(b) Calculate $F_{1,r} = f(x_r, Y_r)$.

(c) Set $x_{r+\frac{1}{2}} = x_r + \frac{1}{2}h$ and $Y_{r+\frac{1}{2}} = Y_r + \frac{1}{2}hF_{1,r}$.

(d) Calculate $F_{2,r} = f(x_{r+\frac{1}{2}}, Y_{r+\frac{1}{2}})$.

(e) Set $x_{r+1} = x_r + h$ and

$$Y_{r+1} = Y_r + hF_{2,r}. \qquad (2.6)$$

Y_{r+1} is the approximation to $y(x_{r+1})$.

(f) If further approximate values are required, increase r by 1 and return to sub-step (b).

Example 2.2

Consider again the initial-value problem (0.1):

$$\frac{dy}{dx} = 3(x-1)^2 + 20(y - (x-1)^3), \qquad y(0) = -1.$$

The exact solution is $y(x) = (x-1)^3$.

Use the Euler-midpoint method, with step size $h = 0.02$, to find an approximation to $y(0.02)$. Compare this approximation with that obtained in Example 2.1 using Euler's method and step size 0.01.

Solution

Starting with $x_0 = 0$, $Y_0 = y_0 = -1$:

$$F_{1,0} = f(0,-1) = 3;$$

$$x_{\frac{1}{2}} = 0.01, \quad Y_{\frac{1}{2}} = -1 + 0.01 \times 3 = -0.97;$$

$$F_{2,0} = f(x_{\frac{1}{2}}, Y_{\frac{1}{2}}) = f(0.01, -0.97)$$

$$= 3(-0.99)^2 + 20(-0.97 - (-0.99)^3) = 2.946\,28;$$

and from Equation (2.6):

$$Y_1 = Y_0 + hF_{2,0} = -1 + 0.02(2.946\,28) = -0.941\,074.$$

So, at $x = 0.02$, the Euler-midpoint method with step size $h = 0.02$ gives the approximation $y(0.02) \simeq -0.941\,074$. Since the correct value is $-0.941\,192$, the global error is $0.000\,118$, a considerable improvement on Euler's method with half the step size. ■

Euler's method, using step size 0.01, gave $y(0.02) \simeq -0.940\,537$ (see Example 2.1), with a global error of $0.000\,655$.

The most numerically complex part of a step-by-step approximation method for an initial-value problem tends to be the evaluation of the function f; thus, using Euler's method to estimate $y(0.02)$ with step size 0.01 requires roughly the same amount of calculation as the Euler-midpoint method with step size 0.02, namely two evaluations of the function. Thus the advantage of the Euler-midpoint method for this example is clear: greater accuracy has been achieved with the same amount of calculation.

Exercise 2.2

Consider again the initial-value problem of Exercise 2.1:

$$\frac{dy}{dx} = (2x+1)y, \qquad y(0) = 1.$$

Use the Euler-midpoint method, with step size $h = 0.1$ to find an approximation to $y(0.1)$, and compare the global error with the global error obtained using Euler's method with step size $h = 0.05$.

Euler-trapezoidal method

Another reasonably obvious way to improve on Euler's method would be to evaluate the slope at both the points x_r and x_{r+1} and use the mean of the two values. However, in order to evaluate the slope at x_{r+1}, we need to have a corresponding value of y which, ideally, would be the value Y_{r+1} that is being sought. The only approximation available is that given by Equation (2.3) (Euler's method itself). Let us call this value Y_{E} (where E stands for Euler) in this context. Thus, the slope we want to use is the mean of the slopes $f(x_r, Y_r)$ at (x_r, Y_r) and $f(x_{r+1}, Y_{\mathrm{E}})$ at $(x_{r+1}, Y_{\mathrm{E}})$. The iteration formula that is obtained in this way is

$$Y_{r+1} = Y_r + \tfrac{1}{2}h(f(x_r, Y_r) + f(x_{r+1}, Y_{\mathrm{E}})),$$

where $Y_{\mathrm{E}} = Y_r + hf(x_r, Y_r)$.

This is the iteration formula for the *Euler-trapezoidal method*, and again requires two function evaluations at each step. One step of the method is illustrated in Figure 2.4

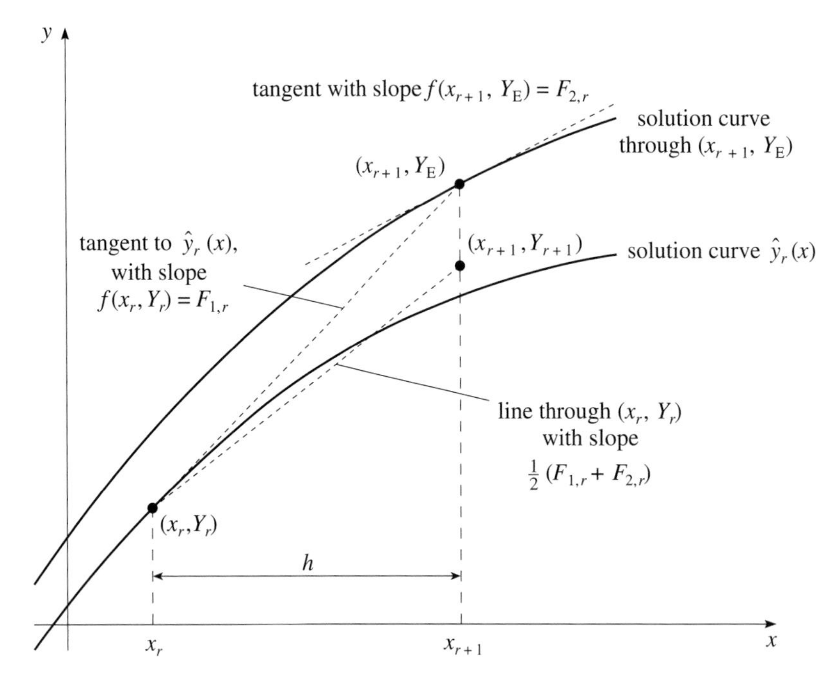

Figure 2.4

The procedure is very similar to that for the Euler-midpoint method.

Euler-trapezoidal method

To apply the Euler-trapezoidal method to the initial-value problem

$$\frac{dy}{dx} = f(x, y), \qquad y(x_0) = y_0,$$

proceed as follows.

(a) Take x_0 and $Y_0 = y_0$ as starting values, choose a step size h, and set $r = 0$.

(b) Calculate $F_{1,r} = f(x_r, Y_r)$.

(c) Set $x_{r+1} = x_r + h$ and $Y_E = Y_r + hF_{1,r}$.

(d) Calculate $F_{2,r} = f(x_{r+1}, Y_E)$.

(e) Set

$$Y_{r+1} = Y_r + \tfrac{1}{2}h(F_{1,r} + F_{2,r}). \qquad (2.7)$$

Y_{r+1} is the approximation to $y(x_{r+1})$.

(f) If further approximate values are required, increase r by 1 and return to sub-step (b).

Example 2.3

Consider once again the initial-value problem (0.1):

$$\frac{dy}{dx} = 3(x-1)^2 + 20(y - (x-1)^3), \qquad y(0) = -1.$$

Use the Euler-trapezoidal method, with step size $h = 0.02$, to find approximations to $y(0.02)$ and $y(0.04)$.

Solution

As before, $x_0 = 0$, $Y_0 = -1$. Thus, $F_{1,0} = f(x_0, Y_0) = 3$, $x_1 = 0.02$ and

$$Y_E = -1 + 0.02(3) = -0.94.$$

Then $F_{2,0} = f(x_1, Y_E) = 2.905\,04$, so that (from Equation (2.7))

$$Y_1 = -1 + 0.01(3 + 2.905\,04) = -0.940\,950.$$

So, at $x = 0.02$, the Euler-trapezoidal method, with step size $h = 0.02$, gives the approximation

$$y(0.02) \simeq Y_1 = -0.940\,950.$$

The error here is 0.000 242, which in this case is about twice as large as the corresponding error using the Euler-midpoint method; nevertheless, it is an improvement over Euler's method.

For the second step, we need to calculate

$$F_{1,1} = f(x_1, Y_1) = f(0.02, -0.940\,950) = 2.886\,048.$$

Now, $x_2 = 0.04$ and

$$Y_E = Y_1 + hf(x_1, Y_1) = -0.940\,950 + 0.02(2.886\,048) = -0.883\,229.$$

Next, $F_{2,1} = f(x_2, Y_E) = 2.794\,947$, so that Equation (2.7) gives finally:

$$Y_2 = -0.940\,950 + 0.01(2.886\,048 + 2.794\,947) = -0.884\,140.$$

So, at $x = 0.04$, the Euler-trapezoidal method, with step size $h = 0.02$, gives the approximation

$$y(0.04) \simeq Y_2 = -0.884\,140. \quad \blacksquare$$

Note in Example 2.3 that the values of $F_{1,r}$ and $F_{2,r}$ are all similar in value and the values of Y_r and Y_E are all similar in value. This is a good check, in hand calculations, that we are not making arithmetic errors.

***Exercise 2.3**

Consider again the initial-value problem of Exercises 2.1 and 2.2:

$$\frac{dy}{dx} = (2x + 1)y, \qquad y(0) = 1.$$

Use the Euler-trapezoidal method, with step size $h = 0.1$, to find an approximation to $y(0.1)$, and compare the global error with the global errors obtained using Euler's method with step size $h = 0.05$ and the Euler-midpoint method with step size $h = 0.1$.

It is no accident that in general the Euler-midpoint and Euler-trapezoidal methods give considerably better approximations than Euler's method. It turns out (though we shall not prove this) that the local truncation error for these methods is $O(h^3)$ (as opposed to $O(h^2)$ for Euler's method) and so we expect the global errors to be $O(h^2)$.

In fact, the Euler-midpoint and Euler-trapezoidal methods are just two of a whole class of second-order iteration methods for initial-value problems. The next subsection considers this class and a similar class of fourth-order methods.

2.3 Runge–Kutta methods

The boxed descriptions of the Euler-midpoint and Euler-trapezoidal methods have been set out so as to display the strong correspondence between the two methods. The only differences are in sub-steps (c), (d) and (e) of the two methods, and even here the calculations are similar.

In sub-step (c) we set $x_{r+\frac{1}{2}}$ equal to $x_r + \frac{1}{2}h$ for the Euler-midpoint method and x_{r+1} equal to $x_r + h$ for the Euler-trapezoidal method. Then in each case we calculate a new Y-value by adding an appropriate multiple of $F_{1,r}$ to Y_r.

In sub-step (d) we calculate the slope, $F_{2,r}$, at this new point.

In sub-step (e) we calculate Y_{r+1} by starting from Y_r, and adding h times $F_{2,r}$ for the Euler-midpoint method and h times the average of $F_{1,r}$ and $F_{2,r}$ for the Euler-trapezoidal method.

These are special cases of the following more general sub-steps, depending on a parameter α, where $0 < \alpha \leq 1$.

(c) Set $x_{r+\alpha} = x_r + \alpha h$ and $Y_{r+\alpha} = Y_r + \alpha h F_{1,r}$.

(d) Calculate $F_{2,r} = f(x_{r+\alpha}, Y_{r+\alpha})$.

(e) Set

$$Y_{r+1} = Y_r + h\left(\left(1 - \frac{1}{2\alpha}\right)F_{1,r} + \frac{1}{2\alpha}F_{2,r}\right).$$

Y_{r+1} is the approximation to $y(x_{r+1})$.

Note that, to avoid confusion between $Y_{r+\alpha}$ and Y_{r+1} in sub-step (c), we used E instead of $r + \alpha$ for the Euler-trapezoidal method.

Exercise 2.4

Which choices of parameter are needed in order to convert these general sub-steps into sub-steps (c), (d) and (e) of the Euler-midpoint and the Euler-trapezoidal methods?

In general, any value of α with $0 < \alpha \leq 1$ may be chosen, and will give a second-order approximation method with a local truncation error $\varepsilon(x_r) = O(h^3)$ and consequently an expected global error $O(h^2)$. These methods are known as **two-stage Runge–Kutta methods**. The Euler-trapezoidal method (with $\alpha = 1$) will usually be taken, in this course, as representative of such methods.

Exercise 2.5

(a) Extend the work of Exercise 2.3 by determining an approximate value for y at $x = 0.2$, using the Euler-trapezoidal method with step size $h = 0.1$.

(b) Determine the global error at $x = 0.1$ and $x = 0.2$.

The Runge–Kutta approach can be continued, to produce approximation methods of higher than second order. An n-stage Runge–Kutta method requires n evaluations of the slope function, $F_{1,r}, F_{2,r}, F_{3,r}, \ldots, F_{n,r}$, each evaluated at a point that depends on the previous evaluations. Finally, Y_{r+1} is obtained from Y_r by adding h times a suitably weighted average of the $F_{1,r}, \ldots, F_{n,r}$. The weightings are chosen so that (considered as a function of h) Y_{r+1} agrees with y in as many terms as possible of the corresponding Taylor series.

The most commonly used Runge–Kutta methods are four-stage methods, which are of fourth order. These require four values, $F_{1,r}$, $F_{2,r}$, $F_{3,r}$, $F_{4,r}$, of the slope function $f(x, y)$, evaluated at points (x, y) with $x = x_r$, $x_r + \beta_2 h$, $x_r + \beta_3 h$, $x_r + h$, for suitable values of the parameters β_2, β_3.

The following very popular Runge–Kutta method forms the basis of many computer packages, including the standard numerical method incorporated in the computer algebra package for this course.

Classical fourth-order Runge–Kutta method

To apply the classical fourth-order Runge–Kutta method to the initial-value problem

$$\frac{dy}{dx} = f(x,y), \qquad y(x_0) = y_0,$$

proceed as follows.

(a) Take x_0 and $Y_0 = y_0$ as starting values, choose a step size h, and set $r = 0$.

(b) Calculate an approximation to the derivative at x_r, two approximations at $x_r + \frac{1}{2}h$, and approximations to the derivative and the solution $y(x)$ at $x_{r+1} = x_r + h$, using the formulae

$$\begin{cases} F_{1,r} = f(x_r, Y_r), \\ F_{2,r} = f(x_r + \frac{1}{2}h, Y_r + \frac{1}{2}hF_{1,r}), \\ F_{3,r} = f(x_r + \frac{1}{2}h, Y_r + \frac{1}{2}hF_{2,r}), \\ F_{4,r} = f(x_r + h, Y_r + hF_{3,r}), \\ Y_{r+1} = Y_r + \frac{1}{6}h(F_{1,r} + 2F_{2,r} + 2F_{3,r} + F_{4,r}). \end{cases} \qquad (2.8)$$

Y_{r+1} is the approximation to $y(x_{r+1})$.

(c) If further approximate values are required, increase r by 1, and return to sub-step (b).

You are *not* expected to memorize these Runge–Kutta formulae.

In this method, $F_{1,r}$ approximates the slope at x_r; $F_{4,r}$ approximates the slope at $x_r + h$; while $F_{2,r}$ and $F_{3,r}$ are two different approximations to the slope at $x_r + \frac{1}{2}h$. Finally, the overall slope is the weighted mean value $\frac{1}{6}(F_{1,r} + 2F_{2,r} + 2F_{3,r} + F_{4,r})$.

Example 2.4

Consider the initial-value problem

$$\frac{dy}{dx} = 3(x-1)^2 + 20(y - (x-1)^3), \qquad y(0) = -1.$$

Use the classical fourth-order Runge–Kutta method, with step size $h = 0.04$, to obtain an approximate value for y at $x = 0.04$.

Solution

The given initial condition gives $Y_0 = y_0 = -1$ at $x_0 = 0$. Using each of Equations (2.8) in turn, with $h = 0.04$:

$$\begin{aligned} F_{1,0} &= f(x_0, Y_0) = 3 \times (-1)^2 + 20(-1 - (-1)^3) = 3, \\ F_{2,0} &= f(x_0 + \tfrac{1}{2}h, Y_0 + \tfrac{1}{2}hF_{1,0}) = f(0.02, -0.94) \\ &= 3 \times (-0.98)^2 + 20(-0.94 - (-0.98)^3) = 2.905\,04, \\ F_{3,0} &= f(x_0 + \tfrac{1}{2}h, Y_0 + \tfrac{1}{2}hF_{2,0}) = f(0.02, -0.941\,899) \\ &= 3 \times (-0.98)^2 + 20(-0.941\,899 - (-0.98)^3) = 2.867\,056, \\ F_{4,0} &= f(x_0 + h, Y_0 + hF_{3,0}) = f(0.04, -0.885\,318) \\ &= 3 \times (-0.96)^2 + 20(-0.885\,318 - (-0.96)^3) = 2.753\,165, \\ Y_1 &= Y_0 + \tfrac{1}{6} \times 0.04(F_{1,0} + 2F_{2,0} + 2F_{3,0} + F_{4,0}) \\ &= -1 + \frac{0.04}{6}(3 + 2 \times 2.905\,04 + 2 \times 2.867\,056 + 2.753\,165) \\ &= -0.884\,684. \end{aligned}$$

So, at $x = 0.04$, the classical fourth-order Runge–Kutta method with step size $h = 0.04$ gives the approximation $y(0.04) \simeq Y_1 = -0.884\,684$. ■

As might have been expected, this fourth-order method, using a step size $h = 0.04$, gives a much better approximation (global error 0.000 052) to the exact value of $y(0.04) = -0.884\,736$, than did the Euler-trapezoidal method, in Example 2.3, using a step size $h = 0.02$ (global error 0.000 596). The two methods required roughly the same amount of calculation, since the fourth-order method, given by Equations (2.8), required four evaluations of the function $f(x, y)$ to complete a single step, while the Euler-trapezoidal method, given by Equation (2.7), required two evaluations of $f(x, y)$ on each of two steps. In this example, the advantage of using a fourth-order method has been clearly exhibited, by the reduction in the size of the global error, for the same amount of calculation.

Exercise 2.6

(a) Use the classical fourth-order Runge–Kutta method, with step size $h = 0.2$, to obtain an approximate value for y at $x = 0.2$, for the initial-value problem

$$\frac{dy}{dx} = (2x + 1)y, \qquad y(0) = 1.$$

(b) Compare the result, at $x = 0.2$, with that obtained in Exercise 2.5, using the Euler-trapezoidal method.

End-of-section Exercise

Exercise 2.7

Consider the differential equation

$$\frac{dy}{dx} = 10(4x - y).$$

(a) Verify that the general solution of this differential equation is $y = 4x - 0.4 + Ae^{-10x}$, where A is an arbitrary constant.

(b) Use Euler's method, with step size $h = 0.025$, to obtain an approximation to $y(0.1)$, given the initial condition $y(0) = -4$. Determine the global error at $x = 0.1$.

(c) Use the Euler-trapezoidal method, with step size $h = 0.05$, to obtain an approximation to $y(0.1)$, given the initial condition $y(0) = -4$. Determine the global error at $x = 0.1$.

(d) Use the classical fourth-order Runge–Kutta method, with step size $h = 0.1$, to obtain an approximation to $y(0.1)$, given the initial condition $y(0) = -4$. Compare the result, at $x = 0.1$, with those obtained in parts (b) and (c).

3 Numerical experimentation

Section 2 has provided an introduction to second-order and fourth-order Runge–Kutta methods, and to their errors, in particular the local truncation error. Some hand calculations were carried out over one or two steps. However, these numerical methods are of limited use without a computer. In this section, you are asked to make use of your computer, using each of the numerical methods discussed in Section 2, to obtain approximate solutions to the first three initial-value problems (0.1), (0.2), (0.3), stated in the Introduction:

Euler's method can be considered as a first-order Runge–Kutta method.

$$\frac{dy}{dx} = 3(x-1)^2 + 20(y-(x-1)^3), \qquad y(0) = -1, \tag{3.1}$$

$$\frac{dy}{dx} = 20x(2-x) - 20y, \qquad y(0) = 0, \tag{3.2}$$

$$\frac{dy}{dx} = y(20-y), \qquad y(0) = 12. \tag{3.3}$$

As mentioned in the Introduction, these problems have analytic solutions, which are useful when trying to understand how numerical methods work, and how the global errors of each method behave. The solution of problems (3.1), (3.2) and (3.3) are given below:

These analytic solutions may be obtained using the methods of *Unit 2*.

(3.1) $\quad y(x) = (x-1)^3$;

(3.2) $\quad y(x) = x(2.1-x) - 0.105(1-e^{-20x})$;

(3.3) $\quad y(x) = 60/(3+2e^{-20x})$.

In practice, of course, numerical methods would be used mainly to obtain approximate solutions when no analytic solution is available. In order to do the second of the activities below, you will need to know that we measure the **efficiency** of a numerical method, used to obtain a solution of specified accuracy, by the number of function evaluations required to obtain that level of accuracy. (The greater the number of function evaluations, the lower the efficiency.)

We shall use the idea of *efficiency* again later in the unit.

Use your computer to complete the following activities.

Activity 3.1

Consider the initial-value problem (3.1) over the interval $0 \le x \le 0.2$. Use:

We will refer to the results from these activities in Section 4.

(a) Euler's method;

(b) the Euler-trapezoidal method;

(c) the classical fourth-order Runga–Kutta method;

to obtain approximate solutions to this problem, using each of the step sizes $h = 0.04, 0.02, 0.01, 0.005, 0.0025$.

Observe, for each method, how the global error, in particular at the end of the interval at $x = 0.2$, is reduced as the step size h is reduced. Attempt to deduce in what way the global error depends on the step size, and how this dependency relates to the order of the method. Compare the global errors obtained using the three methods for the same amount of calculation.

Activity 3.2

Consider the initial-value problem (3.2) over the interval $0 \leq x \leq 2$. Use:

(a) Euler's method;

(b) the Euler-trapezoidal method;

(c) the classical fourth-order Runge–Kutta method;

to obtain approximate solutions to this problem, using each of the step sizes $h = 0.2, 0.1, 0.05, 0.025, 0.0125$.

Observe, for each method, how the global error, in particular at the end of the interval at $x = 2$, behaves as the step size h is reduced. Attempt to deduce in what way the global error depends on the step size, and how this dependency relates to the order of the method. Compare the global errors obtained using the three methods and comment on the relative efficiency of the three methods for obtaining:

(i) two-decimal-place accuracy;

(ii) four-decimal-place accuracy.

Activity 3.3

Consider the initial-value problem (3.3) over the interval $0 \leq x \leq 0.6$. Use:

(a) Euler's method;

(b) the Euler-trapezoidal method;

(c) the classical fourth-order Runge–Kutta method;

to obtain approximate solutions to this problem, using each of the step sizes $h = 0.2, 0.15, 0.12, 0.1, 0.075, 0.06, 0.05, 0.025, 0.0125$.

For each method, compare these approximate solutions with a graph of the exact solution, and note their general behaviour. Observe and comment on the behaviour of the global error, at the end of the interval at $x = 0.6$, as the step size h becomes smaller. Compare the global errors obtained using the three methods.

Activities 3.1 and 3.2 should have confirmed that, for sufficiently small step sizes h, Euler's method is $O(h)$, the Euler-trapezoidal method is $O(h^2)$ and the classical Runge–Kutta method is $O(h^4)$. However, you will also have seen how, when h is not small enough, you can sometimes obtain an approximate solution that bears no resemblance to the true solution. This provides a warning that numerical methods should not be applied indiscriminately without further analysis of the plausibility of the solutions obtained. The reasons why such inaccurate solutions arise are given in Section 4.

4 Analysis of numerical methods

In Section 2, development of second-order and fourth-order Runge–Kutta methods was based, principally, on discussion of the *local truncation error*. However, as was pointed out there, in practice it is the *global error* that is more important. The activities in Section 3 should have given you a feeling for the ways in which the global error can behave, depending upon the order of the method and the step size which is used. Subsection 4.1 looks at the strange behaviour that you may have noticed when the step size is not small enough, and introduces the important concept of *absolute instability* to give some explanation of that behaviour. When the step size *is* small enough, however, it would appear that the global error is approximately proportional to some power of that step size. Subsection 4.2 presents a theorem that provides a reason why this should be so, and Subsection 4.3 provides a method of choosing a step size that gives the degree of accuracy that is actually required in practice.

4.1 Ill-conditioning and instability

You may have noticed in performing the activities in Section 3, that for some of the problems and some of the numerical methods, the answers were absurd for certain values of the step size h. However, if h was made small enough, the methods eventually gave reasonable results.

For initial-value problem (0.1) there is an inherent reason for this: the problem is extremely ill-conditioned.

The concept of ill-conditioning was introduced in *Unit 9*.

> ***Definition***
>
> Suppose that small changes are made to the data for a problem. The problem is **absolutely ill-conditioned** if it is possible for the absolute change in the solution to be significantly larger than the absolute change in the data. A problem that is not absolutely ill-conditioned is said to be **absolutely well-conditioned**.

There is also a concept of *relative ill-conditioning* that we do not discuss in this course.

The general solution of the differential equation

$$\frac{dy}{dx} = 3(x-1)^2 + 20(y - (x-1)^3) \tag{4.1}$$

is $y(x) = (x-1)^3 + Ae^{20x}$, and the particular solution satisfying the initial condition $y(0) = -1$ is $y(x) = (x-1)^3$. Now the exponential function e^{20x} grows enormously faster than the polynomial function $(x-1)^3$ once x exceeds 0.1 or so, and all the numerical methods in this unit proceed by attempting to solve a new initial-value problem at each step, consisting of the *same* differential equation with a *new* initial condition. Thus, a term Ae^{20x} (with $A \neq 0$) will inevitably creep into the function that the method is trying to find, since $A = 0$ only for the initial condition $y(0) = -1$. It will quickly dominate unless h is small enough to keep it very strictly under control.

The situation is not much improved even if the given initial condition is (say) $y(0) = -0.95$.

*Exercise 4.1

Consider the initial-value problem

$$\frac{dy}{dx} = 3(x-1)^2 + 20(y - (x-1)^3), \qquad y(0) = -0.95. \tag{4.2}$$

(a) Verify that the analytic solution to this problem is

$$y(x) = (x-1)^3 + 0.05e^{20x},$$

and evaluate this solution at $x = 0.2$.

(b) Determine the change to the analytic solution at $x = 0.2$, if a small change $\varepsilon = 0.005$ is made to the initial condition, so that $y(0) = -0.945$.

So the initial-value problem (0.1) is absolutely ill-conditioned with respect to small changes in $y(0)$ over the interval $[0, 0.2]$.

In general, whatever the initial condition may be, any initial-value problem involving Equation (4.1) is absolutely ill-conditioned over the interval $[0, 0.2]$, or indeed over any larger interval starting at $x = 0$. The reason is that the solutions are fast-growing functions, so that small errors inevitably grow as rapidly as the solutions themselves.

For such absolutely ill-conditioned problems, it is usually necessary to use a very small step size to achieve a reasonable accuracy. However, even well-conditioned problems can require careful attention to step size, as otherwise the numerical method can generate an iteration formula that is itself ill-conditioned! This is a phenomenon known as *induced instability*.

Induced instability is where errors in the data may be magnified by the method chosen (rather than by the problem itself).

In investigating ill-conditioning and induced instability, we shall only look at what happens if the right-hand side of the initial condition is changed from Y_0 to $Y_0 + \varepsilon$, and we shall say that the method suffers from *induced instability* if the solution changes by significantly more than ε.

Example 4.1

Consider the initial-value problem

$$\frac{dy}{dx} = -4y, \qquad y(0) = 1. \tag{4.3}$$

(a) Show that this problem is absolutely well-conditioned over the interval from $x = 0$ to $x = 3$.

(b) Show that Euler's method, with step size $h = 1$, when applied to this problem leads to an absolutely ill-conditioned iteration formula and to an absurd estimate of $y(3)$.

Solution

(a) The general solution of this differential equation is $y = Ae^{-4x}$, so the analytic solution of (4.3) is $y = e^{-4x}$. Suppose that the initial condition is perturbed so that $\overline{y}(0) = 1 + \varepsilon$; then the new solution is

$$\overline{y} = (1+\varepsilon)e^{-4x} = e^{-4x} + \varepsilon e^{-4x} = y + \varepsilon e^{-4x},$$

so that at any point b the solution is perturbed by εe^{-4b}, and this is less than ε if b is positive. Thus the problem is absolutely well-conditioned over any interval from $x = 0$ to $x = a$ for positive a, and in particular this is true if $a = 3$.

Strictly speaking, the problem is absolutely well-conditioned 'with respect to small changes in the initial condition'.

(b) Euler's method involves the iteration formula

$$Y_{r+1} = Y_r + hf(x_r, Y_r) = Y_r + h(-4Y_r) = -3Y_r \quad (\text{if } h = 1).$$

The solution of this iteration problem with $Y_0 = 1$ is $Y_r = (-3)^r$. Suppose we change the initial condition to $\overline{Y}_0 = 1 + \varepsilon$. The solution of

$$\overline{Y}_{r+1} = -3\overline{Y}_r \qquad (\text{with } \overline{Y}_0 = 1 + \varepsilon)$$

is $\overline{Y}_r = (-3)^r(1 + \varepsilon)$. Thus an error in $\overline{Y}_0$ of ε has led to a change in Y_N of $\varepsilon(-3)^N$ and so the iteration problem is absolutely ill-conditioned. The true solution of the initial-value problem is $y(3) = 0.000\,006\,144$, while Euler's method gives $Y_3 = -27$, a hopeless estimate! ■

The real problem here is that Euler's method is based on the tangent approximation to the function being sought, and if the second derivative of this function is large then h must be small in order for the tangent approximation to be any good. In the case of Example 4.1, the function we are trying to estimate is e^{-4x}, whose second derivative is $16e^{-4x}$. Thus at $x = 0$ the second derivative is 16, so a step size of 1 will estimate the function very poorly. That is to say, Euler's method suffers from *induced instability* when applied to initial-value problem (4.3) with $h = 1$. However, if we reduce h to 0.1 the iteration formula in Example 4.1(b) would be $Y_{r+1} = 0.6Y_r$ and the problem of using this formula with $Y_0 = 1$ is then absolutely well-conditioned.

From Section 1, the error in the first step is $\varepsilon(h) = -\frac{1}{2}h^2 y''(c_h)$. With $h = 1$ and $y''(0) = 16$ the magnitude of the error in the first step could be as high as 8.

You should have found that induced instability occurred in the activities in Section 3. Problems (3.2) and (3.3) are both absolutely well-conditioned, over any interval and in particular over the intervals [0, 2] and [0, 0.6] that were used. However, all three numerical methods give rise to iteration formulae that are absolutely ill-conditioned, for the number of steps required, when h is too large.

The following definition applies to a numerical method, rather than to an initial-value problem which it is intended to solve.

Definition

When a numerical method is applied to a well-conditioned initial-value problem, it gives rise to an iteration problem. If that iteration problem is absolutely ill-conditioned, for a given step size and large numbers N of steps, the method is said to be **absolutely unstable**. If the iteration problem is absolutely well-conditioned, for a given step size, for all values of N, the method is **absolutely stable**.

In fact we do not need to know the solution of the iteration problem in order to judge whether it is absolutely ill-conditioned. We only need to look at an error ε in Y_r to see whether it leads to a larger or smaller error in Y_{r+1}. If it is smaller, for all r, we deduce that the iteration problem is absolutely well-conditioned, and the method does not suffer from induced instability. If the error in Y_{r+1} is larger than the error in Y_r for some values of r then we deduce that (for sufficiently large N) the iteration problem may be absolutely ill-conditioned and the method may suffer from induced instability. Our aim in analysing a particular well-conditioned problem is to choose a step size so that an error in Y_r leads to a smaller error in Y_{r+1}, for all values of r.

For a problem whose differential equation is $dy/dx = \lambda y$ for some negative λ, where the exact solution, $y = Ae^{\lambda x}$, tends to zero as x increases, the corresponding iteration formula is $Y_{r+1} = (1 + \lambda h)Y_r$, and so we require $-1 < 1 + \lambda h < 1$ for absolute stability, that is,

$$-2 < \lambda h < 0. \tag{4.4}$$

Exercise 4.2

For what step sizes is Euler's method absolutely stable, for the initial-value problem

$$\frac{dy}{dx} = -10y, \qquad y(0) = 1?$$

For a more general initial-value problem, the calculation of Y_{r+1} from Y_r might be more complicated.

Example 4.2

Consider the following initial-value problem:

$$\frac{dy}{dx} = (2x - 4)y, \qquad y(0) = 1.$$

This problem is absolutely well-conditioned only for $0 \le x \le 2$.

Under what condition is Euler's method absolutely stable for this problem on the interval $0 \le x \le 1$?

Solution

Here, the iteration formula for Euler's method is

$$\begin{aligned} Y_{r+1} &= Y_r + hf(x_r, Y_r) \\ &= Y_r + h(2x_r - 4)Y_r \\ &= (1 + h(2x_r - 4))Y_r. \end{aligned}$$

In this case, then, an error in Y_r will diminish if $-1 < 1 + h(2x_r - 4) < 1$, so that $h(2x_r - 4)$ must lie in the interval between -2 and 0. On the interval $0 \le x \le 1$, for positive h, $h(2x_r - 4)$ lies between $-4h$ and $-2h$. So Euler's method is absolutely stable if $h < 0.5$. ■

All the initial-value problems studied in this unit take the general form

$$\frac{dy}{dx} = f(x, y), \qquad y(x_0) = y_0,$$

and (as we saw in Section 2) Euler's method for this general problem, on the interval $[x_0, x_N]$, produces the iteration formula

$$Y_{r+1} = Y_r + hf(x_r, Y_r).$$

Now, if Y_r is replaced by $Y_r + \varepsilon$, then Y_{r+1} is replaced by

$$Y_r + \varepsilon + hf(x_r, Y_r + \varepsilon),$$

and (from *Unit 12*) the difference between $f(x_r, Y_r)$ and $f(x_r, Y_r + \varepsilon)$ is approximately $\varepsilon \times \frac{\partial f}{\partial y}(x_r, Y_r)$; that is,

$$f(x_r, Y_r + \varepsilon) \simeq f(x_r, Y_r) + \varepsilon \frac{\partial f}{\partial y}(x_r, Y_r).$$

Thus, Y_{r+1} is replaced by (approximately)

$$Y_r + \varepsilon + hf(x_r, Y_r) + h\varepsilon \frac{\partial f}{\partial y}(x_r, Y_r).$$

That is to say, the error ε in the value of Y_r becomes (approximately) an error of $\varepsilon \left(1 + h\frac{\partial f}{\partial y}(x_r, Y_r)\right)$ in the value of Y_{r+1}.

If ε is small (which we hope it is!), then this estimate of the error in the next step is reliable, and so the requirement that an initial error in Y_0 should be diminished rather than increased with each step is expressed by the formula

$$-1 < 1 + h\frac{\partial f}{\partial y}(x_r, Y_r) < 1 \qquad (r = 0, \dots, N-1)$$

or equivalently

$$-2 < h\frac{\partial f}{\partial y}(x_r, Y_r) < 0 \qquad (r = 0, \dots, N-1). \tag{4.5}$$

One immediate consequence is that if $\partial f/\partial y > 0$, then Euler's method is unstable for all step sizes. If $\partial f/\partial y < 0$, however, then there will be a range of values of h for which Euler's method is absolutely stable.

If $\partial f/\partial y > 0$, it can be shown that, over a sufficiently large interval, the initial-value problem is absolutely ill-conditioned.

Both expressions (4.4) and (4.5) indicate that a multiple of h that can be calculated from the original differential equation should remain within the interval $(-2, 0)$ during the calculation. This interval is known as the **interval of absolute stability** for Euler's method.

*Exercise 4.3

Euler's method is to be used to solve the logistic equation

$$\frac{dy}{dx} = 10y\left(1 - \frac{y}{1000}\right)$$

with the initial condition $y(0) = 2000$. Given that under this condition y is a decreasing function of x, tending to the equilibrium value 1000, determine a bound on the value of h that will guarantee that Euler's method is absolutely stable for this problem.

It turns out (though we shall not prove this) that each of the numerical methods developed in Section 2 has an interval of absolute stability, which can be used in exactly the same way as above in order to find a value of h that guarantees absolute stability. These intervals are given in Table 4.1.

Table 4.1 Intervals of absolute stability

Method	Interval of absolute stability
Euler's method	$(-2, 0)$
Euler-midpoint method	$(-2, 0)$
Euler-trapezoidal method	$(-2, 0)$
classical fourth-order Runge–Kutta method	$(-2.78, 0)$

Absolute stability of numerical methods

For the general initial-value problem

$$\frac{dy}{dx} = f(x, y), \qquad y(x_0) = y_0,$$

a numerical method with step size h is absolutely stable on the interval $[x_0, x_N]$ if $h(\partial f/\partial y)(x_r, Y_r)$ remains within the method's interval of absolute stability for all points (x_r, Y_r), $r = 0, \dots, N-1$.

If $\partial f/\partial y > 0$ then there is *no* step size that gives absolute stability.

Exercise 4.4

Consider the initial-value problem (3.2):

$$\frac{dy}{dx} = 20x(2-x) - 20y, \qquad y(0) = 0.$$

Determine under what conditions the Euler-trapezoidal method is absolutely stable for this problem. Use this result to explain what happened, for $h \geq 0.1$, in Activity 3.2, when the Euler-trapezoidal method was applied to the initial-value problem.

Exercise 4.5

Consider the initial-value problem (3.3):

$$\frac{dy}{dx} = y(20 - y), \qquad y(0) = 12.$$

Determine conditions under which the classical fourth-order Runge–Kutta method is absolutely stable for this problem. Use this result to explain what happened, for $h > 0.1$, in Activity 3.3, when the classical fourth-order Runge–Kutta method was applied to the initial-value problem.

4.2 Global error and convergence

In the development of Section 2, a numerical method was described as being *of order* p if the local truncation error was $O(h^{p+1})$. Thus, Euler's method is a method of order 1 (with local truncation error $O(h^2)$), and the other methods developed in Section 2 have order $p > 1$. These facts ensure that, if the step size h is reduced sufficiently, then the local truncation error tends to zero. However, knowing that each *local* truncation error tends to zero is not very useful in itself. What is important, in practice, is the *global error* at a particular point, and it is necessary to examine how the local truncation errors accumulate to form the global error.

If we wish to solve the initial-value problem

$$\frac{dy}{dx} = f(x, y), \qquad y(x_0) = y_0, \tag{4.6}$$

over some interval $[a, b]$ in the domain of interest, it is not very informative to know the local truncation error on each step of size h, or to know that the local truncation error on each step tends to zero as the step size h is reduced. As the step size is reduced, the number of steps needed to cover the interval $[a, b]$ increases, and it is not always clear what might be the effect of an accumulation of an increasing number of local truncation errors, even if each individual error is reduced.

In Section 3, the numerical solutions of each of the three initial-value problems (3.1), (3.2) and (3.3) were compared at a single value of the independent variable x. In each case, and for each method, it was found that, as the step size h was reduced to sufficiently small values, the numerical solution corresponding to the grid point at that fixed value of x appeared to *converge* to the value of the true analytic solution at that point. Thus, even though the number of steps was necessarily increasing as the step size h was reduced, it appeared that the global error at that point was tending to zero. If calculations are carried out exactly, then it is a desirable property of any numerical method that the global error, at any given value of the independent variable, and for any initial-value problem of the general form (4.6), should tend to zero as the step size h is reduced. Taking some particular value x of the independent variable (say $x = 0.2$) and computing the approximations to y at that point using smaller and smaller step sizes, should result in these approximations getting closer and closer to the true solution at that point. Figure 4.1 illustrates how a sequence of numerical solutions might converge to the true solution.

In practice, if the step size were made too small, then the global error would begin to increase again, owing to the build-up of rounding errors in the increasing number of calculations.

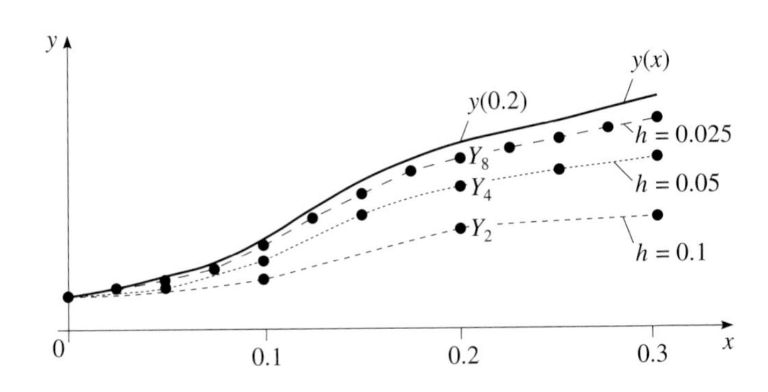

Figure 4.1

For a given numerical method, consider the global error at a fixed value of the independent variable x, and the way in which it changes as h is reduced. In order that the value of x should remain fixed, it is necessary to vary the number of steps N which are needed to reach x. In fact, N is related to h by the equation

$$Nh = x - x_0.$$

The global error at x,

$$Y_N - y(x),$$

depends upon h, not only because h appears as a parameter in the iteration formula for Y_r, but also because the number of steps, N, depends upon h.

If the global error at x tends to zero as $h \to 0$, with $N = (x - x_0)/h$, then the numerical method is said to be *convergent* at x. A method that gives convergence at a particular point b will also (usually) be convergent at any point between x_0 and b, and in general it will be possible to find some interval, $x_0 \le x \le b$, throughout which convergence is guaranteed. This leads to the following definition of convergence of a numerical method.

> ***Definition***
> A numerical method is **convergent**, for a given initial-value problem of the form $dy/dx = f(x, y)$, $y(x_0) = y_0$, over some interval $[x_0, b]$ if, for all points x in the interval, as $h \to 0$, and $N = (x - x_0)/h$, then $Y_N \to y(x)$.

If the method is to give useful information about the true solution of the initial-value problem, then this property is essential.

For one-step methods the following theorem (which we do not prove) not only establishes a criterion for convergence, but also gives an indication of the rate of convergence.

> ***Theorem 4.1 Convergence Theorem***
> Consider an initial-value problem of the form
>
> $$\frac{dy}{dx} = f(x, y), \qquad y(x_0) = y_0,$$
>
> on an interval $[x_0, b]$, with a well-behaved function $f(x, y)$. A one-step method is convergent if, and only if, the method is of order p for some integer $p \geq 1$, i.e. its local truncation error is $O(h^{p+1})$. The global error at a fixed point x, for sufficiently small values of h, is then of the form
>
> $$Y_N - y(x) \simeq Ch^p,$$
>
> where $Nh = x - x_0$, and C is a constant that does not depend on h.

The function $f(x, y)$ is 'well-behaved' in this context if it can be differentiated $p + 1$ times. If it cannot, it would be better to use a lower-order method where this property does hold.

The Convergence Theorem does not provide a bound on the error, since C is an unknown constant, but it indicates that, when the step size h is small enough, if h is further divided by two, say, then the error in the approximation to $y(x)$ should be reduced by a factor of 2^p, even though it is necessary to take twice as many steps. This means that, when high accuracy is required, this is more efficiently obtained (requires fewer function evaluations) using a higher-order method. When less accuracy is required, it may be more efficiently obtained using a simpler, lower-order, method.

If you look back at the results of your Section 3 activities, you should see that this property seems to hold.

Example 4.3

Use the Convergence Theorem to establish that, for an initial-value problem of the general form $dy/dx = f(x, y)$, $y(x_0) = y_0$, on an interval $[x_0, b]$, with well-behaved function $f(x, y)$, Euler's method is convergent, and give the form of its global error at a fixed point x, for sufficiently small values of the step size h.

In particular, consider the initial-value problem (3.2):

$$\frac{dy}{dx} = 20x(2 - x) - 20y, \qquad y(0) = 0.$$

Use the results of Activity 3.2(a) to estimate the form of the global error at a fixed point x, for sufficiently small values of the step size h.

Solution
Since its local truncation error is $O(h^2)$, Euler's method is a first-order method. Therefore $p = 1$ and by Theorem 4.1 the method is convergent. Its global error, at a fixed point x, takes the form

$$Y_N - y(x) \simeq Ch$$

for sufficiently small values of h, where $Nh = x - x_0$, and C is a constant which does not depend on h.

In the case of the initial-value problem (3.2), the results of Activity 3.2(a) indicate that the global error at $x = 2$ takes the values in Table 4.2.

Table 4.2

h	Global error at $x = 2$
0.2	5609.67
0.1	0.105
0.05	0.0025
0.025	0.001 25
0.0125	0.000 625

Since $\partial f/\partial y = -20$ the method is only absolutely stable if $h < 0.1$.

For $h \leq 0.05$, the global error satisfies, to six decimal places, $Y_N - y(2) = 0.05\,h = Ch$, where C takes the value 0.05. ■

Exercise 4.6

Use the Convergence Theorem to establish that, for an initial-value problem of the general form $dy/dx = f(x, y)$, $y(x_0) = y_0$, with well-behaved function $f(x, y)$, the classical fourth-order Runge–Kutta method is convergent, and give the form of its global error at a fixed point x, for sufficiently small values of the step size h.

Exercise 4.7

Consider the initial-value problem (3.3):

$$\frac{dy}{dx} = y(20 - y), \qquad y(0) = 12.$$

Use the results of Activity 3.3(c) to estimate the form of the global error at $x = 0.6$, for sufficiently small values of the step size h, when the classical fourth-order Runge–Kutta method is used to solve the problem.

4.3 Determination of step size

Convergence is a very important property of a numerical method, as it guarantees that, if the step size h is made small enough, and if the calculations are carried out to a sufficient number of decimal places, then any predetermined accuracy can be obtained in the solution of an initial-value problem. The methods developed in Section 2 are one-step methods, with orders $p = 1, 2$ and 4 and are therefore convergent for any initial-value problem of the general form (4.6) with a well-behaved function $f(x, y)$. This is reassuring, but the global error formula in the Convergence Theorem contains an unknown constant C, and gives no indication, when the exact solution of the problem is not known, as to just how small the step size h needs to be in order to achieve a given accuracy. Finding a suitable step size to achieve a predetermined accuracy is the topic of this subsection.

Consider again the results of Activity 3.2(a) for the initial-value problem

$$\frac{dy}{dx} = 20x(2 - x) - 20y, \qquad y(0) = 0. \tag{4.7}$$

To obtain approximations to $y(2)$ using Euler's method for the step sizes $h = 0.2, 0.1, 0.05, 0.025, 0.0125$, the corresponding number of steps required are $N = 10, 20, 40, 80, 160$, so as to maintain the relationship

$$Nh = x - x_0 = 2.$$

The results obtained are shown in Table 4.3.

Table 4.3

h	N	x_N	Y_N
0.2	10	2	5609.76
0.1	20	2	0.2
0.05	40	2	0.0975
0.025	80	2	0.096 25
0.0125	160	2	0.095 625

The result for $h = 0.2$ certainly gives little confidence, though without prior knowledge of the nature of the solution, the most obvious indication that something is wrong is that the solution over the range $x = 0$ to $x = 2$ appears to be oscillating at every step, with ever increasing amplitude (as in Figures 4.2 and 4.3, which show the situations using two different scales).

You can deduce from Exercise 4.4 that the condition $0 < h < 0.1$ is needed for absolute stability. Thus the erratic behaviour at $h = 0.1$ and the wild behaviour at $h = 0.2$ are not surprising.

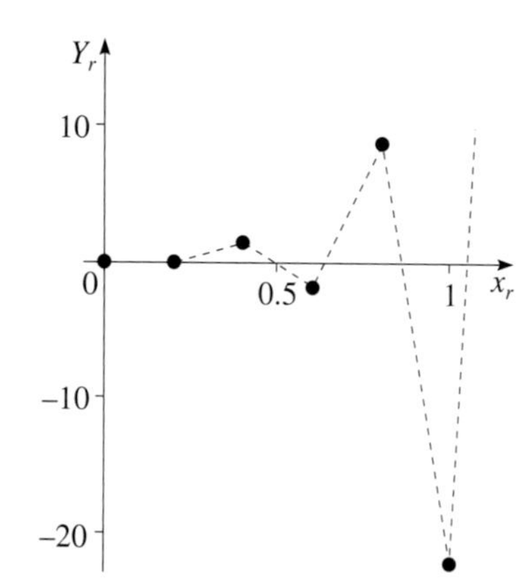

Figure 4.2 Results for $h = 0.2$

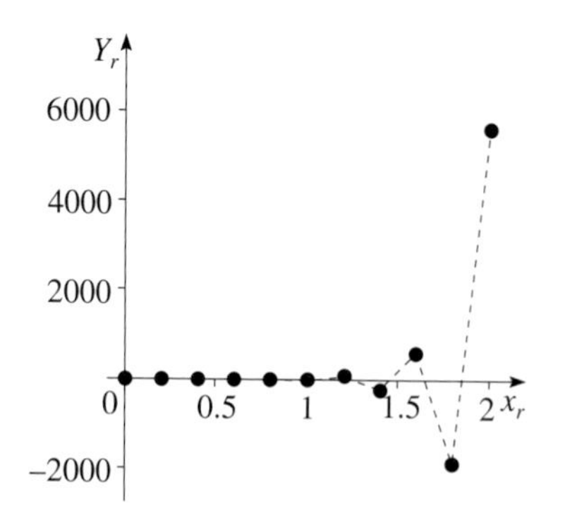

Figure 4.3 Results for $h = 0.2$ (large scale)

For $h = 0.1$, the oscillations in the solution are quite small and are not growing (Figure 4.4). However, they are not decaying either, and the rather crude solution gives little more than a rough idea of the nature of the true solution. The fact that the oscillations are neither growing nor decaying suggests that $h = 0.1$ is just on the limit of absolute stability (as we know that it is), and it would be expected that a smaller value of the step size h should be used.

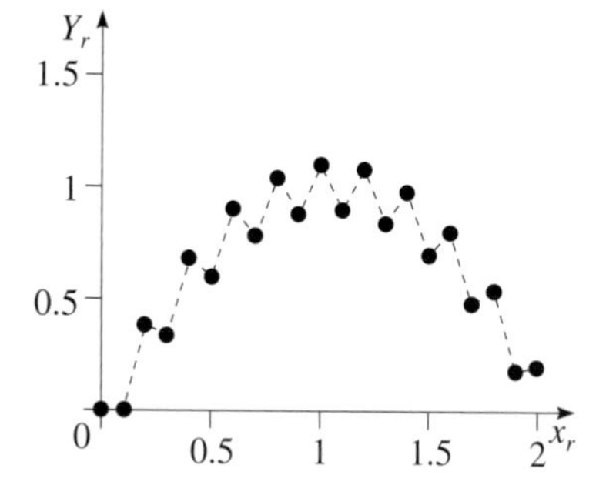

Figure 4.4 Results for $h = 0.1$

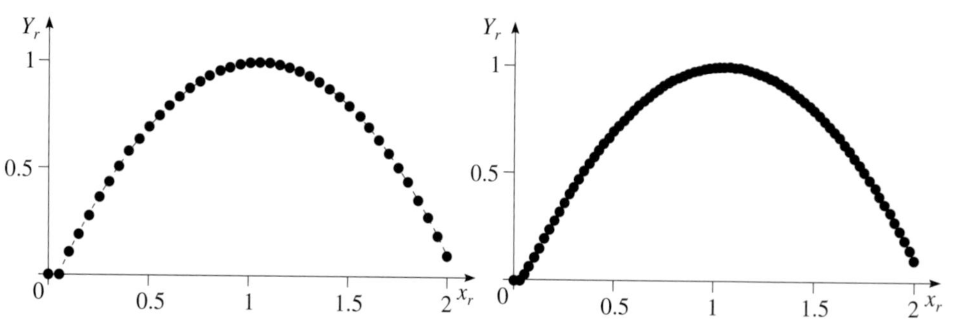

Figure 4.5 Results for $h = 0.05$ and $h = 0.025$

The results obtained with $h = 0.05$ and $h = 0.025$ both look quite sensible, showing no visible oscillation (Figure 4.5). If the analytic solution were not known, how would it be possible to decide upon the accuracy of these two results? A first observation would be to note that the values for $x = 2$ differ by only $0.0975 - 0.096\,25 = 0.001\,25$. They are therefore both, probably, correct to two decimal places. Suppose that the result was required correct to three decimal places; how much smaller would the step size h need to be? Suppose that the result was required correct to six decimal places; how much smaller would the step size h need to be?

Using the Convergence Theorem to analyse the results of Euler's method ($p = 1$) at $x_N = x = 2$, we have

$$Y_N - y(2) \simeq Ch.$$

So, how small must h be, in order that we may assume that the global error is proportional to h^p? In this case, it would certainly be far from true for $h = 0.2$ ($N = 10$). It would be unwise to assume any proportionality for $h = 0.1$ ($N = 20$). It would, however, be reasonable to look for an approximate proportionality for $h \leq 0.05$. To do this, we plot a graph of Y_N against h, as shown in Figures 4.6 and 4.7.

In general we would need to plot Y_N against h^p.

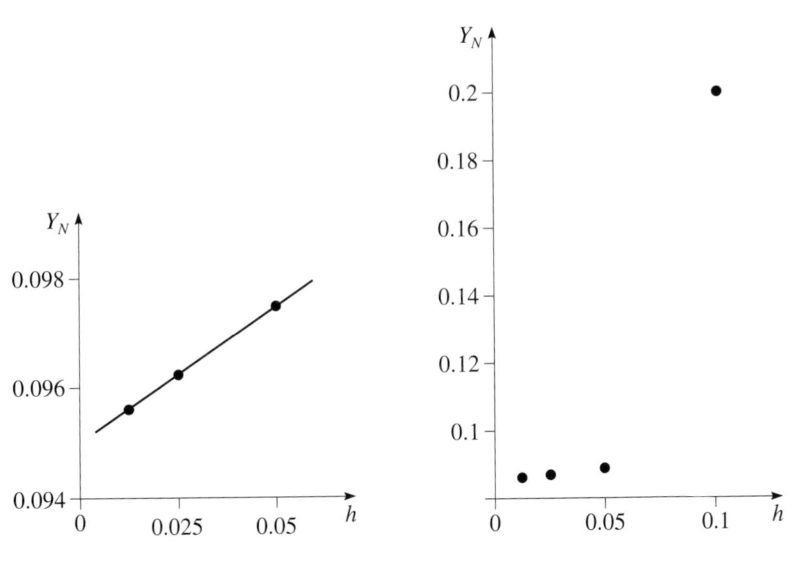

Figure 4.6 *Figure 4.7*

In order to confirm the proportionality, we plot the results for at least three different values of the step size h. In this case, the results for $h = 0.0125, 0.025, 0.05$ have been plotted. They lie remarkably close to a straight line, thus confirming that the values of $Y_N - y(2)$ are proportional to h for this range of values of h. If the result for $h = 0.1$ is included, the corresponding point does not lie on the straight line (Figure 4.7), thus showing that this value of h is too large. In many practical cases, it is unlikely that such a good straight-line fit will be obtained for such relatively large step sizes as in Figure 4.6, but when a reasonable straight-line fit is obtained by plotting Y_N against h^p, it may be assumed that

$$Y_N \simeq y(x) + Ch^p \tag{4.8}$$

for the corresponding range of values of h.

In the approximate formula (4.8), the values of the step size h may be chosen, and the corresponding values Y_N of the numerical solution may be calculated. However, the constant C and the true solution $y(x)$ are, in general, unknown. In the particular case of Euler's method applied to the initial-value problem (4.7),

$$Y_N \simeq y(2) + Ch,$$

and values of Y_N are known for certain values of h. If this were an exact identity, then, in Figure 4.6, the slope of the straight line would be C, and its intercept with the y-axis would be $y(2)$.

It is tempting to try to calculate the true solution $y(2)$ in this way. Using the tabulated results for the smallest two available step sizes, namely $h = 0.025$ and $h = 0.0125$:

$$\begin{cases} Y_{80} = 0.096\,25 \simeq y(2) + C \times 0.025, \\ Y_{160} = 0.095\,625 \simeq y(2) + C \times 0.0125. \end{cases} \tag{4.9}$$

Multiplying the second equation by 2, and subtracting the first, the intercept with the y-axis is given approximately by

$$y(2) \simeq 2Y_{160} - Y_{80} = 2 \times 0.095\,625 - 0.096\,25 = 0.095.$$

Because of the good straight-line fit, this gives a remarkably accurate solution in this case. (In fact, $y(2) = 0.095 + 0.105e^{-40}$.) However, in general, because of the approximations involved, a result obtained in this way would still contain some significant error. In this case, if the results for $h = 0.1$ and $h = 0.05$ had been used, there would certainly have been a large error. What has been done is to eliminate a term Ch^p, but this leaves some term $O(h^{p+1})$, which should be small compared to Ch^p if h is sufficiently small, but is generally non-zero. The disadvantage of this way of estimating the true solution at x is that we do not know how accurate it is.

However, there is a more reliable way of using Equations (4.9). They contain two unknowns, the constant C and the true solution $y(2)$. In the analysis above, the constant C was eliminated in order to estimate the true solution $y(2)$. It is in general more useful to eliminate the true solution $y(2)$ in order to estimate the slope C of the straight line in Figure 4.6. Subtracting one equation from the other,

$$C(0.025 - 0.0125) \simeq Y_{80} - Y_{160} = 0.096\,25 - 0.095\,625 = 0.000\,625,$$

so that

$$C \simeq \frac{0.000\,625}{0.0125} = 0.05.$$

This may not be a particularly accurate value, but it is to be expected that, for values of $h \leq 0.05$, the global error at $x = 2$ is approximately

$$Ch \simeq 0.05h.$$

If the value of $y(2)$ were required to three decimal places, then it should be sufficient to choose a new value of h satisfying

$$0.05h \leq 0.5 \times 10^{-3},$$

so that $h \leq 0.01$, and to repeat the calculation using Euler's method with that step size. In order to confirm the accuracy of the result, it would be sensible to repeat the process with a value of h half the size again, to check that the two results differ by less than 0.5×10^{-3}.

If the value of $y(2)$ were required to six decimal places, then it should be sufficient to choose a new value of h satisfying

$$0.05h \leq 0.5 \times 10^{-6},$$

so that $h \leq 0.000\,01$, and to repeat the calculation using Euler's method with that step size. This, however, would require 200 000 steps, and would take a relatively large amount of calculation; it may therefore suffer from the build up of rounding errors.

Example 4.4

Analyse the results of Activity 3.2(b) for the initial-value problem (3.2),

$$\frac{dy}{dx} = 20x(2-x) - 20y, \qquad y(0) = 0,$$

using the Euler-trapezoidal method, in order to determine what step size h would be needed in order to determine $y(2)$:

(a) correct to three decimal places;

(b) correct to six decimal places.

Compare the efficiency of this method with that of Euler's method for this problem.

Recall that the efficiency is given by the product of the number of steps × the number of function evaluations per step, the more efficient method being the one with the smaller product.

Solution

The results obtained for the step sizes $h = 0.2, 0.1, 0.05, 0.025, 0.0125$ ($N = 10, 20, 40, 80, 160$) may be tabulated as in Table 4.4.

Table 4.4

h	N	x_N	Y_N
0.2	10	2	830 078.24
0.1	20	2	0.00
0.05	40	2	0.0925
0.025	80	2	0.094 583
0.0125	160	2	0.094 911

The result for $h = 0.2$ gives little confidence, particularly when compared with the results for smaller values of h. The solution over the range $x = 0$ to $x = 2$ does not oscillate, but increases exponentially. However, a quick look at the differential equation indicates that, for large values of y, the slope function $f(x, y)$ should be negative.

Exercise 4.4 showed that we need $h < 0.1$ for absolute stability, so the poor results for $h = 0.2$ and 0.1 are to be expected.

For $h = 0.1$ the solution behaves more reasonably, but still differs significantly from the results for smaller values of h.

The results obtained with $h = 0.05$ and $h = 0.025$ look more sensible, and their values for $x = 2$ differ by only $0.094\,583 - 0.0925 = 0.002\,083$, suggesting that they are both, probably, correct to two decimal places.

Since the Euler-trapezoidal method is of order two, it is expected that, if h is small enough,

$$Y_N - y(2) \simeq Ch^2.$$

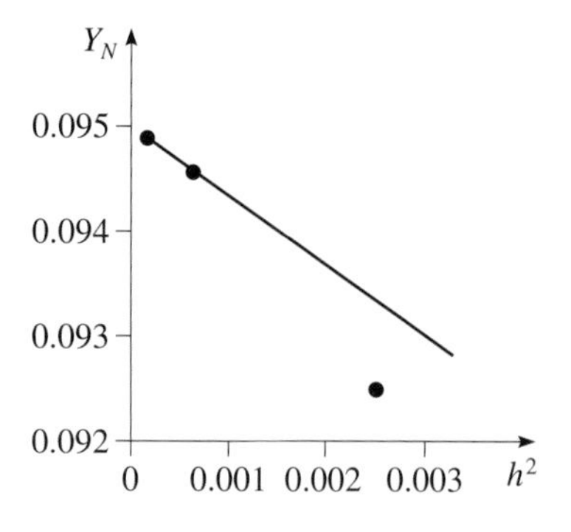

Figure 4.8

This is certainly not true for $h = 0.2$ ($N = 10$), and is unlikely to be reliable for $h = 0.1$ ($N = 20$) (see the note above). It might, however, be a reasonable approximation for $h \leq 0.05$, as the method is absolutely stable for these values of h. To test the approximate proportionality, we plot a graph of Y_N against h^2, for the three smallest values of h used in Activity 3.2(b) (Figure 4.8) and draw the line through the two points for which h has the smallest values, since this is the best we can do. While the third point is not particularly close to this straight line, it does suggest a reasonable proportionality between the global error at $x = 2$ and h^2, so that for $h < 0.05$ we can use

$$Y_N \simeq y(2) + Ch^2.$$

Using the tabulated results for the two smallest values $h = 0.025$ and $h = 0.0125$,

$$\begin{cases} Y_{80} &= 0.094\,583 \simeq y(2) + C \times 0.025^2 \\ Y_{160} &= 0.094\,911 \simeq y(2) + C \times 0.0125^2. \end{cases} \qquad (4.10)$$

We now estimate the constant C by subtracting one of Equations (4.10) from the other:

$$C(0.025^2 - 0.0125^2) \simeq Y_{80} - Y_{160} = 0.094\,583 - 0.094\,911 = -0.000\,328,$$

so that $C \simeq -0.000\,328/0.000\,468\,75 \simeq -0.700$. While this may not be a particularly accurate value, it is to be expected that, for values of $h \leq 0.05$, the global error at $x = 2$ is approximately

$$Ch^2 \simeq -0.700h^2.$$

(a) If the value of $y(2)$ is required to three decimal places, then it should be sufficient to choose a new value of h satisfying

$$0.700h^2 \leq 0.5 \times 10^{-3},$$

so that $h^2 \leq 0.000\,71$, and $h \leq 0.0267$. In order to have a convenient integer number N of steps, it would be appropriate to choose $h = 0.025$ or $h = 0.02$. Given that the Euler-trapezoidal method requires twice as many function evaluations per step as Euler's method, it is only marginally more efficient for three-decimal-place accuracy than Euler's method, which needs a step size of $h = 0.01$ for this same accuracy.

(b) If the value of $y(2)$ is required to six decimal places, then it should be sufficient to choose a new value of h satisfying

$$0.700h^2 \leq 0.5 \times 10^{-6},$$

so that $h^2 \leq 0.000\,000\,71$, and $h \leq 0.000\,85$. In order to have a convenient integer number N of steps, it would be appropriate to choose $h = 0.0005$. This is 50 times bigger than the corresponding step size using Euler's method, and reduces the number of steps required from 200 000 to 4000. Thus, the Euler-trapezoidal method appears to be a more efficient method for obtaining accuracy to six decimal places, in this case. ■

The approach based on estimating C has a further advantage over the direct estimation of $y(x)$ from equations such as (4.9) or (4.10). When the appropriate step size h has been determined, and the calculation is repeated using that step size, not only is $y(x)$ determined to within the specified accuracy, but it is likely that an accurate solution has been obtained over the whole interval from $x = x_0$ up to the particular value of x where the analysis was carried out.

Procedure 4.1 Determination of step size

When using a numerical method of order p to solve the initial-value problem

$$\frac{dy}{dx} = f(x, y), \qquad y(x_0) = y_0,$$

from $x = x_0$ to $x = b$, proceed as follows.

(a) Choose at least three different values of the step size h, say, $h_0 = (b - x_0)/N_0$, $h_1 = (b - x_0)/N_1$, $h_2 = (b - x_0)/N_2$.

(b) Use the numerical method to obtain approximate solutions over the interval $[x_0, b]$, using each of those step sizes.

(c) Check that the solutions behave in a similar way. On a graph of Y_N against h^p, check that the three points (h_0^p, Y_{N_0}), (h_1^p, Y_{N_1}), (h_2^p, Y_{N_2}) lie close to the straight line through the two points involving the smallest values of h. If not, choose a smaller step size, discard the largest step size, and return to (b).

(d) When a reasonable straight-line fit is obtained, then

$$Y_N \simeq y(b) + Ch^p$$

and choosing the smallest two step sizes (h_1 and h_2 say)

$$Y_{N_1} \simeq y(b) + Ch_1^p,$$
$$Y_{N_2} \simeq y(b) + Ch_2^p.$$

The difference

$$Y_{N_1} - Y_{N_2} \simeq C(h_1^p - h_2^p)$$

gives an approximate value for the slope C.

(e) To achieve n-decimal-place accuracy in the estimate Y_N for $y(b)$ it is necessary to choose an appropriate step size h so that

$$|Ch^p| \leq 0.5 \times 10^{-n}, \qquad \text{so that } h \leq \sqrt[p]{0.5 \times 10^{-n}/|C|}.$$

Halving the step size is a good strategy here. It is not sensible, for example, to use consecutive integers for N_0, N_1 and N_2.

**Exercise 4.8*

Analyse the results of Activity 3.1(a) for the initial-value problem (3.1),

$$\frac{dy}{dx} = 3(x-1)^2 + 20(y - (x-1)^3), \qquad y(0) = -1,$$

using Euler's method, in order to determine what step size h would be needed in order to determine $y(0.2)$:

(a) correct to three decimal places;

(b) correct to six decimal places.

Exercise 4.9

Analyse the results of Activity 3.1(b) for the initial-value problem (3.1), using the Euler-trapezoidal method, in order to determine what step size h would be needed in order to determine $y(0.2)$:

(a) correct to three decimal places;

(b) correct to six decimal places.

Compare the efficiency of this method with that of Euler's method (Exercise 4.8) for this problem.

End-of-section Exercises

Exercise 4.10

Consider the initial-value problem (3.3):

$$\frac{dy}{dx} = y(20 - y), \qquad y(0) = 12.$$

Determine conditions under which the Euler-trapezoidal method is absolutely stable for this problem. Analyse the results of Activity 3.3(b) for the initial-value problem, using the Euler-trapezoidal method, explaining the behaviour of the results. Estimate what step size h would be needed in order to determine $y(0.6)$ correct to six decimal places.

Exercise 4.11

The classical fourth-order Runge–Kutta method is to be used to solve the initial-value problem

$$\frac{dy}{dx} = -xy + \frac{1}{1+x^2}, \qquad y(0) = 1,$$

for $0 \le x \le 10$. Determine a bound on the values of h which will guarantee that the classical fourth-order Runge–Kutta method is absolutely stable.

5 Practical computation

In this final section you are given the opportunity to put into practice the analysis of Section 4, so as to obtain the solution of an initial-value problem to a given, pre-determined accuracy.

Use your computer to complete the following activity.

PC

Activity 5.1

Consider the initial-value problem (3.2)

$$\frac{dy}{dx} = 20x(2-x) - 20y, \qquad y(0) = 0,$$

over the interval $0 \leq x \leq 0.2$. Determine under what conditions each of:

(a) Euler's method;

(b) the Euler-trapezoidal method;

(c) the classical fourth-order Runge–Kutta method;

is absolutely stable for this problem. For each method, use Procedure 4.1, with an initial step size $h_0 = 0.02$, to estimate the step size required to determine $y(0.2)$ correct to six decimal places, and use each method to obtain the value of $y(0.2)$ correct to six decimal places. Compare the efficiencies of the methods for obtaining six-decimal-place accuracy.

Previous questions concerning initial-value problem (3.2) have considered the solution over the interval $0 \leq x \leq 2$. In this case, you are only asked about the smaller interval to $x = 0.2$.

In this unit, a process has been discussed by which it is possible to determine a fixed step size h for any given problem, so that a given method should provide the solution to a specified accuracy. In many practical problems, it is more efficient to vary the step size throughout the interval of interest, and there exist many general-purpose computer packages, for the numerical solution of initial-value problems, which are designed to change the step size for the problem as they advance through the interval. The criterion for choosing an appropriate step size is similar to that given here, and is applied to almost every step. However, the step size is calculated using an estimate of the local truncation error, rather than the global error, and so cannot guarantee the results will have the desired accuracy. Nevertheless, such general-purpose packages are very reliable.

Outcomes

After studying this unit, you should be able to:

- understand the concept of a truncation error;
- understand the nature of, and distinguish between, local truncation error and global error, for numerical methods for differential equations;
- set up the iteration formulae arising from the Euler-trapezoidal method for solving an initial-value problem, and carry out one or two steps of the method by hand;
- set up the iteration formulae arising from the classical fourth-order Runge–Kutta method for solving an initial-value problem, and carry out one step of the method by hand;
- use the computer to apply each of the above methods with a large number of steps;
- understand the concept of convergence of a numerical method for differential equations and the relationship between the order of a one-step method and the order of its local truncation error;
- use the Convergence Theorem to determine what step size is appropriate to obtain a pre-determined accuracy, when using a one-step method;
- understand the concepts of absolute ill-conditioning of an initial-value problem, and absolute stability of a numerical method;
- determine conditions on the step size under which a one-step numerical method will be absolutely stable for a given initial-value problem.

Solutions to the exercises

Section 1

1.1 With $f(x) = e^{2x}$, we have $f'(x) = 2e^{2x}$, $f''(x) = 4e^{2x}$, $f'''(x) = 8e^{2x}$ and $f^{(4)}(x) = 16e^{2x}$, and so $f(0) = 1$, $f'(0) = 2$, $f''(0) = 4$, $f'''(0) = 8$ and $f^{(4)}(0) = 16$. Thus,

$$p_1(x) = 1 + 2x,$$

$$p_2(x) = p_1(x) + \tfrac{4}{2!}x^2 = 1 + 2x + 2x^2,$$

$$p_3(x) = p_2(x) + \tfrac{8}{3!}x^3 = 1 + 2x + 2x^2 + \tfrac{4}{3}x^3,$$

$$p_4(x) = p_3(x) + \tfrac{16}{4!}x^4 = 1 + 2x + 2x^2 + \tfrac{4}{3}x^3 + \tfrac{2}{3}x^4.$$

1.2 With $f(x) = x^{\frac{1}{2}}$, we have $f'(x) = \frac{1}{2}x^{-\frac{1}{2}}$, $f''(x) = -\frac{1}{4}x^{-\frac{3}{2}}$, $f'''(x) = \frac{3}{8}x^{-\frac{5}{2}}$, and so $f(1) = 1$, $f'(1) = \frac{1}{2}$, $f''(1) = -\frac{1}{4}$, $f'''(1) = \frac{3}{8}$. Thus,

$$p_2(x) = 1 + \tfrac{1}{2}(x-1) - \tfrac{1}{8}(x-1)^2,$$

$$p_3(x) = 1 + \tfrac{1}{2}(x-1) - \tfrac{1}{8}(x-1)^2 + \tfrac{1}{16}(x-1)^3.$$

With $x = 1.44$, the value of $x - 1$ is 0.44. Then $p_2(1.44) = 1.1958$ and $p_3(1.44) = 1.201\,124$. This may be compared with $f(1.44) = \sqrt{1.44} = 1.2$. At $x = 1.44$, the second-order Taylor polynomial matches the function $f(x) = x^{\frac{1}{2}}$ to two decimal places as does the third-order polynomial (although the error in $p_3(1.44)$ is only about one-quarter of that in $p_2(1.44)$).

1.3 **(a)** With $f(x) = \ln x$, we have $f'(x) = \frac{1}{x}$, $f''(x) = -\frac{1}{x^2}$, $f'''(x) = \frac{2}{x^3}, \ldots, f^{(n)}(x) = (-1)^{n+1}\frac{(n-1)!}{x^n}$. At $x = 1$, the values are $f(1) = \ln 1 = 0$, $f'(1) = 1$, $f''(1) = -1$, $f'''(1) = 2, \ldots, f^{(n)}(1) = (-1)^{n+1}(n-1)!$ Hence, the nth-order Taylor polynomial approximating $f(x) = \ln x$ about $x = 1$ is

$$p_n(x) = (x-1) - \tfrac{1}{2}(x-1)^2 + \tfrac{1}{3}(x-1)^3 - \cdots + (-1)^{n+1}\tfrac{1}{n}(x-1)^n$$

as required.

(b) Thus, $p_3(x) = (x-1) - \frac{1}{2}(x-1)^2 + \frac{1}{3}(x-1)^3$, so that $p_3(1.6) = 0.492$, while

$$p_4(x) = (x-1) - \tfrac{1}{2}(x-1)^2 + \tfrac{1}{3}(x-1)^3 - \tfrac{1}{4}(x-1)^4,$$

so that $p_4(1.6) = 0.4596$. Now, $\ln 1.6 = 0.4700$, so at $x = 1.6$ both polynomials match the function to just one decimal place (although the error in $p_4(1.6)$ is less than half that in $p_3(1.6)$).

1.4 **(a)** We know that $-1 \le \cos c \le 1$ for all c, and hence $|\cos c| \le 1$.

(b) With $f(x) = \sin x$, we have $f'(x) = \cos x$, $f''(x) = -\sin x$, $f'''(x) = -\cos x$, $f^{(4)}(x) = \sin x$, $f^{(5)}(x) = \cos x$, $f^{(6)}(x) = -\sin x$, $f^{(7)}(x) = -\cos x$. At $x = 0$, the values are $f(0) = 0$, $f'(0) = 1$, $f''(0) = 0$, $f'''(0) = -1$, $f^{(4)}(0) = 0$, $f^{(5)}(0) = 1$, $f^{(6)}(0) = 0$, $f^{(7)}(0) = -1$.

Hence, the sixth-order Taylor polynomial approximating $f(x) = \sin x$ about $x = 0$ is

$$p_6(x) = x - \tfrac{1}{6}x^3 + \tfrac{1}{120}x^5.$$

An estimate of the truncation error is provided by the next term of the Taylor expansion, so that

$$\varepsilon(x) \simeq \tfrac{1}{5040}x^7.$$

That is to say, $\varepsilon(x) = O(x^7)$.

(c) Taylor's Theorem, with $f(x) = \sin x$, gives

$$\sin x = x - \tfrac{1}{6}x^3 + \tfrac{1}{120}x^5 - \varepsilon(x),$$

where

$$\varepsilon(x) = -\tfrac{1}{5040}x^7 f^{(7)}(c_x) = \tfrac{1}{5040}x^7 \cos c_x.$$

The estimate in part (b) was obtained by evaluating $f^{(7)}$ at 0 instead of at c_x. However, by part (a), we know that $|\cos c_x| \le 1$. Therefore $|\varepsilon(x)| \le \frac{1}{5040}|x|^7$ for all x, and in particular $|\varepsilon(x)| \le \frac{1}{5040}$ if $0 \le x \le 1$.

1.5 **(a)** With $f(x) = x^5$, we have $f'(x) = 5x^4$, $f''(x) = 20x^3$, $f'''(x) = 60x^2$, $f^{(4)}(x) = 120x$. The truncation error for the third-order Taylor polynomial approximating $f(x) = x^5$ about $x = 1$ is given by

$$\varepsilon(x) \simeq -\tfrac{1}{4!}h^4 f^{(4)}(1),$$

where $h = x - 1$. So $\varepsilon(x) \simeq -5(x-1)^4$, and

$$\varepsilon(x) = O(h^4).$$

(b) Taylor's Theorem, with $f(x) = x^5$, gives

$$\varepsilon(x) = -\tfrac{1}{4!}h^4 f^{(4)}(c_x),$$

where $h = x - 1$, and $1 \le c_x \le x \le 1.5$. Therefore $|f^{(4)}(c_x)| = |120c_x| \le 180$, and

$$|\varepsilon(x)| = \left|-\tfrac{1}{24}h^4 f^{(4)}(c_x)\right| \le 7.5h^4 \text{ for } 1 \le x \le 1.5,$$

where $h = x - 1$.

1.6 The approximation $\sin x \simeq x$ uses the first or second-order Taylor polynomial approximating $f(x) = \sin x$ about $x = 0$. Since the term in x^2 disappears, it is appropriate to consider the second-order polynomial in order to estimate the truncation error. An estimate of the truncation error is provided by the next term of the Taylor expansion, so, making use of Solution 1.4(b),

$$\varepsilon(x) \simeq \tfrac{1}{6}x^3.$$

So $\left|\varepsilon\left(\frac{\pi}{180}\right)\right| \simeq \left|\frac{1}{6}\left(\frac{\pi}{180}\right)^3\right| \simeq 0.000\,000\,886$ and the approximation is accurate to almost six decimal places.

1.7 **(a)** With $f(x) = x^{-2}$, we have $f'(x) = -2x^{-3}$, $f''(x) = 6x^{-4}$, $f'''(x) = -24x^{-5}$, $f^{(4)}(x) = 120x^{-6}$. At $x = 1$, the values are $f(1) = 1$, $f'(1) = -2$, $f''(1) = 6$, $f'''(1) = -24$, $f^{(4)}(1) = 120$. Hence, the third-order Taylor polynomial approximating $f(x) = x^{-2}$ about $x = 1$ is

$$p_3(x) = 1 - 2(x-1) + 3(x-1)^2 - 4(x-1)^3.$$

An estimate of the truncation error is provided by the next term of the Taylor expansion, so that

$$\varepsilon(x) \simeq -5(x-1)^4.$$

(b) Writing the Taylor polynomial in terms of $h = x - 1$,

$$p_3(1+h) = 1 - 2h + 3h^2 - 4h^3.$$

With $x = 1.05$, the value of $h = x - 1$ is 0.05. Then $p_3(1.05) = 0.907$.
Taylor's Theorem, with $f(x) = x^{-2}$, gives

$$\varepsilon(x) = -\tfrac{1}{4!}h^4 f^{(4)}(c_x),$$

where $h = x - 1$, and $1 \le c_x \le 1.05$.
Therefore $|f^{(4)}(c_x)| = |120c_x^{-6}| \le 120$, and

$$|\varepsilon(x)| = \left|-\tfrac{1}{24}h^4 f^{(4)}(c_x)\right| \le 5h^4,$$

and with $h = 0.05$, $|\varepsilon(x)| \le 0.000\,031\,25$.

(The actual value of $f(1.05)$ is $0.907\,029\,48$, and so the actual truncation error is $-0.000\,029\,48$, which is slightly smaller in magnitude than the error bound. The error estimate, from part (a), is

$$\varepsilon(x) \simeq -5(x-1)^4 = -0.000\,031\,25,$$

which, in this case, has the same magnitude as the error bound, and is larger than the actual truncation error.)

Section 2

2.1 **(a)** If $y = Ae^{x(x+1)}$, then $y'(x) = A(2x+1)e^{x(x+1)} = (2x+1)y$.
Thus, $y = Ae^{x(x+1)}$ is a solution of the differential equation for any value of the constant A, and as it is a linear first-order differential equation, this must be the general solution.

(b) We have $x_0 = 0$, $Y_0 = y_0 = 1$ and $f(x_r, Y_r) = (2x_r + 1)Y_r$. The step size is given as $h = 0.05$. Therefore $x_1 = x_0 + h = 0 + 0.05 = 0.05$, and

$$Y_1 = Y_0 + hf(x_0, Y_0) = 1 + 0.05(1) = 1.05.$$

For the second step, $x_2 = x_1 + h = 0.05 + 0.05 = 0.1$, and

$$Y_2 = Y_1 + hf(x_1, Y_1) = 1.05 + 0.05(1.1 \times 1.05) = 1.107\,75.$$

So Euler's method, with step size 0.05, gives the approximations

$$y(0.05) \simeq Y_1 = 1.05, \quad y(0.1) \simeq Y_2 = 1.107\,75.$$

(c) The exact solution of the given initial-value problem is $y(x) = e^{x(x+1)}$, which (to six decimal places) takes the value $y(0.1) = 1.116\,278$.

The global error at $x = 0.1$ is given by

$$Y_2 - y(0.1) = 1.107\,75 - 1.116\,278 = -0.008\,528.$$

2.2 Once again, $x_0 = 0$ and $Y_0 = y_0 = 1$. Now $F_{1,0} = (2x_0 + 1)Y_0 = 1$; then

$$x_{\frac{1}{2}} = 0.05,\ Y_{\frac{1}{2}} = 1.05,\ F_{2,0} = (2x_{\frac{1}{2}} + 1)Y_{\frac{1}{2}} = 1.155,$$
$$x_1 = 0.1,$$
$$Y_1 = Y_0 + 0.1(F_{2,0}) = 1.1155.$$

Thus, the Euler-midpoint method gives $y(0.1) \simeq 1.1155$, with global error $1.1155 - 1.116\,278 = -0.000\,778$. This is considerably smaller than the global error for two steps of Euler's method, which was $-0.008\,528$.

2.3 For the Euler-trapezoidal method $x_0 = 0$, $Y_0 = y_0 = 1$ and $F_{1,0} = 1$, as in Solution 2.2, and $Y_{\mathrm{E}} = Y_0 + 0.1 = 1.1$; so

$$F_{2,0} = f(0.1, 1.1) = 1.2 \times 1.1 = 1.32,$$
$$Y_1 = Y_0 + \tfrac{1}{2}(0.1)(1 + 1.32) = 1.116.$$

The Euler-trapezoidal method gives $y(0.1) \simeq 1.116$, with global error $-0.000\,278$. This is considerably smaller than the global error for two steps of Euler's method. It is also smaller than the global error for one step of the Euler-midpoint method.

2.4 The Euler-midpoint method uses $\alpha = \frac{1}{2}$ while the Euler-trapezoidal method uses $\alpha = 1$.

2.5 **(a)** From Exercise 2.3, $x_1 = 0.1$, $Y_1 = 1.116$ and $h = 0.1$; thus $F_{1,1} = (2x_1 + 1)Y_1 = 1.3392$, $x_2 = 0.2$, $Y_{\mathrm{E}} = Y_1 + 0.1(F_{1,1}) = 1.249\,92$, and $F_{2,1} = (2x_2 + 1)Y_{\mathrm{E}} = 1.749\,888$. This leads to $Y_2 = Y_1 + 0.05(F_{1,1} + F_{2,1}) = 1.270\,454$. Thus, the Euler-trapezoidal method gives $y(0.2) \simeq Y_2 = 1.270\,454$.

(b) The global error at $x = 0.1$ is $-0.000\,278$ (from Exercise 2.3), while the global error at $x = 0.2$ is $Y_2 - e^{0.24} = 1.270\,454 - 1.271\,249 = -0.000\,795$ to six decimal places.

2.6 **(a)** $x_0 = 0$, $Y_0 = y_0 = 1$, $h = 0.2$.

$$F_{1,0} = f(x_0, Y_0) = (2x_0 + 1)Y_0 = 1,$$
$$Y_0 + \tfrac{1}{2}hF_{1,0} = 1.1,$$
$$F_{2,0} = f(x_0 + \tfrac{1}{2}h, Y_0 + \tfrac{1}{2}hF_{1,0}) = (2 \times 0.1 + 1) \times 1.1 = 1.32,$$
$$Y_0 + \tfrac{1}{2}hF_{2,0} = 1.132,$$
$$F_{3,0} = f(x_0 + \tfrac{1}{2}h, Y_0 + \tfrac{1}{2}hF_{2,0}) = (2 \times 0.1 + 1) \times 1.132 = 1.3584,$$
$$Y_0 + hF_{3,0} = 1.271\,68,$$
$$F_{4,0} = f(x_0 + h, Y_0 + hF_{3,0}) = (2 \times 0.2 + 1) \times 1.271\,68 = 1.780\,352,$$
$$Y_1 = Y_0 + \tfrac{1}{6}h(F_{1,0} + 2F_{2,0} + 2F_{3,0} + F_{4,0}) = 1.271\,238.$$

So, at $x = 0.2$, the classical fourth-order Runge–Kutta method, with step size $h = 0.2$, gives the approximation $y(0.2) \simeq Y_1 = 1.271\,238$.

(b) The global error at $x = 0.2$ is approximately $-0.000\,011$, compared with the global error of $-0.000\,795$, at the same point, which was obtained in Exercise 2.5, using the Euler-trapezoidal method and the same amount of calculation.

2.7 **(a)** If $y = 4x - 0.4 + Ae^{-10x}$ then

$$\frac{dy}{dx} = 4 - 10Ae^{-10x}.$$

Substituting the given solution into the right-hand side of the differential equation,

$$10(4x - (4x - 0.4 + Ae^{-10x})) = 4 - 10Ae^{-10x}$$

which matches the left-hand side, and so $y = 4x - 0.4 + Ae^{-10x}$ is a solution of the differential equation for any value of the constant A. Since the differential equation is linear and first-order, this is also the general solution.

(b) $x_0 = 0$, $Y_0 = y_0 = -4$, $h = 0.025$.
$f(x_0, Y_0) = 10(4x_0 - Y_0) = 40$,
$Y_1 = Y_0 + h\,f(x_0, Y_0) = -4 + 0.025 \times 40 = -3$,
$x_1 = 0.025$,
$f(x_1, Y_1) = 10(4x_1 - Y_1) = 31$,
$Y_2 = Y_1 + h\,f(x_1, Y_1) = -3 + 0.025 \times 31 = -2.225$,
$x_2 = 0.05$,
$f(x_2, Y_2) = 10(4x_2 - Y_2) = 24.25$,
$Y_3 = Y_2 + h\,f(x_2, Y_2)$
$\quad = -2.225 + 0.025 \times 24.25 = -1.61875$,
$x_3 = 0.075$,
$f(x_3, Y_3) = 10(4x_3 - Y_3) = 19.1875$,
$Y_4 = Y_3 + h\,f(x_3, Y_3)$
$\quad = -1.618\,75 + 0.025 \times 19.1875 = -1.139\,063$,
$x_4 = 0.1$.

So, at $x = 0.1$, Euler's method, with step size $h = 0.025$, gives the approximation $y(0.1) \simeq Y_4 = -1.139\,063$.
The exact solution of the given problem is
$y(x) = 4x - 0.4 - 3.6e^{-10x}$, so that
$y(0.1) = -1.324\,366$.
The global error at $x = 0.1$ is given by $Y_4 - y(0.1)$, where $y(0.1)$ is the value of the exact solution of the original problem. So the global error at $x = 0.1$ is

$$\begin{aligned} Y_4 - (-1.324\,366) &= -1.139\,063 - (-1.324\,366) \\ &= 0.185\,303. \end{aligned}$$

(c) $x_0 = 0$, $Y_0 = y_0 = -4$, $h = 0.05$,
$F_{1,0} = f(x_0, Y_0) = 10(4x_0 - Y_0) = 40$,
$x_1 = 0.05$,
$Y_\mathrm{E} = Y_0 + hF_{1,0} = -4 + 0.05 \times 40 = -2$,
$F_{2,0} = f(x_1, Y_\mathrm{E}) = 10(4 \times 0.05 - (-2)) = 22$,
$Y_1 = Y_0 + \frac{1}{2}h(F_{1,0} + F_{2,0})$
$\quad = -4 + 0.025(40 + 22) = -2.45$,
$F_{1,1} = f(x_1, Y_1) = 10(4x_1 - Y_1) = 26.5$,
$x_2 = 0.1$,
$Y_\mathrm{E} = Y_1 + hF_{1,1}$
$\quad = -2.45 + 0.05 \times 26.5 = -1.125$,
$F_{2,1} = f(x_2, Y_\mathrm{E}) = 10(4 \times 0.1 - (-1.125)) = 15.25$,
$Y_2 = Y_1 + \frac{1}{2}h(F_{1,1} + F_{2,1})$
$\quad = -2.45 + 0.025(26.5 + 15.25) = -1.406\,25$.

So, at $x = 0.1$, the Euler-trapezoidal method, with step size $h = 0.05$, gives the approximation $y(0.1) \simeq Y_2 = -1.406\,25$.

The global error at $x = 0.1$ is given by $Y_2 - y(0.1)$, where $y(0.1)$ is the value of the exact solution of the original problem. So the global error at $x = 0.1$ is

$$\begin{aligned} Y_2 - (-1.324\,366) &= -1.406\,25 - (-1.324\,366) \\ &= -0.081\,884. \end{aligned}$$

(d) $x_0 = 0$, $Y_0 = y_0 = -4$, $h = 0.1$.
$F_{1,0} = f(x_0, Y_0) = 10(4x_0 - Y_0) = 40$,
$Y_0 + \frac{1}{2}h\,F_{1,0} = -4 + 0.05 \times 40 = -2$,
$F_{2,0} = f(x_0 + \frac{1}{2}h, Y_0 + \frac{1}{2}h\,F_{1,0})$
$\quad = 10(4 \times 0.05 - (-2)) = 22$,
$Y_0 + \frac{1}{2}h\,F_{2,0} = -4 + 0.05 \times 22 = -2.9$,
$F_{3,0} = f(x_0 + \frac{1}{2}h, Y_0 + \frac{1}{2}h\,F_{2,0})$
$\quad = 10(4 \times 0.05 - (-2.9)) = 31$,
$Y_0 + h\,F_{3,0} = -4 + 0.1 \times 31 = -0.9$,
$F_{4,0} = f(x_0 + h, Y_0 + h\,F_{3,0})$
$\quad = 10(4 \times 0.1 - (-0.9)) = 13$,
$Y_1 = Y_0 + \frac{1}{6}h(F_{1,0} + 2F_{2,0} + 2F_{3,0} + F_{4,0}) = -1.35$.
So, at $x = 0.1$, the classical fourth-order Runge–Kutta method, with step size $h = 0.1$, gives the approximation $y(0.1) \simeq -1.35$.
The global error at $x = 0.1$ is

$$\begin{aligned} Y_1 - (-1.324\,366) &= -1.35 - (-1.324\,366) \\ &= -0.025\,634, \end{aligned}$$

compared with the global error of $-0.081\,884$, at the same point, obtained using the Euler-trapezoidal method, and the global error of $0.185\,303$ obtained using Euler's method. With the step sizes given, each of the three methods required the same amount of calculation, and the classical fourth-order Runge–Kutta method produced a more accurate result than either of the other methods.

Section 4

4.1 **(a)** Differentiating the given function:

$$\begin{aligned} y'(x) &= 3(x-1)^2 + e^{20x} = 3(x-1)^2 + \left(\tfrac{y(x)-(x-1)^3}{0.05}\right) \\ &= 3(x-1)^2 + 20(y - (x-1)^3). \end{aligned}$$

Also, $y(0) = (-1)^3 + 0.05 = -0.95$, as required.
Then $y(0.2) = -0.512 + 0.05e^4 = 2.217\,908$ to six decimal places.

(b) The general solution (as discussed in the text) is $y(x) = (x-1)^3 + Ae^{20x}$, so that $y(0) = -1 + A$. Thus, if $y(0) = -0.945$, then $A = 1 - 0.945 = 0.055$. Thus the new analytic solution, evaluated at $x = 0.2$, is $-0.512 + 0.055e^4 = 2.490\,898$. The change in the analytic solution at $x = 0.2$ is thus $2.490\,898 - 2.217\,908 = 0.272\,990$, more than 54 times the change to the initial condition. From the definition of absolute ill-conditioning, we conclude that the problem is absolutely ill-conditioned.

4.2 Here, Euler's method involves the iteration formula

$$Y_{r+1} = Y_r + hf(x_r, Y_r) = Y_r + h(-10Y_r) = (1 - 10h)Y_r.$$

Thus an error in Y_r will diminish if $-1 < 1 - 10h < 1$ and will grow otherwise. Thus, for absolute stability, we require $1 - 10h$ to lie in this interval (equivalently, $10h$ must lie in the interval between 0 and 2). Thus, the method is absolutely stable if $0 < h < 0.2$.

4.3 $f(x,y) = 10y\left(1 - \frac{y}{1000}\right)$, and so $\frac{\partial f}{\partial y} = 10 - \frac{y}{50}$, which varies from step to step. However, we are told that, for this problem, y lies between 1000 and 2000, and so $-30 \le \frac{\partial f}{\partial y} \le -10$. Euler's method will be absolutely stable if $-2 < h\frac{\partial f}{\partial y} < 0$ throughout the interval. Since $\frac{\partial f}{\partial y} < 0$, this means that we need $h < 2/\left|\frac{\partial f}{\partial y}\right|$ for the largest possible value of $\left|\frac{\partial f}{\partial y}\right|$, and so $h < \frac{2}{30} = \frac{1}{15}$.

4.4 $f(x,y) = 20x(2-x) - 20y$, and so $\frac{\partial f}{\partial y} = -20$. The Euler-trapezoidal method is absolutely stable if $-2 < h\frac{\partial f}{\partial y} < 0$. So, in this case, $-2 < -20h < 0$, or in other words, $0 < h < 0.1$ for absolute stability. (Since $\partial f/\partial y$ is constant, the absolute stability criterion does not depend on x and so the result holds for the whole of the x-interval $[0, \infty)$.) This explains some of the results of Activity 3.2(b), where the Euler-trapezoidal method was applied to the initial-value problem (3.2). For $h = 0.2$, the method is absolutely unstable, and the numerical results grew exponentially. For $h = 0.1$, the errors were growing gradually because the step size is just on the limit of absolute stability.

4.5 $f(x,y) = y(20-y)$, and so $\frac{\partial f}{\partial y} = 20 - 2y$. The exact solution of this problem increases from $y(0) = 12$ to a limit value of $y = 20$ as x increases without limit.

So y lies between 12 and 20, and $-20 \leq \frac{\partial f}{\partial y} \leq -4$. The classical fourth-order Runge–Kutta method will be absolutely stable if $-2.78 < h\frac{\partial f}{\partial y} < 0$ throughout the interval. Since $\frac{\partial f}{\partial y} < 0$, this means that $h < 2.78/\left|\frac{\partial f}{\partial y}\right|$ for the largest possible value of $\left|\frac{\partial f}{\partial y}\right|$, and so $h < \frac{2.78}{20} = 0.139$. (Again, as $\partial f/\partial y$ does not depend on x, the result holds for the whole of the x-interval $[0, \infty)$.)

This explains some of the results of Activity 3.3(c), where the classical fourth-order Runge–Kutta method was applied to the initial-value problem (3.3). For $h = 0.2$, and for $h = 0.15$, the method is absolutely unstable, and cannot settle down to a limit value of $y = 20$. In one case ($h = 0.15$) it settles down to another, spurious, value around $y = 15.2$, while in the other it oscillates around that value. For $h = 0.12$, the method is absolutely stable, but large errors on the early steps are only decaying very slowly, and the solution is taking much too long in its approach to the limit value of $y = 20$.

4.6 Since a fourth-order Runge–Kutta method is of order $p = 4$, by Theorem 4.1 the method is convergent. Its global error, at a fixed point x, takes the form

$$Y_N - y(x) \simeq Ch^4$$

for sufficiently small values of h, where $Nh = x - x_0$, and C is a constant which does not depend on h.

4.7 In the case of initial-value problem (3.3), the results of Activity 3.3(c) indicate that the global error at $x = 0.6$ takes the following values for $h \leq 0.05$:

h	global error
0.05	−0.000 017
0.025	−0.000 001
0.0125	−0.000 000

These results are consistent with the global error being Ch^4, although more accuracy and possibly smaller step sizes would be required to confirm this.

4.8 The results obtained in Activity 3.1(a), for the step sizes $h = 0.04, 0.02, 0.01, 0.005, 0.0025$ ($N = 5, 10, 20, 40, 80$) are as follows.

h	N	x_N	Y_N
0.04	5	0.2	−0.410 226
0.02	10	0.2	−0.432 371
0.01	20	0.2	−0.458 681
0.005	40	0.2	−0.480 371
0.0025	80	0.2	−0.494 640

The results all appear to be fairly consistent, but differ in the second decimal place, suggesting that the last three, with $h \leq 0.01$, may be correct to one decimal place. Since Euler's method is of order one, it is expected that, if h is small enough,

$$Y_N - y(0.2) \simeq Ch.$$

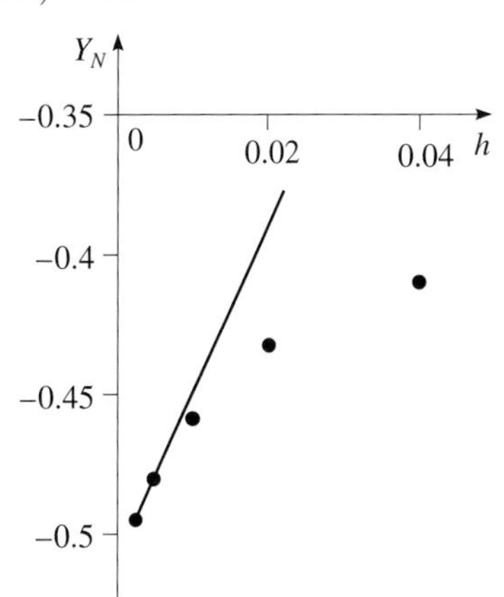

Plotting a graph of Y_N against h, the straight line through the two points involving the smallest values of h does not fit all of the points well, but does suggest a reasonable proportionality between the global error at $x = 0.2$ and h, at least for $h \leq 0.01$. So $Y_N \simeq y(0.2) + Ch$. Using the two smallest tabulated values, $h = 0.005$ and $h = 0.0025$,

$$Y_{40} = -0.480\,371 \simeq y(0.2) + C \times 0.005,$$
$$Y_{80} = -0.494\,640 \simeq y(0.2) + C \times 0.0025.$$

Subtracting Y_{80} from Y_{40}:

$$Y_{40} - Y_{80} = -0.480\,371 - (-0.494\,64) \simeq C(0.005 - 0.0025),$$

so that $C \simeq \frac{0.014\,269}{0.0025} = 5.7076$.

This may not be an accurate value, but it is expected that, for values of $h \leq 0.01$, the global error at $x = 0.2$ is approximately $Ch \simeq 5.7h$.

(a) If the value of $y(0.2)$ is required to three decimal places, then it should be sufficient to choose a value of h satisfying $5.7h \leq 0.5 \times 10^{-3}$, so that $h \leq \frac{0.5\times10^{-3}}{5.7} = 0.000\,0876$. In order to have a convenient integer number N of steps, it would be appropriate to choose $h = 0.000\,08$, giving 2500 steps.

(b) If the value of $y(0.2)$ is required to six decimal places, then it should be sufficient to choose a value of h satisfying $5.7h \leq 0.5 \times 10^{-6}$, so that $h \leq \frac{0.5\times10^{-6}}{5.7} = 0.000\,000\,0876$. In order to have a convenient integer number N of steps, it would be appropriate to choose $h = 0.000\,000\,08$, giving 2.5 million steps!

4.9 The results obtained in Activity 3.1(b), for the step sizes $h = 0.04, 0.02, 0.01, 0.005, 0.0025$ ($N = 5, 10, 20, 40, 80$) are as follows.

h	N	x_N	Y_N
0.04	5	0.2	−0.442 282
0.02	10	0.2	−0.487 972
0.01	20	0.2	−0.505 062
0.005	40	0.2	−0.510 153
0.0025	80	0.2	−0.511 525

While the result for $h = 0.04$ does not look so good, the others behave more reasonably, and agree to one decimal place. The results for $h \leq 0.01$ agree to two decimal places. Since the Euler-trapezoidal method is of order two, it is expected that, if h is small enough,

$$Y_N - y(0.2) \simeq Ch^2.$$

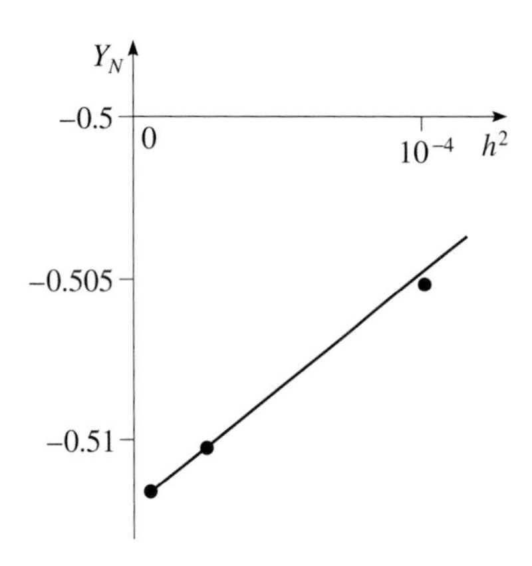

Plotting a graph of Y_N against h^2, for the three smallest values of h, the straight line through the smallest two values of h is quite a good fit, and suggests a reasonable proportionality between the global error at $x = 0.2$ and h^2, at least for $h \leq 0.01$. So $Y_N \simeq y(0.2) + Ch^2$. Using the tabulated values for $h = 0.005$ and $h = 0.0025$,

$$Y_{40} = -0.510\,153 \simeq y(0.2) + C \times 0.005^2,$$
$$Y_{80} = -0.511\,525 \simeq y(0.2) + C \times 0.0025^2.$$

Subtracting Y_{80} from Y_{40}:

$$Y_{40} - Y_{80} = -0.510\,153 - (-0.511\,525) \simeq C(0.005^2 - 0.0025^2),$$

so that $C \simeq \frac{0.001\,372}{0.000\,018\,75} \simeq 73.1733$.

This may not be an accurate value, but it is expected that, for values of $h \leq 0.01$, the global error at $x = 0.2$ is approximately $Ch^2 \simeq 73h^2$.

(a) If the value of $y(0.2)$ is required to three decimal places, then it should be sufficient to choose a value of h satisfying $73h^2 \leq 0.5 \times 10^{-3}$, so that $h^2 \leq \frac{0.5\times10^{-3}}{73} = 0.000\,0068$, and $h \leq 0.0026$. This suggests that the result obtained with $h = 0.0025$ is already correct to three decimal places (as is indeed the case).

(b) If the value of $y(0.2)$ is required to six decimal places, then it should be sufficient to choose a value of h satisfying $73h^2 \leq 0.5 \times 10^{-6}$, so that $h^2 \leq \frac{0.5\times10^{-6}}{73} = 0.000\,000\,0068$, and $h \leq 0.000\,083$. In order to have a convenient integer number N of steps, it would be appropriate to choose $h = 0.000\,08$.

Using Euler's method (Exercise 4.8), the step size $h = 0.000\,08$ gave only three-decimal-place accuracy; by doubling the number of function evaluations, the Euler-trapezoidal method gives six-decimal-place accuracy for $h = 0.000\,08$.

4.10 $f(x, y) = y(20 - y)$, and so $\frac{\partial f}{\partial y} = 20 - 2y$. The exact solution of this problem increases from $y(0) = 12$ to a limit value of $y = 20$ as x increases without limit. So y lies between 12 and 20, and $-20 \leq \frac{\partial f}{\partial y} \leq -4$. The Euler-trapezoidal method will be absolutely stable if $-2 < h\frac{\partial f}{\partial y} < 0$ throughout the interval. Since $\frac{\partial f}{\partial y} < 0$, this means that $h < 2/\left|\frac{\partial f}{\partial y}\right|$ for the largest possible value of $\left|\frac{\partial f}{\partial y}\right|$, and so $h < \frac{2}{20} = 0.1$. (As $\partial f/\partial y$ does not depend on x, this result holds for the whole of the x-interval $[0, \infty)$.)

This explains some of the results of Activity 3.3(b), where the Euler-trapezoidal method was applied to the initial-value problem (3.3). For $h = 0.2$, this method is absolutely unstable, and the numerical results diverge rapidly. For $h = 0.15$, and for $h = 0.12$, the method is still absolutely unstable, and cannot settle down to a limit value of $y = 20$. In one case ($h = 0.12$) it settles down to another, spurious, value of $y = 12.8056$, while in the other it oscillates. For $h = 0.1$, the step size is just on the limit of absolute stability, but with large errors on the early steps, the solution is taking much too long in its approach to the limit value of $y = 20$. The results obtained, at $x = 0.6$, for $h < 0.1$, are as follows.

h	N	x_N	Y_N
0.075	8	0.6	19.885 335
0.06	10	0.6	19.990 009
0.05	12	0.6	19.997 899
0.025	24	0.6	19.999 845
0.0125	48	0.6	19.999 906

The results after the first two behave reasonably, and agree to two decimal places. Since the Euler-trapezoidal method is of order two, it is expected that, if h is small enough,

$$Y_N - y(0.6) \simeq Ch^2.$$

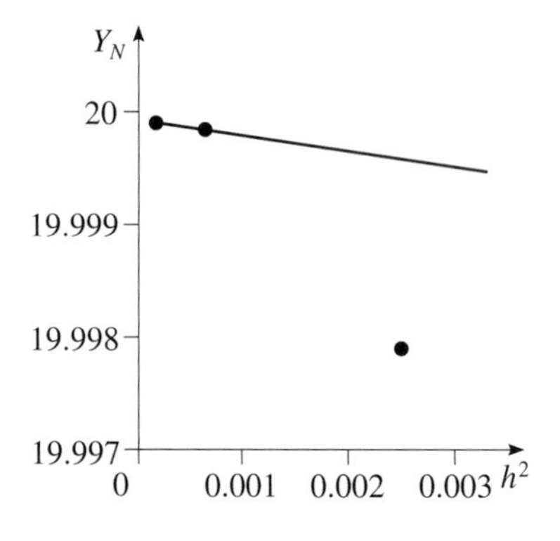

Plotting a graph of Y_N against h^2, for the three smallest values of h, the straight-line fit through the two smaller values is quite a poor fit to the third value, and suggests that the step size may not be small enough for the global error to be proportional to h^2, at least for $h = 0.05$. Assuming that the proportionality is acceptable for $h \leq 0.025$, and using the tabulated values for $h = 0.025$ and $h = 0.0125$,

$$Y_{24} = 19.999\,845 \simeq y(0.6) + C \times 0.025^2,$$
$$Y_{48} = 19.999\,906 \simeq y(0.6) + C \times 0.0125^2.$$

Subtracting Y_{48} from Y_{24}:

$$\begin{aligned} Y_{24} - Y_{48} &= 19.999\,845 - 19.999\,906 \\ &\simeq C(0.025^2 - 0.0125^2), \end{aligned}$$

so that $C \simeq \frac{-0.000\,061}{0.000\,468\,75} \simeq -0.130\,133$.
This may not be an accurate value, but it is expected that, for values of $h \leq 0.025$, the global error at $x = 0.6$ is approximately $Ch^2 \simeq -0.13h^2$.
If the value of $y(0.6)$ is required to six decimal places, then it may be sufficient to choose a value of h satisfying $0.13h^2 \leq 0.5 \times 10^{-6}$, so that
$h^2 \leq \frac{0.5 \times 10^{-6}}{0.13} = 0.000\,003\,84$, and $h \leq 0.001\,96$.
In order to have a convenient integer number N of steps, it would be appropriate to choose $h = 0.0016$, or $h = 0.0012$. In view of the uncertainty as to the proportionality of the global error to h^2, for $h \leq 0.025$, it would be well to confirm the accuracy of the result by using two such values of h, and checking that the two results differ by less than 0.5×10^{-6}.

4.11 $f(x, y) = -xy + \frac{1}{1+x^2}$, and so $\frac{\partial f}{\partial y} = -x$, which varies from step to step. However, the problem is to be solved over the interval $0 \leq x \leq 10$. Therefore $-10 \leq \frac{\partial f}{\partial y} \leq 0$, and the classical fourth-order Runge–Kutta method will be absolutely stable if $-2.78 < h\frac{\partial f}{\partial y} < 0$ throughout the interval. Since $\frac{\partial f}{\partial y} \leq 0$, this means that $h < 2.78/\left|\frac{\partial f}{\partial y}\right|$ for the largest possible value of $\left|\frac{\partial f}{\partial y}\right|$, and so $h < \frac{2.78}{10} = 0.278$.

UNIT 27 Rotating bodies and angular momentum

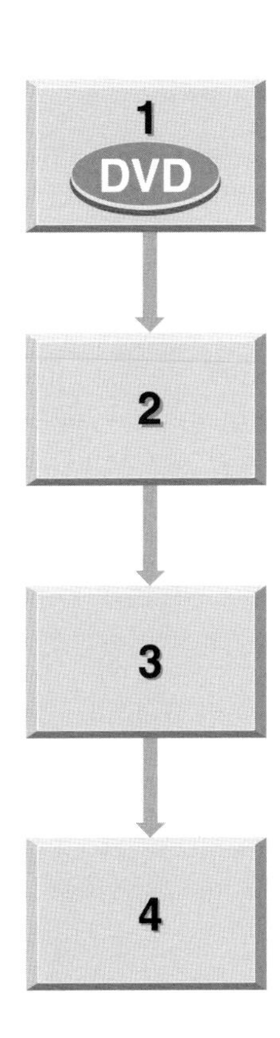

Study guide for Unit 27

This unit draws together many aspects of the mechanics that you have met earlier in the course. It makes use of ideas from *Units 5, 6, 8, 14, 19, 20* and *25*. In particular, it picks up the study of torque and the rotational motion of particles from *Unit 20*, and generalizes these concepts to extended bodies. (As you may recall, you studied extended bodies *in equilibrium* in *Unit 5*, and considered their moments of inertia in *Unit 25*.) The important prerequisite knowledge is *Unit 20*, and especially Section 4 of that unit. (An understanding of the methods of computing multiple integrals in *Unit 25* is not needed here.)

Section 1 is based on a video sequence. Through examples, the video provides an introduction to the central ideas in the unit, and so it is important that you view the video when you begin studying the unit. The material in the unit needs to be studied in the order in which it appears.

The sections are of similar lengths, with the exception of Section 1 which is rather shorter than the others.

Introduction

When an ice skater is performing a spin, if she brings her arms in and folds them across her chest, her rate of rotation will increase. Why is this? Take another example. Suppose that two cylindrical objects have equal size and mass but one is hollow and the other is solid. If they are released together from the top of a slope, will they roll down at the same rate? If not, which cylinder will reach the bottom of the slope first?

To answer such questions, we need to bring together a number of ideas that have been introduced earlier in the course. In the early mechanics units, such as *Units 6*, *7* and *8*, we modelled moving objects as particles. However, this approach is inadequate for dealing with the questions above, because we are now concerned with extended bodies, i.e. objects that have size, and we are interested in aspects of their motion where that size is important. In *Unit 19*, you saw that the motion of an extended body can often be modelled by the motion of a representative particle located at the centre of mass of the body. But, in the case of the spinning skater, the centre of mass may well be more or less stationary — it is the skater's rotation about the centre of mass that is of interest. For the rolling cylinders, it is perhaps less obvious that the particle model is inappropriate, but again, rotation about the centre of mass is a crucial part of the motion.

An *extended* body has one or more of length, breadth and depth.

In this unit we deal with the motion of extended bodies, and in particular with their rotational motion. In *Unit 5*, we considered such bodies when stationary: you learned that for a rigid body in equilibrium, the sum of all the external forces must be zero, and that the sum of the external *torques* must be zero. In *Unit 20*, you saw that if a non-zero torque is applied to a particle, then this changes the rotational motion of the particle. Now, we combine these ideas and consider the motion of an *extended body* subject to a *non-zero torque*.

A *rigid* body is an extended body whose shape does not change.

The video sequence in Section 1 shows a variety of examples of motion involving the rotation of an extended body. Several of these examples come from sports, and a number are modelled in later sections. In Section 1 we take an overview of the unit and freely apply principles that are not formally established until Section 4. Section 2 begins by reviewing concepts from earlier units, and then goes on to develop a theoretical basis for modelling the motion of extended bodies. Section 3 looks at the rotation of extended bodies about an axis that is fixed, such as the spinning ice skater. In Section 4 we explore situations where rotational motion is combined with other types of motion. For example, consider a diver in flight after leaving a high diving board (Figure 0.1). From *Unit 19* we would expect the diver's centre of mass to follow a parabolic trajectory (if we ignore air resistance), but the diver's rotation about her centre of mass is also a major factor in the success of the dive.

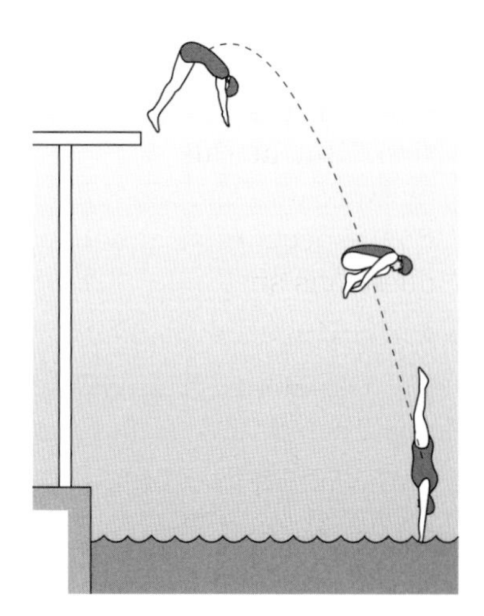

Figure 0.1

1 Rotating bodies

Rotation is an important aspect of motion in many situations, notably in several sports, such as ice skating, diving and tossing the caber. The video associated with this unit shows a number of these sporting situations. Understanding such motion involves various mechanical concepts that you have met earlier in the course: these include torque (*Unit 5*), angular momentum (*Unit 20*), and moment of inertia (*Unit 25*).

To get an idea of some of the factors involved in analysing rotational motion, consider someone pushing a roundabout in a playground so as to make it move (see Figure 1.1). Initially the roundabout is stationary, but when it is pushed, it rotates with increasing rotational speed. Even after the person stops pushing, the roundabout will continue to rotate.

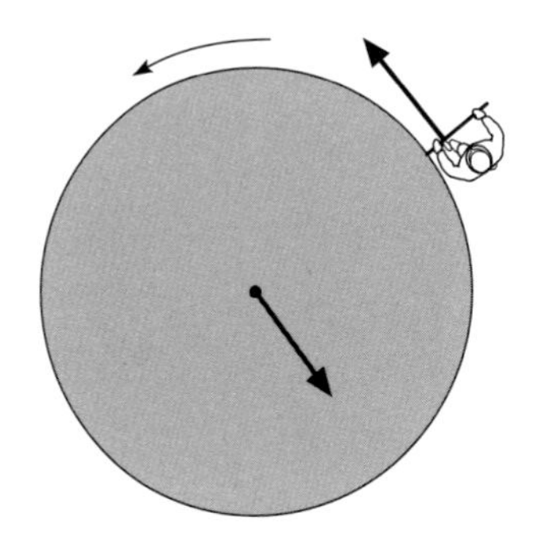

Figure 1.1

While the roundabout is being pushed, the total force on it is zero: the force supplied by the pusher is balanced by a force exerted by the support at the centre of the roundabout. The roundabout 'as a whole' is not going anywhere, i.e. its centre of mass is not moving. However, although the two forces shown in Figure 1.1 are equal in magnitude and opposite in direction, they have different lines of action. As a result, there is a torque on the roundabout. This torque initiates the rotation of the roundabout and gives it angular momentum. In *Unit 20*, you saw that, for a particle, if there is no torque being applied, then the angular momentum is constant. As you will see later, this result can be generalized to extended bodies. This means that, even when the pushing stops, the roundabout will maintain its angular momentum and will continue to rotate; indeed, in the absence of resistive forces, it would go on rotating for ever without the need for further pushing (but in practice resistive forces are always present).

Later in this unit we shall develop quantitative models of rotational motion. But at this stage you should obtain an overview of rotational motion by watching the video for the unit — concentrating mainly on the qualitative aspects of the motion. In the various examples in the video, consider questions such as the following.

- Is the total torque that is acting on the moving object zero?
- If it is not, what torque is being applied to the object?
- If the rotational speed of an object is changing, why is this?
- Is the moment of inertia of a rotating object (about the axis of rotation) fixed, or is it changing?
- If the moment of inertia is changing (for example, because a diver or skater is changing body shape), is it increasing or decreasing?

Watch the video for this unit now.

Some key points from the video are summarized below.

- The motion of an extended body can be treated in two parts: the motion of an equivalent particle located at the centre of mass, and rotation about the centre of mass. This result will be established in Section 4.
- A torque applied to an extended body that is initially stationary will initiate rotation and supply angular momentum.
- Once an extended body has angular momentum, that momentum will remain constant provided that no further torque is applied to the body.
- The component l of the angular momentum along the axis of rotation of an extended body that is rotating about a fixed axis is the product

of the angular speed ω and the moment of inertia I about that axis, i.e.

$$l = I\omega. \tag{1.1}$$

You will see later, in Subsection 3.1, that this scalar equation can be obtained from a vector equation by resolving in the direction of the (fixed) axis of rotation.

This scalar equation is sufficient for the needs of this section.

- An ice skater can vary their speed of rotation during a spin by changing body shape. This is in accord with Equation (1.1) since, although the angular momentum l is constant, the moment of inertia is changing. When modelling *rigid* bodies the moment of inertia is a constant, but the human body is flexible and its moment of inertia can change.

In the following examples and exercises we shall carry out similar analyses of some of the other sporting situations that you saw in the video, thus exploring further the relationships between angular momentum, moment of inertia and rotational motion.

Example 1.1

(a) A diver is executing a simple dive in which the diver's body shape remains constant, as illustrated in Figure 1.2 (top). The diver starts in a handstand position. The subsequent motion can be divided into two phases: firstly, rotation about the point O while the diver remains in contact with the diving board; secondly, motion in flight after the diver lets go of the board, but before she enters the water.

(i) In the first phase, how is the diver's angular momentum about O changing?

(ii) In the second phase, what would you expect to happen to the angular momentum about the diver's centre of mass? Assume that resistive forces are negligible.

(b) Suppose that the diver goes into a tuck position (see Figure 1.2 (bottom)) in the second phase. What aspect of the motion will be different from that in part (a)?

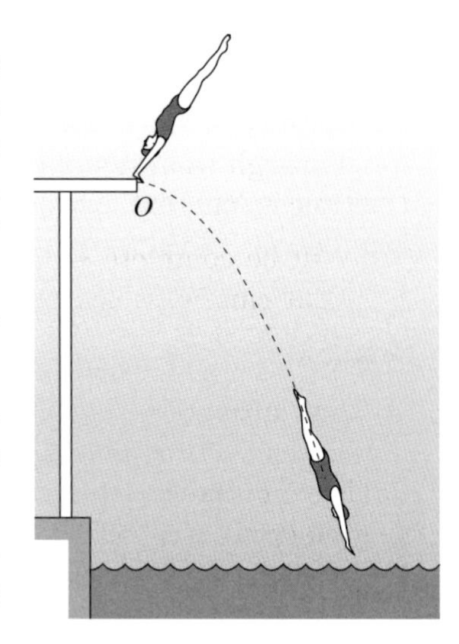

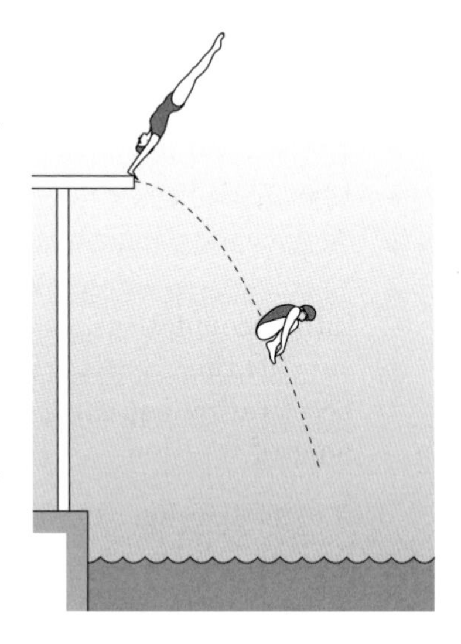

Figure 1.2

Solution

(a) (i) In the first phase, the diver's weight provides a torque which will act to increase the angular momentum about O. During this phase of the motion, the angular momentum (and angular speed) about O are increasing.

(ii) In the second phase, the only force on the diver is her weight, which acts through her centre of mass. This means there is no torque about the centre of mass, and consequently the angular momentum about the centre of mass will be constant.

(b) In the situation in part (a), the diver's body shape and, hence, moment of inertia remain constant throughout the dive, so the angular speed of rotation about the diver's centre of mass does not change after she has let go of the board. However, if the diver adopts a tuck position after letting go of the board, this will reduce her moment of inertia, and will increase her angular speed of rotation about her centre of mass. ■

In Example 1.2 and Exercise 1.1 below, we shall make use of the idea implicit in Example 1.1(a)(ii): that angular momentum about the centre of mass is constant for an (effectively rigid) extended body in flight (assuming that the body is subject only to gravity, i.e. that resistive forces are negligible). This result will be established in Section 4.

Example 1.2

Figure 1.3 shows a gymnast, rotating anticlockwise around a bar 3 m above the ground, at the point of letting go of the bar and dismounting. Assume that the gymnast does not change body shape so that he can be modelled as a rigid rod of length 2.4 m. Also assume that his centre of mass is at his midpoint, i.e. a distance $R = 1.2$ m from O, while he is contact with the bar. Just before he lets go of the bar, his centre of mass is moving in a circle at a speed of $4\,\mathrm{m\,s^{-1}}$. At the moment of release, his body makes an angle of $\frac{\pi}{3}$ with the vertical.

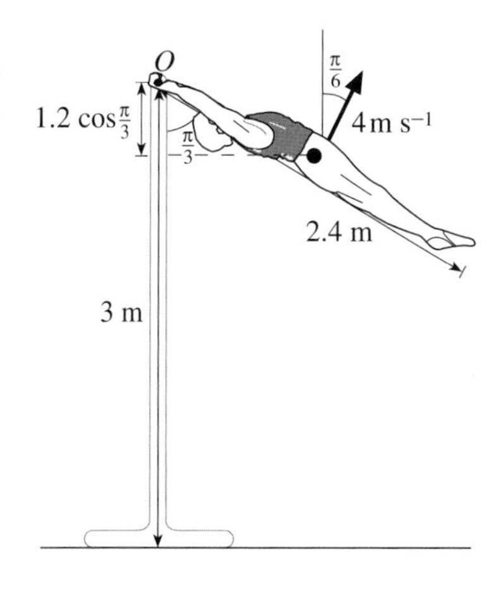

Figure 1.3

(a) What is the gymnast's angular speed about his centre of mass just after he releases the bar?

(b) If the gymnast is to land successfully, i.e. on his feet with his body in a vertical position, what angle must he rotate through while in the air? How long will it take him to rotate through this angle?

(c) Consider the vertical movement of an equivalent particle located at the centre of mass of the gymnast. What is the vertical component of the velocity of the centre of mass just after the gymnast releases the bar? Through what distance will the gymnast's centre of mass fall during the time calculated in part (b)?

(d) Will he complete a dismount successfully using this approach? If not, what can he do to achieve a successful dismount?

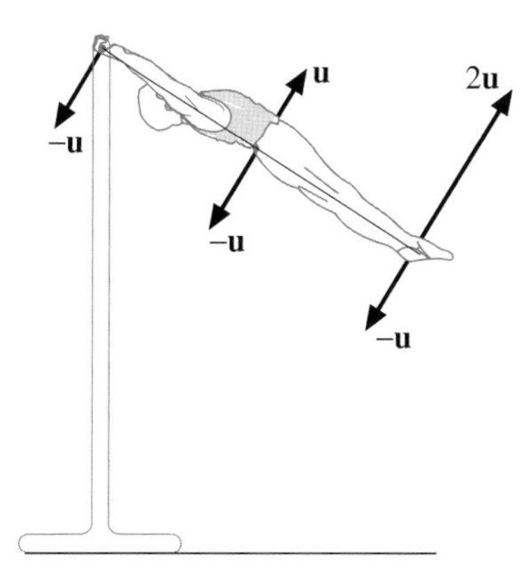

Figure 1.4 Motion relative to the centre of mass

Solution

(a) Just after releasing the bar, the gymnast's hands are stationary, and his centre of mass has the same velocity (say, $\mathbf{u}$) as immediately before leaving the bar. So, relative to the centre of mass, his hands have velocity $-\mathbf{u}$. At that moment, the gymnast is rotating about his centre of mass with angular speed $|\mathbf{u}|/R$ in the direction in which he was circling the bar before letting go. Since $|\mathbf{u}| = 4\,\mathrm{m\,s^{-1}}$ and $R = 1.2$ m, the angular speed of rotation is $4/1.2 = 3\frac{1}{3}$ rad s^{-1}.

To determine motion relative to the centre of mass, add $-\mathbf{u}$ to the velocities throughout the body, as shown in Figure 1.4, and thus take a point of view in which the centre of mass is 'fixed'.

(b) At the time of release, the gymnast's body makes an angle of $\frac{\pi}{3}$ with the vertical, so the gymnast must rotate through $2\pi - \frac{\pi}{3} = \frac{5\pi}{3}$ to achieve a vertical landing. At the angular speed calculated in part (a), this will take $\frac{5\pi}{3} \div 3\frac{1}{3} = \frac{\pi}{2}$ s.

(c) At the moment of release, the gymnast's centre of mass has an upward vertical component of velocity of $4\cos\frac{\pi}{6} = 2\sqrt{3}\,\mathrm{m\,s^{-1}}$. Now, taking into account the constant downward acceleration of magnitude g, and substituting $v_0 = 2\sqrt{3}\,\mathrm{m\,s^{-1}}$, $a_0 = -g$ and $t = \frac{\pi}{2}$ s into the constant-acceleration equation $x = v_0t + \frac{1}{2}a_0t^2$, we find that the vertical component of position will increase in $\pi/2$ seconds by

The constant-acceleration equation was derived in *Unit 6*.

$$2\sqrt{3}\tfrac{\pi}{2} - \tfrac{1}{2}g\left(\tfrac{\pi}{2}\right)^2 \simeq -6.66\,\mathrm{m}.$$

Therefore, in the time it would take for the gymnast to attain a vertical body position for landing, his centre of mass will have fallen through a distance of about 6.66 m.

(d) The gymnast cannot complete a dismount successfully in this way. His centre of mass starts at $3 - 1.2\cos\frac{\pi}{3} = 2.4$ m above the ground. But, as he would have to fall through 6.66 m before his body was vertical, he would hit the ground before he had completed the necessary rotation.

If the gymnast were to adjust his body position while in the air, so as to reduce his moment of inertia, he could increase his angular speed of rotation about his centre of mass. This might allow him to complete the necessary rotation before reaching the ground. ■

*Exercise 1.1

Suppose that the gymnast in Example 1.2 adjusts his body position while in the air so as to achieve a successful dismount, landing on his feet in a vertical position. When he lands, his body is extended with his centre of mass at a height of 1.2 m above the ground.

(a) How long is he in flight between letting go of the bar and landing?

(b) Assume that he is able to adjust his body position instantaneously, so that he is in a tuck position (Figure 1.5) for *all* the time that he is in flight. What is the ratio of the moments of inertia of his body in the tuck and extended positions?

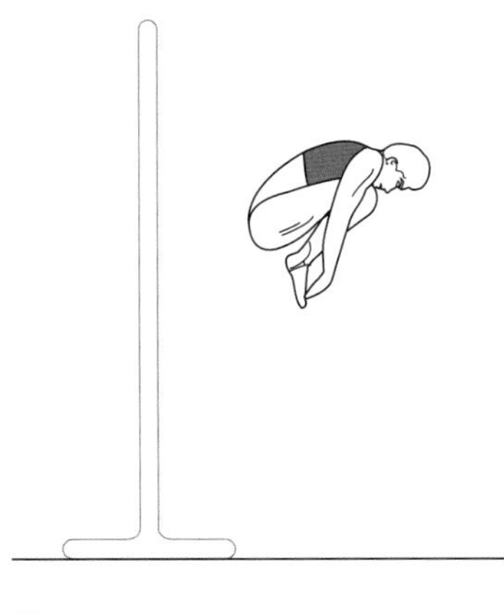

Figure 1.5

End-of-section Exercise

Exercise 1.2

Tossing the caber can be divided into five phases (see Figure 1.6).

(i) The competitor runs forward with the caber held in a vertical position, and then stops.

(ii) The caber rotates forwards about the competitor's hands, which are stationary.

(iii) He pushes upwards on the bottom of the caber, and releases it.

(iv) After the competitor releases the caber, it is in flight prior to hitting the ground.

(v) The end of the caber strikes the ground, but the motion of the caber continues until the caber falls down flat.

For the toss to be successful, the caber must land with the end originally held by the competitor pointing away from him.

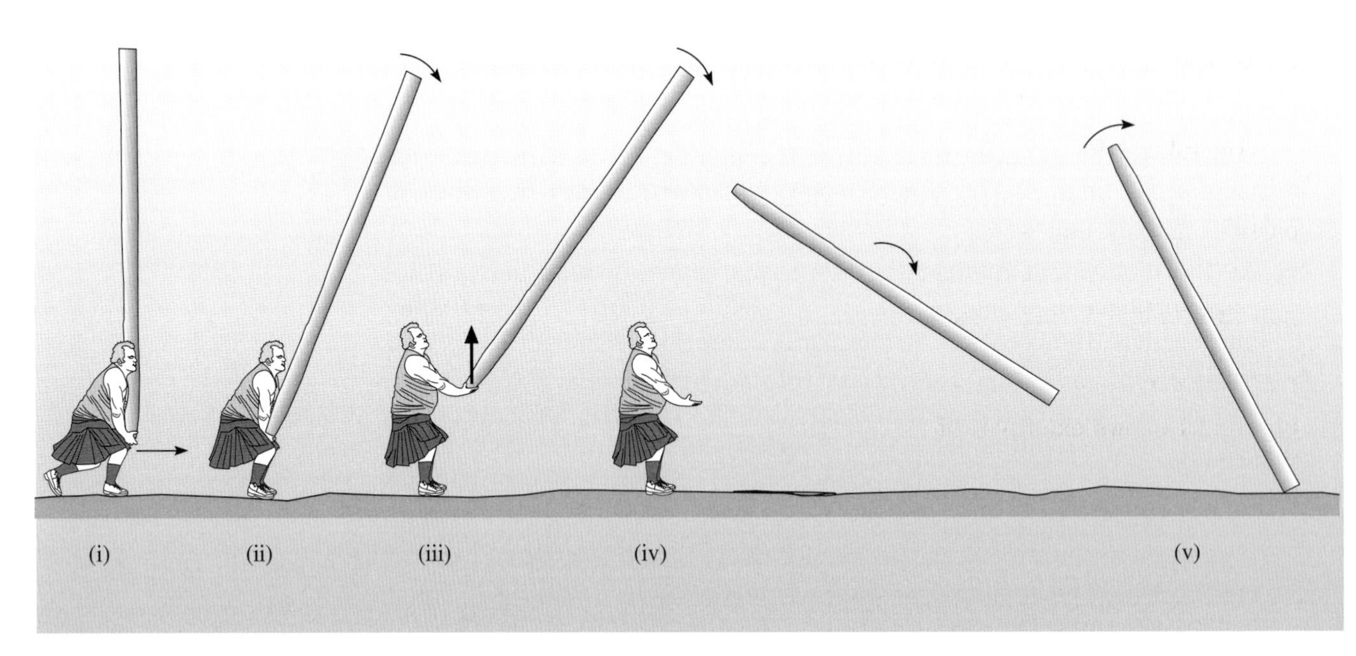

Figure 1.6

(a) Discuss each of these phases qualitatively. Which aspects of the motion of the caber change from phase to phase, and which stay the same? In particular, what happens to the rotational motion of the caber in each phase? (Assume that all the motion is in two dimensions.)

(b) Why is it helpful to have a caber that is tapered, with the thinner end being held by the competitor?

2 Angular momentum

In *Unit 20* we obtained the torque law for a particle,

$$\dot{\boldsymbol{l}} = \boldsymbol{\Gamma},$$

where $\boldsymbol{l}$ is the particle's angular momentum and $\boldsymbol{\Gamma}$ is the torque applied to the particle (each taken about the same point). In this section, you will see that this result can be extended to a system of particles; in that case, $\boldsymbol{l}$ is the total angular momentum of all the particles in the system, and $\boldsymbol{\Gamma}$ is the total torque exerted by all the external forces on the particles in the system. These results can be applied to extended bodies by modelling them as systems of particles.

This section starts by reviewing a number of ideas that you have met earlier: in Subsection 2.1 we review Newton's third law of motion, and in Subsection 2.2 we review angular momentum and the torque law for a particle. Then in Subsection 2.3, we extend the torque law to a system of particles.

2.1 Newton's third law of motion revisited

In order to extend the results of *Unit 20* from particles to extended bodies we need to look again at Newton's third law, which deals with the interaction between particles. In the Introduction to *Unit 5*, Newton's third law was stated as follows:

Law III To every action (i.e. force) by one body on another there is always opposed an equal reaction (i.e. force) — i.e. the actions of two bodies upon each other are always equal in magnitude and opposite in direction.

In symbols this can be expressed by considering two particles, particle 1 and particle 2. Let $\mathbf{I}_{12}$ be the force exerted on particle 1 by particle 2 and let $\mathbf{I}_{21}$ be the force exerted on particle 2 by particle 1. Then the statement of Newton's third law above can be written as $\mathbf{I}_{12} = -\mathbf{I}_{21}$. Alternatively,

$$\mathbf{I}_{12} + \mathbf{I}_{21} = \mathbf{0}. \qquad (2.1)$$

Thus the sum of the forces is zero. Recall that these forces between the particles in a system were called *internal* forces in *Unit 19*.

Exercise 2.1 considers how pairs of inter-particle forces that satisfy Equation (2.1) might be represented diagrammatically.

***Exercise 2.1**

Figure 2.1 shows examples of two forces of equal magnitude acting on particles A and B. For each pair of forces state whether Equation (2.1) is satisfied.

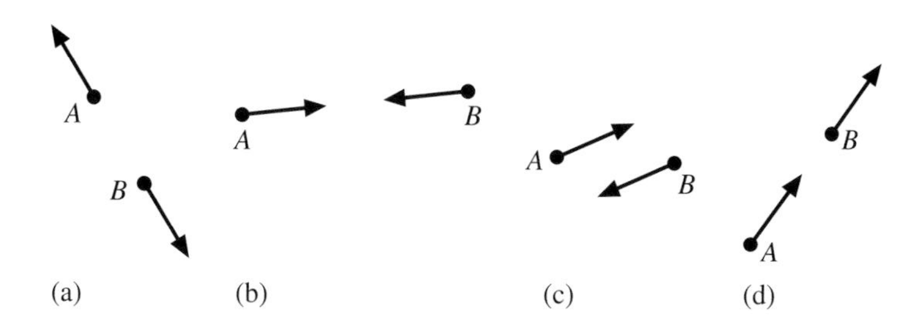

Figure 2.1

What we didn't mention in *Unit 5* was that Newton's third law also states that the pair of equal and opposite forces should have *the same line of action* (this was because the concept of line of action had yet to be introduced in *Unit 5*). Try the following exercise to see what this means.

*Exercise 2.2

Look back at Figure 2.1 and find an example of a pair of forces that satisfy Equation (2.1), but where the forces do *not* have the same line of action.

So there are pairs of forces that satisfy Equation (2.1), but where the forces do *not* act in the same straight line. We therefore need a mathematical condition to test whether the forces are acting in the same straight line, and hence whether Newton's third law is applicable. We shall now develop such a condition.

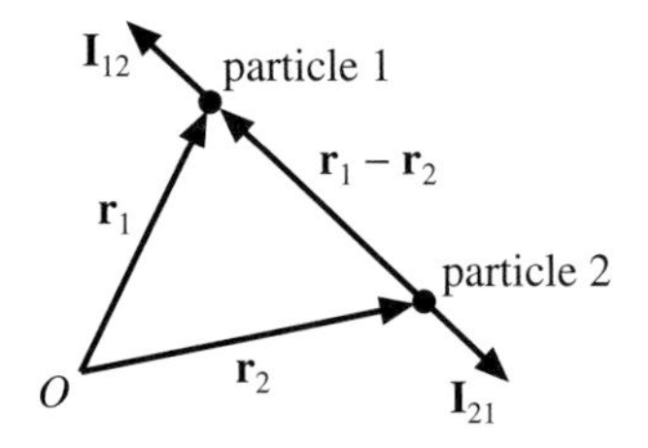

Figure 2.2

Figure 2.2 illustrates a situation where Newton's third law applies: the force $\mathbf{I}_{12}$ exerted on particle 1 by particle 2 is equal and opposite to the force $\mathbf{I}_{21}$ exerted on particle 2 by particle 1, with $\mathbf{I}_{12}$ and $\mathbf{I}_{21}$ having the same line of action. Let $\mathbf{r}_1$ and $\mathbf{r}_2$ be the position vectors of particle 1 and particle 2 respectively. The vectors $\mathbf{I}_{12}$ and $\mathbf{r}_1 - \mathbf{r}_2$ have the same direction, and so their cross product must be $\mathbf{0}$, i.e.

$$(\mathbf{r}_1 - \mathbf{r}_2) \times \mathbf{I}_{12} = \mathbf{0}.$$

Recall from *Unit 4* that the cross product of parallel vectors is zero.

By Equation (2.1) we have $\mathbf{I}_{12} = -\mathbf{I}_{21}$, so this can be rewritten as

$$\begin{aligned}(\mathbf{r}_1 - \mathbf{r}_2) \times \mathbf{I}_{12} &= \mathbf{r}_1 \times \mathbf{I}_{12} - \mathbf{r}_2 \times \mathbf{I}_{12} \\ &= \mathbf{r}_1 \times \mathbf{I}_{12} + \mathbf{r}_2 \times \mathbf{I}_{21} = \mathbf{0}. \qquad (2.2)\end{aligned}$$

Let $\mathbf{\Gamma}_{12} = \mathbf{r}_1 \times \mathbf{I}_{12}$ be the torque about O exerted on particle 1 by the force from particle 2, and similarly let $\mathbf{\Gamma}_{21} = \mathbf{r}_2 \times \mathbf{I}_{21}$ be the torque about O exerted on particle 2 by the force from particle 1. Then, from Equation (2.2), we have

Recall from *Unit 5* that a force $\mathbf{F}$ whose point of action has position vector $\mathbf{r}$ exerts a torque $\mathbf{\Gamma} = \mathbf{r} \times \mathbf{F}$ about the origin O.

$$\mathbf{\Gamma}_{12} + \mathbf{\Gamma}_{21} = \mathbf{0},$$

i.e. the sum of the inter-particle torques is zero when equal and opposite inter-particle forces have the same line of action. In other words, when Newton's third law applies, the sum of the inter-particle torques is zero. Conversely, if the sum of the inter-particle torques is not zero then the line of action of the forces is not the same (by reversing the above argument). Newton's third law can, therefore, be expressed in terms of the properties of the forces and torques between two interacting particles, as follows.

Newton's third law restated

The force $\mathbf{I}_{12}$ exerted on particle 1 by particle 2 is equal in magnitude but opposite in direction to the force $\mathbf{I}_{21}$ exerted on particle 2 by particle 1, with both forces acting along the line joining the two particles. An equivalent condition in symbols is

$$\mathbf{I}_{12} + \mathbf{I}_{21} = \mathbf{0} \quad \text{and} \quad \mathbf{\Gamma}_{12} + \mathbf{\Gamma}_{21} = \mathbf{0},$$

where $\mathbf{\Gamma}_{12} = \mathbf{r}_1 \times \mathbf{I}_{12}$ and $\mathbf{\Gamma}_{21} = \mathbf{r}_2 \times \mathbf{I}_{21}$, with $\mathbf{r}_1$ and $\mathbf{r}_2$ being the position vectors of particles 1 and 2, respectively, relative to the origin.

These equations state that the sum of the inter-particle forces is zero, and the sum of the torques exerted (about the origin) by those forces is also zero.

Almost all inter-particle forces conform to Newton's third law. The gravitational and electrostatic forces between particles obey this law, as do the forces in model springs or model rods joining two particles. All the systems that you will meet in this course conform to Newton's third law.

In electromagnetism there is a type of inter-particle force that does not obey Newton's third law, but this exception need not concern you here.

2.2 The torque law for a particle

Recall, from *Unit 20*, the definition of angular momentum for a particle, which is as follows: for a particle of mass m that has linear momentum $m\dot{\mathbf{r}}$ and position vector $\mathbf{r}$ relative to an origin O, its angular momentum $\boldsymbol{l}$ about O is

$$\boldsymbol{l} = \mathbf{r} \times m\dot{\mathbf{r}}, \tag{2.3}$$

i.e. the angular momentum is the cross product of the particle's position vector and its linear momentum.

Since the position vector is part of the definition, the angular momentum is dependent upon the choice of origin (which is not the case for linear momentum). So the angular momentum will usually not be the same relative to different choices of origin.

***Exercise 2.3**

A particle of mass 20 has position vector $\mathbf{r} = 3\cos(2t)\mathbf{i} + 4\sin(2t)\mathbf{j} + 5\mathbf{k}$ with origin O (working in SI units), where $\mathbf{i}$, $\mathbf{j}$ and $\mathbf{k}$ are Cartesian unit vectors. What is the angular momentum of the particle about O at time $t = 0$?

Exercise 2.4

A particle of mass m moves anticlockwise in a circle of radius R at constant speed v. The circle has its centre at the origin O and lies in the (x, y)-plane. Let $\mathbf{i}$, $\mathbf{j}$ and $\mathbf{k}$ be the Cartesian unit vectors.

(a) What is the angular velocity $\boldsymbol{\omega}$ of the particle?

(b) What is the angular momentum $\boldsymbol{l}$ of the particle about O?

(*Hint*: Work from the definition of angular momentum, and assume that the particle has position $R(\cos(\omega t)\mathbf{i} + \sin(\omega t)\mathbf{j})$ for suitable ω.)

This result is also derived in *Unit 20*.

(c) What is the moment of inertia I of the particle about an axis through O in the $\mathbf{k}$-direction?

(d) Show that $\boldsymbol{l} = I\boldsymbol{\omega}$.

In *Unit 20* we showed that, if a particle is subject to a torque, then the rate of change of the particle's angular momentum $\boldsymbol{l}$ about a fixed point is equal to the applied torque $\boldsymbol{\Gamma}$ about that point, i.e. $\dot{\boldsymbol{l}} = \boldsymbol{\Gamma}$. The derivation of this important result from *Unit 20*, known as the *torque law for a particle*, is repeated below. Using Equation (2.3), we find

$$\begin{aligned}\frac{d}{dt}\boldsymbol{l} &= \frac{d}{dt}(\mathbf{r} \times m\dot{\mathbf{r}}) \\ &= (\dot{\mathbf{r}} \times m\dot{\mathbf{r}}) + (\mathbf{r} \times m\ddot{\mathbf{r}}) \\ &= \mathbf{r} \times m\ddot{\mathbf{r}}.\end{aligned} \tag{2.4}$$

Since $\dot{\mathbf{r}}$ and $m\dot{\mathbf{r}}$ are parallel vectors, $\dot{\mathbf{r}} \times m\dot{\mathbf{r}} = \mathbf{0}$.

Now, by Newton's second law, $\mathbf{F} = m\ddot{\mathbf{r}}$, where $\mathbf{F}$ is the total force on the particle. Substituting for $m\ddot{\mathbf{r}}$ in Equation (2.4), we have

$$\dot{\boldsymbol{l}} = \mathbf{r} \times \mathbf{F}.$$

But the total torque on the particle (relative to the chosen origin) is $\mathbf{r} \times \mathbf{F} = \boldsymbol{\Gamma}$. So we obtain the torque law for a particle:

$$\dot{\boldsymbol{l}} = \boldsymbol{\Gamma}. \tag{2.5}$$

An important special case of this law is when the total external torque is zero. In this case Equation (2.5) becomes $\dot{\boldsymbol{l}} = \mathbf{0}$, and so $\boldsymbol{l}$ is a constant vector. This is called the *law of conservation of angular momentum for a particle*.

Exercise 2.5

Consider any particle moving at constant velocity. By Newton's first law the total force acting on the particle must be zero, so the total torque acting on the particle will also be zero. So, by the torque law, the angular momentum of the particle about any point will be constant.

Now construct an alternative explanation of the conservation of angular momentum, arguing directly from definition (2.3).

Exercise 2.6

(a) If $\mathbf{i}$, $\mathbf{j}$ and $\mathbf{k}$ are Cartesian unit vectors and $\mathbf{r} = x\mathbf{i} + y\mathbf{j}$, show that

$$\mathbf{r} \times \dot{\mathbf{r}} = (x\dot{y} - y\dot{x})\mathbf{k}.$$

(b) Suppose that a particle of mass m is moving in the (x, y)-plane. By expressing x and y in terms of plane polar coordinates r and θ, show that the angular momentum $\boldsymbol{l}$ of the particle about the origin O is

$$\boldsymbol{l} = mr^2\dot{\theta}\mathbf{k}. \qquad (2.6)$$

This result is also derived in *Unit 20*.

Exercise 2.6(b) provides an expression for the angular momentum about the origin of any particle moving in the (x, y)-plane. It generalizes the result obtained in Exercise 2.4 for the angular momentum of a particle travelling in a circle at constant speed. In Exercise 2.4 the particle followed a circle whose centre was at the origin. The next example concerns motion in a circle whose centre is not the origin (indeed, the circle is not in the (x, y)-plane).

Example 2.1

A particle of mass m moves with a constant angular velocity $\boldsymbol{\omega} = \omega\mathbf{k}$ in a circular path of radius R, centred on a fixed point $(0, 0, h)$. At $t = 0$, the particle is at the point $(R, 0, h)$. Let $\mathbf{i}$, $\mathbf{j}$ and $\mathbf{k}$ be Cartesian unit vectors in the x-, y- and z-directions, and let O be the origin.

(a) Express the particle's position vector $\mathbf{r}$ as a function of t.

(b) (i) Calculate the particle's velocity $\dot{\mathbf{r}}$ by differentiation.

(ii) Recall from *Unit 20* that a particle executing circular motion with angular velocity $\boldsymbol{\omega}$ has velocity $\dot{\mathbf{r}} = \boldsymbol{\omega} \times \mathbf{r}$. Verify that this is consistent with your result in part (b)(i).

(c) Calculate the angular momentum of the particle about O.

(d) Show that the torque about O acting to sustain the motion of the particle is $\boldsymbol{\Gamma} = -m\omega h\dot{\mathbf{r}}$.

Solution

(a) The angular velocity is in the $\mathbf{k}$-direction, so the particle must be moving parallel to the (x, y)-plane. The plane of motion is $z = h$. The particle is travelling with constant angular velocity $\omega\mathbf{k}$ in a circle of radius R, and is at $x = R$, $y = 0$ when $t = 0$. Therefore, its position vector is

In *Unit 20*, you saw that the angular velocity is perpendicular to the plane of motion.

$$\mathbf{r} = R\cos(\omega t)\mathbf{i} + R\sin(\omega t)\mathbf{j} + h\mathbf{k}. \qquad (2.7)$$

See *Unit 20*.

(b) (i) Differentiating Equation (2.7) gives the particle's velocity

$$\dot{\mathbf{r}} = -R\omega\sin(\omega t)\mathbf{i} + R\omega\cos(\omega t)\mathbf{j}. \qquad (2.8)$$

(ii) Using $\mathbf{r}$ from Equation (2.7) and $\boldsymbol{\omega} = \omega\mathbf{k}$, we substitute into $\dot{\mathbf{r}} = \boldsymbol{\omega} \times \mathbf{r}$ and obtain

$$\begin{aligned}\dot{\mathbf{r}} &= \omega\mathbf{k} \times (R\cos(\omega t)\mathbf{i} + R\sin(\omega t)\mathbf{j} + h\mathbf{k})\\ &= R\omega\cos(\omega t)\mathbf{j} - R\omega\sin(\omega t)\mathbf{i},\end{aligned}$$

which is consistent with the result in part (b)(i).

(c) By definition (Equation (2.3)), the angular momentum of the particle about O is $\boldsymbol{l} = \mathbf{r} \times m\dot{\mathbf{r}}$. On substituting for $\mathbf{r}$ and $\dot{\mathbf{r}}$ from Equations (2.7) and (2.8), respectively, we obtain

$$\begin{aligned}\boldsymbol{l} &= (R\cos(\omega t)\mathbf{i} + R\sin(\omega t)\mathbf{j} + h\mathbf{k}) \times m(-R\omega\sin(\omega t)\mathbf{i} + R\omega\cos(\omega t)\mathbf{j}) \\ &= m(R^2\omega\cos^2(\omega t)\mathbf{k} + R^2\omega\sin^2(\omega t)\mathbf{k} - hR\omega\sin(\omega t)\mathbf{j} - hR\omega\cos(\omega t)\mathbf{i}) \\ &= mR^2\omega\mathbf{k} - mhR\omega(\sin(\omega t)\mathbf{j} + \cos(\omega t)\mathbf{i}). \qquad (2.9)\end{aligned}$$

(d) From the torque law for a particle, we have $\mathbf{\Gamma} = \dot{\boldsymbol{l}}$. Now, by differentiating Equation (2.9) we get

$$\dot{\boldsymbol{l}} = -mhR\omega^2(\cos(\omega t)\mathbf{j} - \sin(\omega t)\mathbf{i}). \qquad (2.10)$$

Comparing this with Equation (2.8), we see that

$$\dot{\boldsymbol{l}} = -mh\omega\dot{\mathbf{r}},$$

and hence $\mathbf{\Gamma} = -mh\omega\dot{\mathbf{r}}$. ■

To sum up: in both Exercise 2.4 and Example 2.1 we looked at a particle moving at constant speed in a circle. In Exercise 2.4 you saw that, relative to the centre of the circle, angular momentum is constant and the total torque acting on the particle is zero. In Example 2.1, we considered angular momentum and torque relative to a point on the axis of rotation but *not* at the centre of the circle. Relative to that point, the angular momentum is not constant (although its component in the direction of the angular velocity is constant); consequently, there must be a non-zero total torque on the particle about that point if such motion is to be sustained.

Equation (2.9) shows that the component of $\boldsymbol{l}$ in the $\mathbf{k}$-direction is constant.

Exercise 2.7

For a particle moving as described in Example 2.1, calculate the acceleration $\ddot{\mathbf{r}}$. Use Newton's second law to find the total force $\mathbf{F}$ acting on the particle. Then calculate the total torque $\mathbf{\Gamma}$ on the particle by using $\mathbf{\Gamma} = \mathbf{r} \times \mathbf{F}$, and show that you obtain the same result as in Example 2.1(d).

2.3 The torque law for an n-particle system

We now move on to consider angular momentum and torque for systems involving more than one particle. First, we look at systems that have two particles, then we go on to examine a general system containing an arbitrary number of particles.

Two-particle systems

Consider a two-particle system, as illustrated in Figure 2.3, to which Newton's third law applies. Particle 1, at position $\mathbf{r}_1$ relative to a fixed origin O, may be acted on by any number of external forces, but we shall consider only the resultant of all these external forces, $\mathbf{F}_1$. The only other force on particle 1 is the internal force $\mathbf{I}_{12}$ exerted on it by particle 2. The total external force on particle 2, at position $\mathbf{r}_2$, is $\mathbf{F}_2$, and the only other force on particle 2 is the internal force $\mathbf{I}_{21}$ exerted on it by particle 1. Let the angular momentum of particle 1 relative to O be $\boldsymbol{l}_1$, and that of particle 2 relative to O be $\boldsymbol{l}_2$.

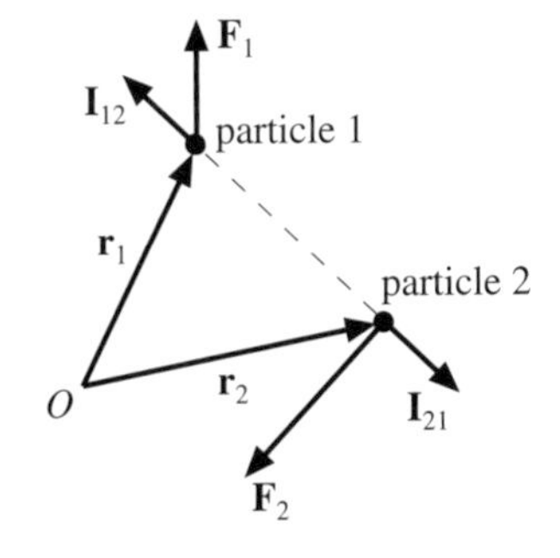

Figure 2.3

Applying the torque law for a particle (Equation (2.5)) to particle 1 gives

$$\dot{\boldsymbol{l}}_1 = \mathbf{r}_1 \times (\mathbf{F}_1 + \mathbf{I}_{12}) = \mathbf{r}_1 \times \mathbf{F}_1 + \mathbf{\Gamma}_{12},$$

where $\mathbf{\Gamma}_{12}$ is the torque about O acting on particle 1 by the internal force from particle 2. Similarly, for particle 2, we have

$$\dot{\boldsymbol{l}}_2 = \mathbf{r}_2 \times (\mathbf{F}_2 + \mathbf{I}_{21}) = \mathbf{r}_2 \times \mathbf{F}_2 + \mathbf{\Gamma}_{21},$$

where $\boldsymbol{\Gamma}_{21}$ is the torque about O acting on particle 2 by the internal force from particle 1. Adding these two equations, we obtain

$$\dot{\boldsymbol{l}}_1 + \dot{\boldsymbol{l}}_2 = \mathbf{r}_1 \times \mathbf{F}_1 + \mathbf{r}_2 \times \mathbf{F}_2 + \boldsymbol{\Gamma}_{12} + \boldsymbol{\Gamma}_{21}.$$

Newton's third law implies that $\boldsymbol{\Gamma}_{12} + \boldsymbol{\Gamma}_{21} = \mathbf{0}$, so this reduces to

$$\dot{\boldsymbol{l}}_1 + \dot{\boldsymbol{l}}_2 = \mathbf{r}_1 \times \mathbf{F}_1 + \mathbf{r}_2 \times \mathbf{F}_2. \qquad (2.11)$$

In Equation (2.11), the right-hand side represents the total torque exerted on the two-particle system by the external forces, while the left-hand side gives the rate of change with time of the total angular momentum of the system. Thus Equation (2.11) extends the torque law to a system of two particles. The *torque law for a two-particle system* can then be stated as follows.

> For a two-particle system, the rate of change of the total angular momentum of the particles in the system is equal to the total torque exerted on the system by external forces (where angular momentum and torque are determined relative to the same fixed point).

*Exercise 2.8

Figure 2.4 is a schematic representation of a type of children's playground roundabout. Two children sit on seats at A and B, and the roundabout is set in motion by pushing at C. It rotates horizontally about a fixed spindle at O. The distances AO, BO and CO are a, b and c, respectively. The mass of the child and seat at A is m_1, and the mass of the child and seat at B is m_2. The positions of the seats are balanced so that $m_1 a = m_2 b$. The mass of the rest of the roundabout is negligible.

There are safety skids under each seat, but we shall assume that these are not touching the ground.

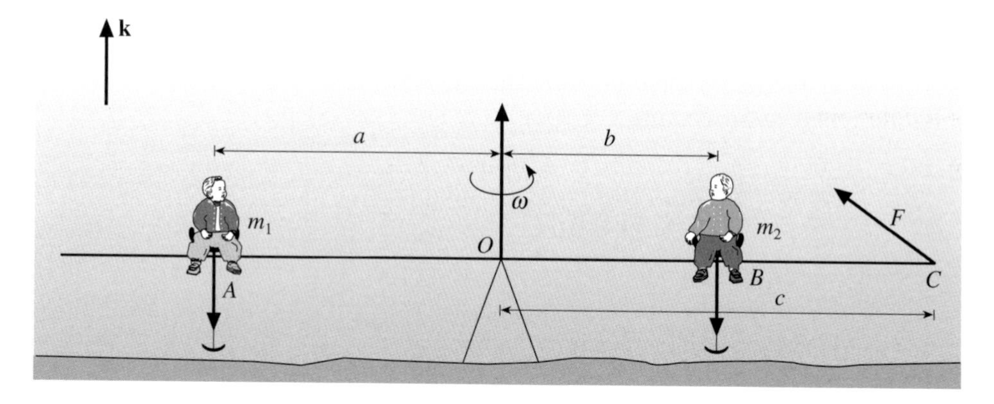

Figure 2.4

(a) Suppose that the roundabout is rotating anticlockwise at an angular speed ω. Model each 'child plus seat' as a particle, and show that the total angular momentum of the roundabout about O is $I\boldsymbol{\omega}$, where $I = m_1 a^2 + m_2 b^2$ and $\boldsymbol{\omega} = \omega\mathbf{k}$, with $\mathbf{k}$ being a unit vector pointing vertically upwards.

(b) Suppose that an adult pushes the roundabout so as to apply a force of constant magnitude F at C, in a horizontal direction at right angles to OC. Assuming resistive forces are negligible, show that

$$I\dot{\omega} = cF.$$

(c) If the distance AO is 1 m, BO is 0.75 m and CO is 1.5 m, and m_1 is 45 kg, m_2 is 60 kg and F is 315 N, then how long will the adult need to push in order to get the roundabout rotating at 0.5 revolutions per second when the roundabout has started from rest?

The next example concerns a two-particle system executing a more complicated motion.

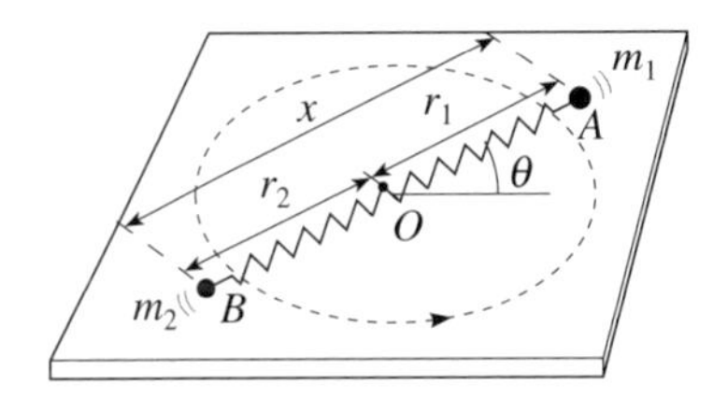

Figure 2.5

Example 2.2

Consider two particles of masses m_1 and m_2, connected by a model spring and resting on a smooth horizontal table, as shown in Figure 2.5. The system is in motion: the two particles are rotating at the same angular speed about the centre of mass of the system, and simultaneously they are oscillating as the spring extends and contracts. The total external force on the system is zero: the weight of each particle is balanced by the normal reaction from the table, and we assume that no other forces are acting. The centre of mass is stationary initially. Therefore it remains stationary throughout the motion because the acceleration of the centre of mass is zero (since the total external force is zero).

This was shown in *Unit 19*.

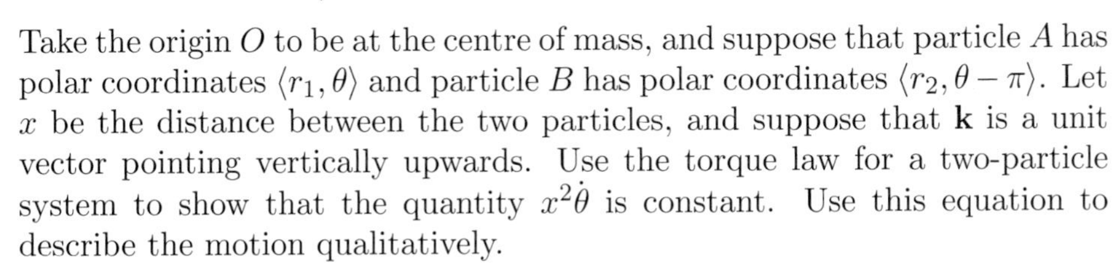

Take the origin O to be at the centre of mass, and suppose that particle A has polar coordinates $\langle r_1, \theta \rangle$ and particle B has polar coordinates $\langle r_2, \theta - \pi \rangle$. Let x be the distance between the two particles, and suppose that $\mathbf{k}$ is a unit vector pointing vertically upwards. Use the torque law for a two-particle system to show that the quantity $x^2\dot{\theta}$ is constant. Use this equation to describe the motion qualitatively.

Solution

The only external forces acting on the system are the weights of the particles and the normal reactions of the table balancing each weight. These normal reactions have the same points of action as the weights; consequently, not only is the total external force on the system zero, but the total external torque on the system is also zero. (The only other force acting on each particle is that from the spring, and this is an internal force.) It follows from the torque law that, as the total external torque is zero, the angular momentum $\boldsymbol{l}$ of the system is a constant.

From Equation (2.6), the angular momentum of particle A about O is $m_1 r_1^2 \dot{\theta}\mathbf{k}$, and that of particle B is $m_2 r_2^2 \dot{\theta}\mathbf{k}$. So the total angular momentum $\boldsymbol{l}$ of the system is

$$\boldsymbol{l} = m_1 r_1^2 \dot{\theta}\mathbf{k} + m_2 r_2^2 \dot{\theta}\mathbf{k} = (m_1 r_1^2 + m_2 r_2^2)\dot{\theta}\mathbf{k}. \tag{2.12}$$

But $\boldsymbol{l}$ is a constant, as noted above, and therefore

$$(m_1 r_1^2 + m_2 r_2^2)\dot{\theta} = c, \tag{2.13}$$

where c is a constant.

Because O is at the centre of mass of the two-particle system,

$$m_1 r_1 = m_2 r_2. \tag{2.14}$$

Now, $x = r_1 + r_2$, so we can substitute for r_1 in Equation (2.14) to obtain $m_1(x - r_2) = m_2 r_2$. Then solving for r_2 gives

$$r_2 = \frac{m_1 x}{m_1 + m_2}. \tag{2.15}$$

Substituting this into Equation (2.14) gives r_1 in terms of x:

$$r_1 = \frac{m_2 x}{m_1 + m_2}. \tag{2.16}$$

Substituting from Equations (2.15) and (2.16) into Equation (2.13) yields

$$\begin{aligned} c &= \left(m_1 \frac{m_2^2 x^2}{(m_1+m_2)^2} + m_2 \frac{m_1^2 x^2}{(m_1+m_2)^2} \right) \dot{\theta} \\ &= \frac{m_1 m_2^2 + m_2 m_1^2}{(m_1+m_2)^2} x^2 \dot{\theta} \\ &= \frac{m_1 m_2}{m_1+m_2} x^2 \dot{\theta}. \end{aligned}$$

Since the masses m_1 and m_2 are constant, we can deduce that $x^2\dot{\theta}$ must be constant.

As the system rotates the spring extends and compresses as the particles oscillate in and out. The rotational motion of the particles is connected to these oscillations since $x^2\dot{\theta}$ is a constant. When the spring is extended (x is larger) the angular speed $\dot{\theta}$ decreases, and vice versa. ■

This is reminiscent of the spinning ice skater holding her arms in or out, whom you saw in the video.

Exercise 2.9

A binary star system consists of two stars of masses m_1 and m_2. Model each star as a particle, and assume that all the forces exerted on the system, other than the gravitational attraction between the two stars, can be ignored. Assume also that the distance d between the stars is constant, and that the common centre of mass of the two stars is fixed. Let the total angular momentum of the binary system have magnitude l. Express the period of rotation of the system in terms of m_1, m_2, d and l.

n-particle systems

You have seen above that the torque law for a two-particle system has the same form as that for a single particle. This is because the sum of the internal torques between the two particles is zero. The situation is analogous for a system of more than two particles. Therefore we can generalize the torque law to any number of particles.

Consider a system of n particles, which we shall call particles $1, 2, 3, \ldots, n$, to which Newton's third law applies. Particle 1 may be acted on by various external forces, but we shall denote the resultant of all the external forces on particle 1 by $\mathbf{F}_1$. In general, for $i = 1, 2, \ldots, n$, $\mathbf{F}_i$ denotes the resultant of all the external forces on particle i. As well as being subject to forces external to the system, particle 1 may be acted on by internal forces exerted by each of the other particles in the system: denote by $\mathbf{I}_{12}$ the force exerted on particle 1 by particle 2, by $\mathbf{I}_{13}$ the force on particle 1 from particle 3, and so on. In general, let $\mathbf{I}_{ij}$ denote the force on particle i exerted by particle j (for i and j between 1 and n, with $i \neq j$). For $i = 1, 2, \ldots, n$, let the position of particle i be $\mathbf{r}_i$ (relative to a fixed origin O), and let the angular momentum of particle i relative to O be $\boldsymbol{l}_i$.

The torque law for a particle when applied to particle 1 gives

$$\dot{\boldsymbol{l}}_1 = \mathbf{r}_1 \times (\mathbf{F}_1 + \mathbf{I}_{12} + \mathbf{I}_{13} + \mathbf{I}_{14} + \cdots + \mathbf{I}_{1n}). \qquad (2.17)$$

If $\boldsymbol{\Gamma}_{ij}$ is the torque exerted on particle i by the internal force from particle j, then $\boldsymbol{\Gamma}_{ij} = \mathbf{r}_i \times \mathbf{I}_{ij}$, and Equation (2.17) becomes

$$\dot{\boldsymbol{l}}_1 = \mathbf{r}_1 \times \mathbf{F}_1 + \boldsymbol{\Gamma}_{12} + \boldsymbol{\Gamma}_{13} + \boldsymbol{\Gamma}_{14} + \cdots + \boldsymbol{\Gamma}_{1n}. \qquad (2.18)$$

Similarly, the torque law for a particle when applied to particle 2 gives

$$\begin{aligned}\dot{\boldsymbol{l}}_2 &= \mathbf{r}_2 \times (\mathbf{F}_2 + \mathbf{I}_{21} + \mathbf{I}_{23} + \mathbf{I}_{24} + \cdots + \mathbf{I}_{2n}) \\ &= \mathbf{r}_2 \times \mathbf{F}_2 + \boldsymbol{\Gamma}_{21} + \boldsymbol{\Gamma}_{23} + \boldsymbol{\Gamma}_{24} + \cdots + \boldsymbol{\Gamma}_{2n}. \end{aligned} \quad (2.19)$$

For particle i, we get

$$\begin{aligned}\dot{\boldsymbol{l}}_i &= \mathbf{r}_i \times (\mathbf{F}_i + \mathbf{I}_{i1} + \mathbf{I}_{i2} + \mathbf{I}_{i3} + \cdots + \mathbf{I}_{in}) \\ &= \mathbf{r}_i \times \mathbf{F}_i + \boldsymbol{\Gamma}_{i1} + \boldsymbol{\Gamma}_{i2} + \boldsymbol{\Gamma}_{i3} + \cdots + \boldsymbol{\Gamma}_{in}. \end{aligned} \quad (2.20)$$

Note that the sum does not contain a term $\boldsymbol{\Gamma}_{ii}$.

Now, to obtain the total angular momentum of the system, we can sum versions of Equation (2.20) for each of $i = 1, 2, \ldots, n$. When we do this, all the internal torques can be 'paired up': thus the term $\boldsymbol{\Gamma}_{12}$ from Equation (2.18) can be paired with the term $\boldsymbol{\Gamma}_{21}$ from Equation (2.19); the term $\boldsymbol{\Gamma}_{13}$ from Equation (2.18) can be paired with the term $\boldsymbol{\Gamma}_{31}$ from the equivalent equation for particle 3; and generally, the term $\boldsymbol{\Gamma}_{ij}$ from the equation for particle i (where $i \neq j$) can be paired with the term $\boldsymbol{\Gamma}_{ji}$ from the equation for particle j. Each pair will sum to $\mathbf{0}$, and so the total of all the internal torques for the n particles comprising the system will be $\mathbf{0}$. If $\boldsymbol{l}$ is the total angular momentum of the system (where $\boldsymbol{l} = \boldsymbol{l}_1 + \boldsymbol{l}_2 + \cdots + \boldsymbol{l}_n$) then, from Equation (2.20) (for $i = 1, 2, \ldots, n$), we have

From Newton's third law, we have $\boldsymbol{\Gamma}_{ij} + \boldsymbol{\Gamma}_{ji} = \mathbf{0}$ (for $i \neq j$).

$$\dot{\boldsymbol{l}} = \mathbf{r}_1 \times \mathbf{F}_1 + \mathbf{r}_2 \times \mathbf{F}_2 + \cdots + \mathbf{r}_n \times \mathbf{F}_n. \quad (2.21)$$

Here, $\mathbf{r}_1 \times \mathbf{F}_1$ is the torque exerted on particle 1 by the external forces acting on that particle, $\mathbf{r}_2 \times \mathbf{F}_2$ is the torque exerted on particle 2 by the external forces acting on it, and so on. Therefore the total external torque on the system is

$$\boldsymbol{\Gamma} = \mathbf{r}_1 \times \mathbf{F}_1 + \mathbf{r}_2 \times \mathbf{F}_2 + \cdots + \mathbf{r}_n \times \mathbf{F}_n.$$

So, Equation (2.21) can be written as

$$\dot{\boldsymbol{l}} = \boldsymbol{\Gamma}.$$

Thus we have shown that the rate of change of the total angular momentum of an n-particle system is equal to the total external torque acting on the system. This extends the torque law to an n-particle system.

Torque law for an n-particle system

Consider a system of n particles. Let $\mathbf{r}_i$ be the position vector (relative to a fixed origin O) of particle i and $\mathbf{F}_i$ be the total external force on particle i for $i = 1, 2, \ldots, n$. The total external torque on the system about O is

$$\boldsymbol{\Gamma} = \sum_{i=1}^{n} \mathbf{r}_i \times \mathbf{F}_i. \quad (2.22)$$

The rate of change of the total angular momentum $\boldsymbol{l}$ of the system about O equals the total external torque acting on the system, i.e.

$$\dot{\boldsymbol{l}} = \boldsymbol{\Gamma}. \quad (2.23)$$

In particular, when the total external torque about O is zero, the total angular momentum vector about O is conserved, i.e. constant.

End-of-section Exercises

Exercise 2.10

Suppose that all the external forces on a system of particles are applied at the same fixed point X. What can you deduce about the angular momentum of the system?

Exercise 2.11

Throughout this exercise, torque and angular momentum are measured about the origin O; also, $\mathbf{i}$, $\mathbf{j}$ and $\mathbf{k}$ are Cartesian unit vectors, with $\mathbf{i}$ and $\mathbf{j}$ in horizontal directions and $\mathbf{k}$ pointing vertically upwards.

(a) Consider a particle following a circular path parallel to the (x, y)-plane, whose position at time t is $R\mathbf{e}_r + h\mathbf{k}$. Here $\mathbf{e}_r = \cos(\omega t)\mathbf{i} + \sin(\omega t)\mathbf{j}$ is a unit vector pointing horizontally from the z-axis towards the particle, and R, h and ω are positive constants. Use Equation (2.9) to deduce that the angular momentum $\boldsymbol{l}$ of the particle is

You met this use of $\mathbf{e}_r$ in *Unit 20*.

The particle is executing the same motion as that in Example 2.1.

$$\boldsymbol{l} = mR^2\omega\mathbf{k} - mRh\omega\mathbf{e}_r. \tag{2.24}$$

(b) Consider a rigid body modelled as a system of n particles that are arranged in a vertical straight line as in Figure 2.6. Each of the particles is moving anticlockwise with constant angular speed ω in a circle of radius R, at a fixed height parallel to the (x, y)-plane.

(i) Use Equation (2.24) to deduce that the angular momentum $\boldsymbol{l}$ of the system is

$$\boldsymbol{l} = MR^2\omega\mathbf{k} - A\omega\mathbf{e}_r,$$

where M is the mass of the body and $A > 0$ is a constant.

(ii) Hence show that the vector

$$\dot{\boldsymbol{l}} = -A\omega\dot{\mathbf{e}}_r \tag{2.25}$$

has a direction normal to $\mathbf{e}_r$ in the (x, y)-plane (and tangential to the circle followed by the body). Deduce that the body must be subject to a non-zero torque in the tangential direction.

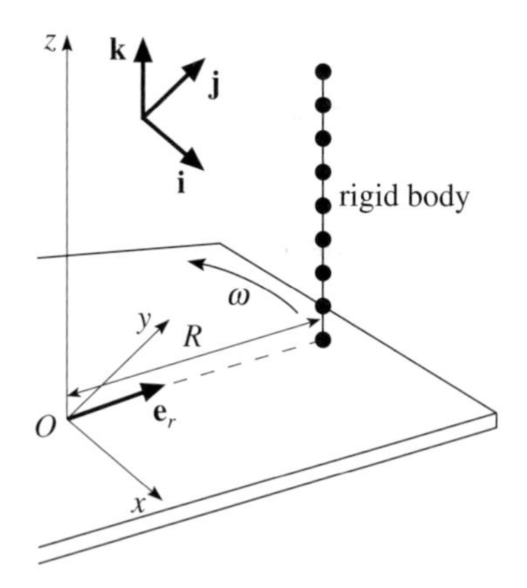

Figure 2.6

(c) Consider a skater whose centre of mass is moving with constant angular speed ω in a circle parallel to the (x, y)-plane.

(i) By analysing the motion of an equivalent particle located at the skater's centre of mass, deduce the direction of the total external force $\mathbf{F}$ on the skater.

(ii) Suppose that the skater tries to follow the circle while remaining perfectly vertical. Use Equation (2.25) to show that this is impossible. What must the skater do if she is to follow such a circle? (Model the skater as a one-dimensional rigid system of particles, as discussed in part (b). Assume that the only forces on the skater are her weight and the force exerted by the ice on her skates.)

3 Rigid-body rotation about a fixed axis

In this section we model a **rigid body** as an n-particle system where all the inter-particle distances remain constant. To simplify matters, we shall consider rigid bodies that are rotating about a fixed axis. For such a body, the rotational motion can be expressed in a very convenient way by using the moment of inertia. This is done in Subsection 3.1.

Rigid bodies were introduced in *Unit 5*.

Moments of inertia were introduced in *Unit 25*.

Unit 25 showed how to use multiple integrals to calculate the moments of inertia of complicated shapes. In this unit we model systems using simple geometric shapes, and we shall give a table of moments of inertia for these in Subsection 3.1. This table covers only moments of inertia about an axis through the centre of mass of the body. You may want to find moments of inertia about other axes, and this is covered in Subsection 3.2. The kinetic energy of a rotating rigid body can also be expressed in terms of its moment of inertia, and we consider that in Subsection 3.3.

3.1 Angular momentum and moments of inertia

In this section we confine our attention to motion in which a rigid body is rotating about a fixed axis. For simplicity, we shall choose a frame of reference in which the z-axis is the axis of rotation.

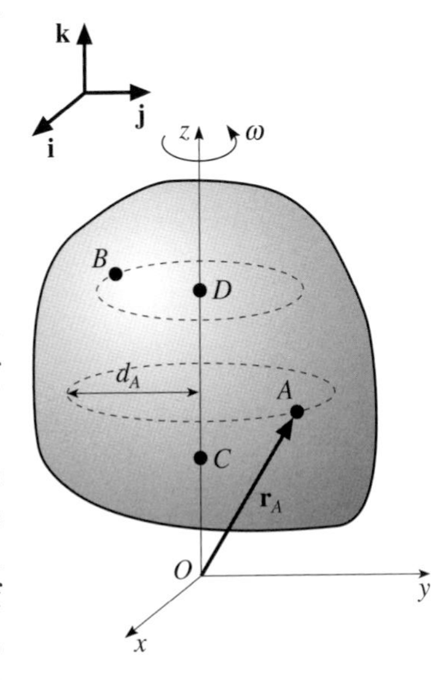

Figure 3.1

We choose x-, y- and z-axes that are fixed in space, and an origin O that is fixed and on the axis of rotation. Here $\mathbf{k}$ is a unit vector in the z-direction.

Now, in order to apply the torque law $\dot{\boldsymbol{l}} = \boldsymbol{\Gamma}$ to a rotating rigid body, we need to find an expression for the angular momentum of the body (relative to a point on the axis of rotation). Suppose that the body is composed of particles, A, B, C and so on. Those particles which lie on the axis of rotation, like C and D in Figure 3.1, do not move. On the other hand, particles like A and B do move, but their distances from the z-axis remain constant, and so they travel in circles centred on a point on the z-axis, and parallel to the (x, y)-plane. Let the angular velocity of the body (and of each of its constituent particles) be $\boldsymbol{\omega} = \omega\mathbf{k}$. First consider particle A, which has mass m_A and position vector $\mathbf{r}_A$. From *Unit 20*, particle A has velocity $\dot{\mathbf{r}}_A = \omega\mathbf{k} \times \mathbf{r}_A$. Therefore its angular momentum is

$$\boldsymbol{l}_A = \mathbf{r}_A \times m_A\dot{\mathbf{r}}_A = \mathbf{r}_A \times m_A\omega(\mathbf{k} \times \mathbf{r}_A). \tag{3.1}$$

If $\mathbf{r}_A = x_A\mathbf{i} + y_A\mathbf{j} + z_A\mathbf{k}$, we have

$$\mathbf{k} \times \mathbf{r}_A = \mathbf{k} \times (x_A\mathbf{i} + y_A\mathbf{j} + z_A\mathbf{k}) = x_A\mathbf{j} - y_A\mathbf{i}.$$

Then, on substituting for $\mathbf{r}_A$ and $\mathbf{k} \times \mathbf{r}_A$ in Equation (3.1), we obtain

$$\begin{aligned}\boldsymbol{l}_A &= (x_A\mathbf{i} + y_A\mathbf{j} + z_A\mathbf{k}) \times m_A\omega(x_A\mathbf{j} - y_A\mathbf{i}) \\ &= m_A\omega(-x_Az_A\mathbf{i} - y_Az_A\mathbf{j} + x_A^2\mathbf{k} + y_A^2\mathbf{k}).\end{aligned} \tag{3.2}$$

Let d_A be the perpendicular distance of particle A from the axis of rotation. Then $d_A^2 = x_A^2 + y_A^2$, and Equation (3.2) simplifies to

$$\boldsymbol{l}_A = m_A\omega(-x_Az_A\mathbf{i} - y_Az_A\mathbf{j} + d_A^2\mathbf{k}).$$

Suppose that the rigid body consists of n particles, where the ith particle (for $i = 1, 2, \ldots, n$) has mass m_i and position vector $\mathbf{r}_i = x_i\mathbf{i} + y_i\mathbf{j} + z_i\mathbf{k}$. The total angular momentum $\boldsymbol{l}$ of the body will be the sum of the angular momenta of all these particles, i.e.

$$\boldsymbol{l} = \omega\sum_{i=1}^{n} m_i(-x_iz_i\mathbf{i} - y_iz_i\mathbf{j} + d_i^2\mathbf{k}).$$

This angular momentum has non-zero components perpendicular to the axis of rotation (in the $\mathbf{i}$- and $\mathbf{j}$-directions). However, in many applications it is only the component in the direction of the axis of rotation that is needed. With our choice of axes, this component is in the z-direction, and is

$$l_z = \omega \sum_{i=1}^{n} m_i d_i^2.$$

This result is very important. For any particular rigid body, the quantity $\sum_{i=1}^{n} m_i d_i^2 = I$ is a constant, since both m_i and d_i are constant for all i. It depends on the distribution of mass about the axis of rotation and, as you saw in *Unit 25*, it is called the moment of inertia. Hence, for a rigid body spinning about a fixed axis, the component of the angular momentum in the direction of the axis can be conveniently expressed in terms of its moment of inertia.

Angular momentum of a rigid body rotating with fixed axis

Suppose that a rigid body is rotating about a fixed axis with angular velocity $\boldsymbol{\omega}$. Let $\boldsymbol{l}$ be the angular momentum of the body about a point O on the axis, and let $\boldsymbol{l}_{\mathrm{a}}$ be the component vector of $\boldsymbol{l}$ in the direction of the axis. Then

$$\boldsymbol{l}_{\mathrm{a}} = I\boldsymbol{\omega}, \qquad (3.3)$$

where I is the moment of inertia of the body about the axis of rotation.

We have established this result with the z-axis as the axis of rotation. However, for any rigid body rotating about a fixed axis, we could choose axes such that the z-axis is the axis of rotation, so there is no loss of generality in our argument.

The angular velocity $\boldsymbol{\omega}$ can be expressed in terms of the angle θ through which the body has rotated about its axis of rotation (see Figure 3.2), thus $\boldsymbol{\omega} = \dot{\theta}\mathbf{k}$, where $\mathbf{k}$ is a unit vector along the axis of rotation. If we look at just the $\mathbf{k}$-components, then the torque law yields

$$\boldsymbol{\Gamma} \cdot \mathbf{k} = \dot{\boldsymbol{l}} \cdot \mathbf{k} = \frac{d}{dt}(\boldsymbol{l} \cdot \mathbf{k}) = \frac{d}{dt}(I\omega) = \frac{d}{dt}(I\dot{\theta}) = I\ddot{\theta}.$$

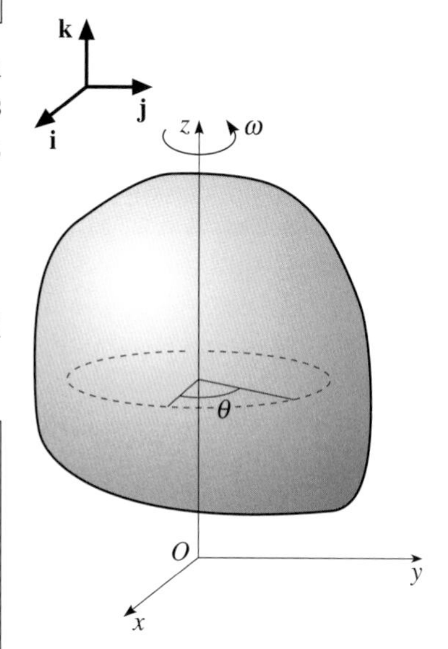

Figure 3.2

So in this situation the torque law leads to the following important and elegant result.

Equation of rotational motion

Suppose that a rigid body is rotating about a fixed axis, and that its angular displacement (from some fixed line normal to the axis) is θ. Then

$$I\ddot{\theta} = \Gamma_{\mathrm{a}}, \qquad (3.4)$$

where Γ_{a} is the component of the total external torque on the body in the direction of the axis of rotation.

The moments of inertia of a number of common regular geometric shapes are given in Table 3.1. In each case we assume that the rigid body is continuous and of uniform density, and we shall only consider objects of this type. The moments of inertia given in the table have been found by integration, as discussed in *Unit 25*. You may use these moments of inertia when doing the exercises in this unit.

The objects are therefore homogeneous rigid bodies, as defined in *Unit 19*.

Table 3.1 Moments of inertia of homogeneous rigid bodies

Object	Axis	Dimensions	Moment of inertia	Figure
solid cylinder	axis of cylinder	radius R	$\frac{1}{2}MR^2$	Figure 3.3, axis AB
solid cylinder	normal to axis of cylinder	radius R length h	$\frac{1}{4}MR^2 + \frac{1}{12}Mh^2$	Figure 3.3, axis CD
hollow cylinder	axis of cylinder	inner radius a outer radius R	$\frac{1}{2}M(R^2 + a^2)$	Figure 3.4, axis AB
hollow cylinder	normal to axis of cylinder	inner radius a outer radius R length h	$\frac{1}{4}M(R^2 + a^2) + \frac{1}{12}Mh^2$	Figure 3.4, axis CD
solid cuboid	normal to one pair of faces	faces normal to axis have sides of lengths a and b	$\frac{1}{12}M(a^2 + b^2)$	Figure 3.5, axis AB
thin straight rod	normal to rod	length h	$\frac{1}{12}Mh^2$	
solid sphere	through centre	radius R	$\frac{2}{5}MR^2$	
hollow sphere	through centre	inner radius a outer radius R	$\frac{2}{5}M\dfrac{R^5 - a^5}{R^3 - a^3}$	
thin spherical shell	through centre	radius R	$\frac{2}{3}MR^2$	

In each case, the mass of the object is M and the axis passes through its centre of mass G.

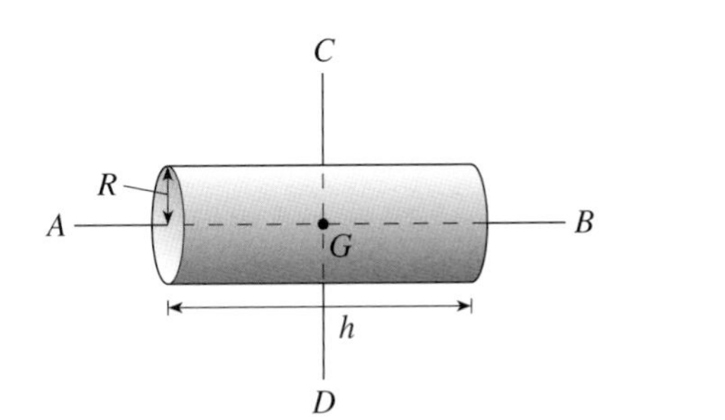

Figure 3.3

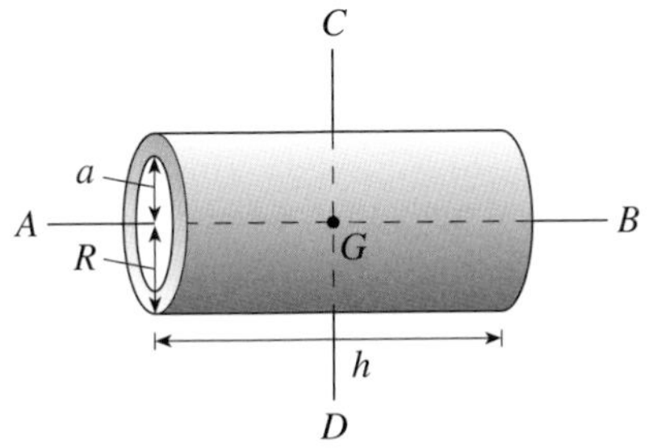

Figure 3.4

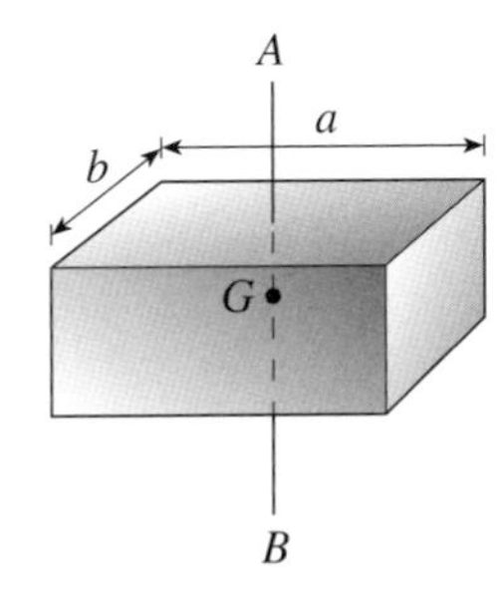

Figure 3.5

The moment of inertia of the 'thin straight rod' in Table 3.1 is calculated using the assumption that all its particles lie on a straight line. While this will never be absolutely true for a three-dimensional object, we sometimes use such limiting cases as convenient models. Similarly, a 'thin spherical shell' is an object whose particles are confined to the surface of a sphere. The moment of inertia of a thin spherical shell is, in fact, the limit of that for a hollow sphere as $a \to R$, but that limit is not obvious, so this case is given separately in the table.

The next example illustrates the use of the table to find the moment of inertia of a 'thin disc', which is another example of a two-dimensional model of a three-dimensional object.

Example 3.1

Consider a uniform solid circular disc of mass M and radius R, and negligible thickness. What is its moment of inertia about an axis normal to the disc and through its centre?

Solution

The distribution of the mass of the disc relative to the specified axis is the same as for a solid cylinder rotating about its own axis. From Table 3.1, the moment of inertia in this case is $\frac{1}{2}MR^2$. ■

To find the moment of inertia of a compound object formed from several simple shapes joined together, we find the moment of inertia of each component part separately, and then sum these. We use this approach in the next example.

Example 3.2

A playground roundabout can be modelled as a uniform solid circular disc of radius 1.2 m and mass 240 kg. The disc is horizontal and rotates about a vertical axis through its centre, making 0.5 revolutions per second. A man of mass 80 kg is standing stationary 0.2 m from the centre O of the disc. Suppose the man moves towards the edge of the disc, stopping when he is 1 m away from the centre. Assume that the only external force on the roundabout acts at the point O. At what rate will the disc be rotating when he is in this new position?

Solution

Since the only external force acts at O, the total external torque about O is zero, and so we can use the conservation of angular momentum about the axis of rotation through O. To do this, we need to know the moment of inertia of the combined 'man-plus-roundabout' system for each of the two positions of the man. Now, the moment of inertia of the roundabout about the axis through O is

$$\tfrac{1}{2}MR^2 = \tfrac{1}{2} \times 240(1.2)^2 = 172.8\,\text{kg}\,\text{m}^2.$$

If we model the man as a particle of mass m located at a distance r from O, then his moment of inertia is mr^2. So when he is 0.2 m from the centre of the disc, the moment of inertia of the combined system is

$$I_1 = 172.8 + 80(0.2)^2 = 176\,\text{kg}\,\text{m}^2.$$

With the man 1 m from the centre of the disc, the moment of inertia of the combined system is

$$I_2 = 172.8 + 80(1)^2 = 252.8\,\text{kg}\,\text{m}^2.$$

When the man is nearer to the centre of the disc, the angular speed ω_1 is 0.5 revolutions per second, i.e. $\omega_1 = \pi\,\text{rad}\,\text{s}^{-1}$. Suppose that the angular speed is ω_2 after the man has moved closer to the edge of the disc. Conservation of angular momentum gives

$$I_1\omega_1 = I_2\omega_2,$$

hence

$$\omega_2 = \frac{176}{252.8}\pi \simeq 2.19\,\text{rad}\,\text{s}^{-1}.$$

Therefore, after the man has moved closer to the edge of the roundabout, the roundabout rotates more slowly, at about 2.19 radians per second, i.e. at about 0.35 revolutions per second. ■

Example 3.3

A bucket used to draw water from a well has mass m and is attached to a light inextensible rope which is wound round a heavy wheel (see Figure 3.6). The wheel is a uniform solid disc, with centre O, radius R and mass M. The distance from O to the surface of the water in the well is h. Suppose that the bucket is released from rest at a point X, level with O, and allowed to fall down the well, causing the wheel to rotate. Model the bucket as a particle and the rope as a model string, and assume that the force supporting the wheel acts at the point O.

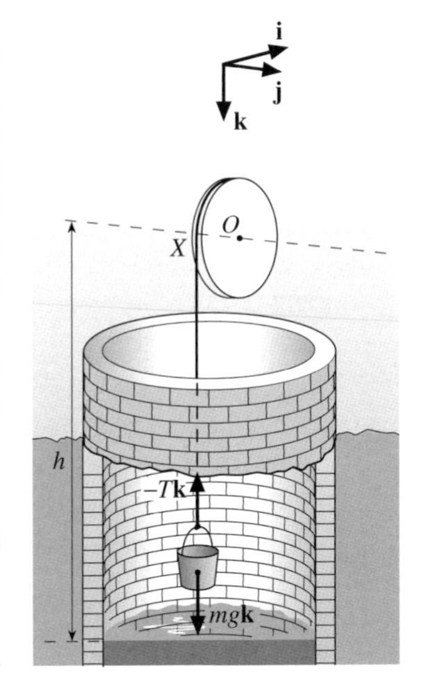

Figure 3.6

(a) If T denotes the tension in the rope, and z the distance that the bucket has travelled down the well in time t, write down the equation of motion for the bucket in terms of m, T and z.

(b) What is the torque acting on the wheel about its centre?

(c) Suppose that the wheel has rotated through an angle θ while the bucket has been falling. What is the relationship between z and θ?

(d) Write down the equation of rotational motion for the wheel.

(e) Find an expression for the acceleration $\ddot{z}$ of the bucket by eliminating T and θ from the equations of motion obtained in parts (a) and (d), and by using the result from part (c).

(f) Hence find the time taken for the bucket to descend the well.

Solution

Choose Cartesian unit vectors with $\mathbf{k}$ pointing vertically downwards, $\mathbf{j}$ in the direction of the axis of rotation of the wheel and $\mathbf{i}$ horizontal, as shown in Figure 3.6. The origin O is at the centre of the wheel.

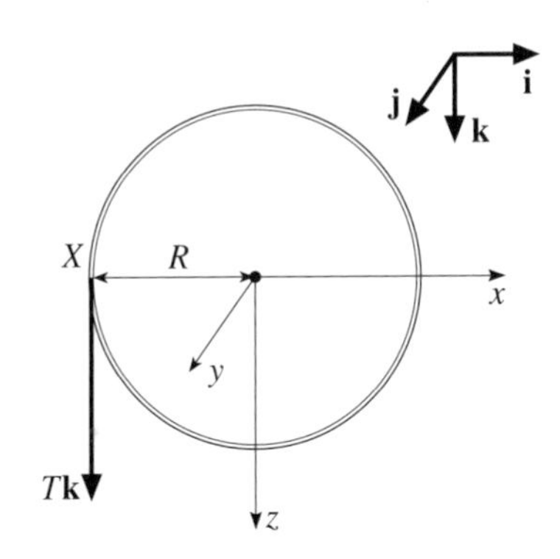

Figure 3.7

(a) The forces acting on the bucket are the tension force in the string, $-T\mathbf{k}$, and the force due to gravity, $mg\mathbf{k}$. So, by Newton's second law,

$$m\ddot{z}\mathbf{k} = mg\mathbf{k} - T\mathbf{k}.$$

Resolving in the $\mathbf{k}$-direction gives the equation of motion:

$$m\ddot{z} = mg - T. \qquad (3.5)$$

(b) The force exerted on the wheel by the rope is $T\mathbf{k}$, acting at the point X whose position relative to O is $-R\mathbf{i}$ (see Figure 3.7). Therefore the torque acting on the wheel about its centre is $(-R\mathbf{i}) \times T\mathbf{k} = RT\mathbf{j}$.

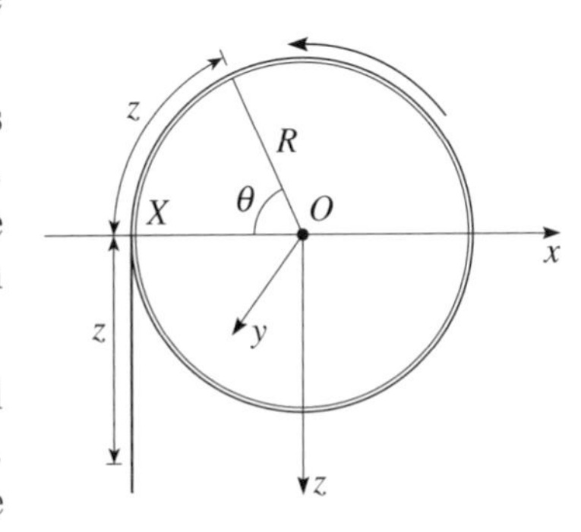

Figure 3.8

(c) If the bucket has fallen a distance z, then the quantity of rope that has unwound from the wheel as the bucket falls must also be of length z. As the bucket falls, the wheel turns through an angle θ, and so the part of the perimeter of the wheel that has moved past the point X in Figure 3.8 has length $R\theta$. Hence $z = R\theta$.

(d) The wheel is a disc turning about an axis through its centre and normal to its plane. It has moment of inertia $\frac{1}{2}MR^2$ about the axis of rotation. Then, from Equation (3.4), the equation of rotational motion of the wheel (in the $\mathbf{j}$-direction) is

$$I\ddot{\theta} = \Gamma_{\text{a}},$$

where $I = \frac{1}{2}MR^2$ and, from part (b), $\Gamma_{\text{a}} = RT$. So we obtain

$$\tfrac{1}{2}MR^2\ddot{\theta} = RT,$$

or equivalently,

$$MR\ddot{\theta} = 2T. \qquad (3.6)$$

(e) From part (c) we have $z = R\theta$, and, since R is constant, $\ddot{z} = R\ddot{\theta}$. On substituting in Equation (3.6), we find

$$M\ddot{z} = 2T. \tag{3.7}$$

Now from Equation (3.5), $T = mg - m\ddot{z}$. So substituting for T in Equation (3.7) yields

$$M\ddot{z} = 2(mg - m\ddot{z}).$$

Hence

$$\ddot{z} = \frac{2mg}{M + 2m}. \tag{3.8}$$

(f) The expression for $\ddot{z}$ in Equation (3.8) is a constant, so using the constant acceleration formula $s = v_0 t + \frac{1}{2}a_0 t^2$ with $s = h$, $v_0 = 0$ and a_0 given by Equation (3.8) we have

$$h = \frac{mg}{M + 2m}t^2.$$

Rearranging this gives the time for the bucket to reach the surface of the water as $\sqrt{h(M + 2m)/mg}$. ■

Exercise 3.1

A roundabout of mass 250 kg is modelled as a uniform solid disc of radius 1.2 m, which turns in a horizontal plane about a vertical axis through its centre O. It is being pushed with a force $\mathbf{F}$, using a handle at X as in Figure 3.9. This force, which has constant magnitude 100 N, is applied at a distance of 1.5 m from O, and is horizontal and normal to OX. A force $\mathbf{R}$ resists the rotational motion. It has magnitude $c\omega$, where c is a constant and ω is the angular speed of the roundabout; its point of action is 0.1 m from O, and its direction is opposite to the velocity of that point on the roundabout.

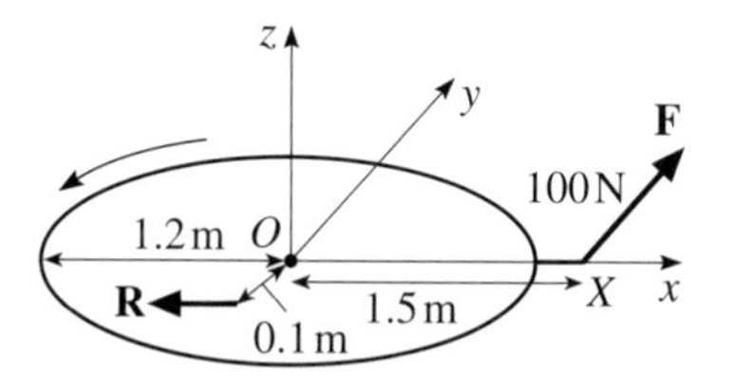

Figure 3.9

(a) Obtain a differential equation in terms of ω for the rotational motion of the roundabout.

(b) If the pushing starts at time $t = 0$ with the roundabout at rest, find ω as a function of t.

(c) If $c = 10$, what is the maximum possible angular speed that the roundabout could reach according to this model? Do you think that this could be achieved in practice?

3.2 The parallel-axes theorem

The moments of inertia of various objects about their centres of mass were given in Table 3.1. To find the moments of inertia about some other axis, we can use the *parallel-axes theorem.*

Theorem 3.1 Parallel-axes theorem

Suppose I_{AB} is the moment of inertia of a rigid body of mass M about a line AB (see Figure 3.10). Let EF be a line through the centre of mass of the body and parallel to AB, let the distance between the lines AB and EF be D, and let I_{EF} be the moment of inertia of the body about EF. Then

$$I_{AB} = I_{EF} + MD^2. \tag{3.9}$$

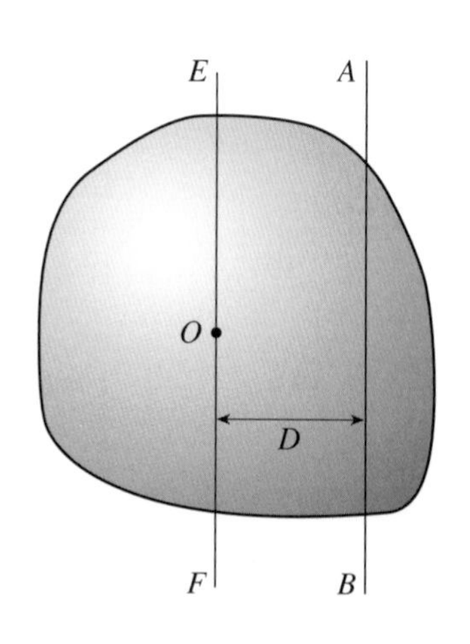

Figure 3.10

Proof of the parallel-axes theorem

Figure 3.11 shows a rigid body of mass M, with the centre of mass O taken as the origin. Suppose that we want to find the moment of inertia of the body about the line AB. Choose as the z-axis a line EF through O and parallel to AB. Let the perpendicular distance between these two parallel lines be D. Choose as the x-axis a line through O that intersects the line AB and is normal to AB.

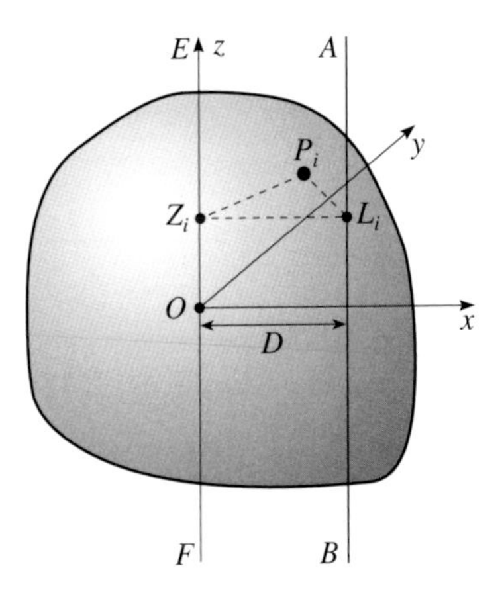

Figure 3.11

Suppose that the rigid body is composed of n particles, P_i, where, for $i = 1, 2, \ldots, n$, the ith particle has mass m_i and position (x_i, y_i, z_i). The distance of particle P_i from the z-axis is d_i (P_iZ_i in Figures 3.11 and 3.12), where $d_i^2 = x_i^2 + y_i^2$. Also, the particle's distance from the line AB is s_i (P_iL_i in Figures 3.11 and 3.12), where

$$\begin{aligned} s_i^2 &= (D - x_i)^2 + y_i^2 \\ &= D^2 - 2x_iD + x_i^2 + y_i^2 \\ &= D^2 - 2x_iD + d_i^2. \end{aligned}$$

By definition (see *Unit 25*), the moment of inertia of the rigid body about the line AB is

$$\begin{aligned} I_{AB} &= \sum_{i=1}^{n} m_i s_i^2 \\ &= \sum_{i=1}^{n} m_i(D^2 - 2x_iD + d_i^2) \\ &= D^2 \sum_{i=1}^{n} m_i - 2D \sum_{i=1}^{n} m_i x_i + \sum_{i=1}^{n} m_i d_i^2. \end{aligned} \tag{3.10}$$

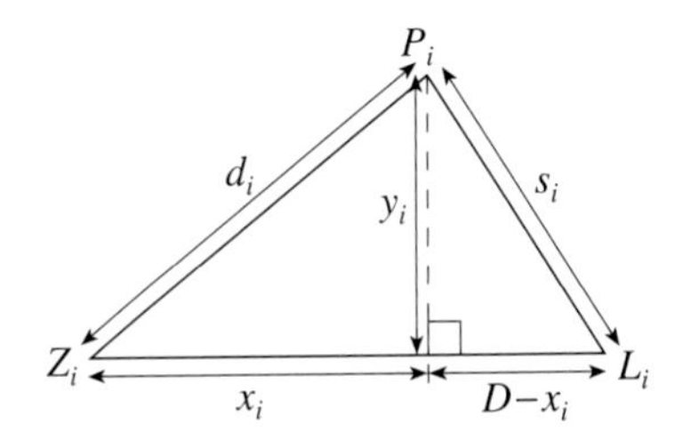

Figure 3.12 Part of a section through the rigid body in Figure 3.11, parallel to the (x, y)-plane.

Now $\sum_{i=1}^{n} m_i = M$ and $\sum_{i=1}^{n} m_i d_i^2 = I_{EF}$, where I_{EF} is the moment of inertia of the object about the z-axis (the line EF). Also, from *Unit 19*, $\frac{1}{M}\sum_{i=1}^{n} m_i x_i$ is the x-coordinate of the centre of mass of the body. Since the origin was chosen at the centre of mass, we have $\sum_{i=1}^{n} m_i x_i = 0$. Hence Equation (3.10) becomes

$$I_{AB} = I_{EF} + MD^2. \quad \blacksquare$$

Example 3.4

An ice skater is rotating about a fixed axis at an angular speed of 8 rad s^{-1}. One of the skater's arms is modelled as a uniform solid cylinder of mass 5.5 kg, length 0.66 m and diameter 0.08 m. The cylinder is normal to the axis of rotation, and the end of the cylinder is 0.09 m from the axis (see Figure 3.13). Find the magnitude of the component of the angular momentum in the direction of the axis of rotation for this model of the arm.

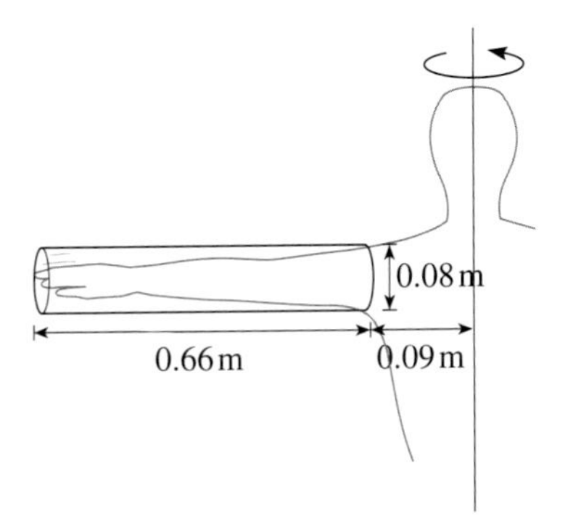

Figure 3.13

Solution

From Table 3.1, the moment of inertia of the cylinder about an axis through its centre of mass and normal to the cylinder is

$$\tfrac{1}{4}MR^2 + \tfrac{1}{12}Mh^2 = \tfrac{1}{4} \times 5.5(0.04)^2 + \tfrac{1}{12} \times 5.5(0.66)^2 \simeq 0.202\,\text{kg m}^2.$$

The axis of rotation is $0.33 + 0.09 = 0.42$ m from the centre of mass of the cylinder, so, from the parallel-axes theorem, the moment of inertia of the cylinder about the axis of rotation is

$$I \simeq 0.202 + 5.5(0.42)^2 \simeq 1.172\,\text{kg m}^2.$$

As the skater's angular speed is $\omega = 8\,\text{rad}\,\text{s}^{-1}$, it follows from Equation (3.3) that, for this model of the arm, the component of angular momentum in the direction of the axis of rotation has magnitude

$$l_a = I\omega \simeq 1.172 \times 8 = 9.376\,\text{kg}\,\text{m}^2\,\text{s}^{-1}. \quad \blacksquare$$

***Exercise 3.2**

The mace used by the leader of a troupe of drum majorettes can be modelled as a sphere of radius r, attached to the end of a uniform cylindrical rod of length d and radius R. The mass of the sphere is M and that of the rod is m. Find the moment of inertia of the mace about an axis AB through the end of the rod and normal to it (as shown in Figure 3.14).

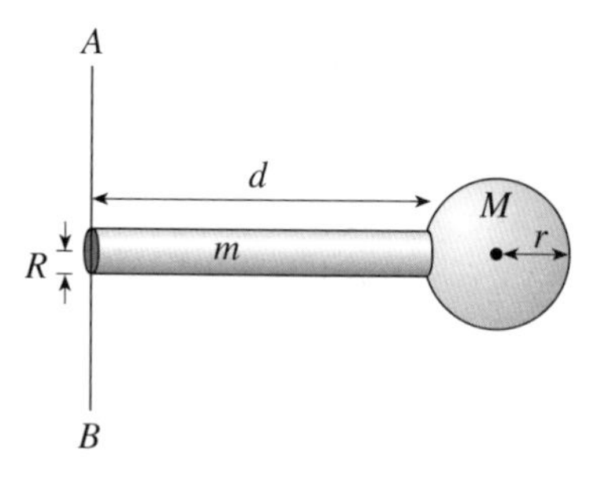

Figure 3.14

3.3 The kinetic energy of a rotating rigid body

You saw in *Unit 25* how the kinetic energy of a rotating particle can be expressed in terms of its moment of inertia. The kinetic energy of a rotating rigid body can be expressed in a similar way. Consider a rigid body rotating about a fixed axis with angular velocity $\omega\mathbf{k}$. The kinetic energy of the body is the sum of the kinetic energies of all its constituent particles. If the ith particle is a distance d_i from the axis of rotation, then its speed is $d_i\omega$ and its kinetic energy is $\frac{1}{2}m_i(d_i\omega)^2$. Hence the total kinetic energy of the body is

$$\sum_{i=1}^{n} \tfrac{1}{2}m_i(d_i\omega)^2 = \tfrac{1}{2}\left(\sum_{i=1}^{n} m_i d_i^2\right)\omega^2 = \tfrac{1}{2}I\omega^2,$$

where I is the body's moment of inertia about the axis of rotation.

Kinetic energy of a rigid body rotating with fixed axis

Suppose that a rigid body is rotating with angular speed ω about a fixed axis. Let I be the moment of inertia of the body about the axis of rotation. Then the kinetic energy of the body is

$$T = \tfrac{1}{2}I\omega^2.$$

Note that, so long as rotation is about a fixed axis, the expression $\frac{1}{2}I\omega^2$ gives the *total* kinetic energy of the body.

Example 3.5

A planet is modelled as a uniform solid sphere of radius 6400 km and mass 6.0×10^{24} kg. It is turning on its axis once every 24 hours. If the axis of rotation is fixed, what is the kinetic energy of the planet?

Solution

The planet's kinetic energy is $\frac{1}{2}I\omega^2$, where

$$\omega = \frac{2\pi}{24 \times 60^2}\ \text{rad s}^{-1}$$

and, from Table 3.1,

$$I = \tfrac{2}{5}MR^2 = \tfrac{2}{5} \times 6 \times 10^{24} \times (6.4 \times 10^6)^2\,\text{kg}\,\text{m}^2.$$

Therefore, the kinetic energy of the planet is

$$\tfrac{1}{2} \times \tfrac{2}{5} \times 6 \times 10^{24} \times (6.4 \times 10^6)^2 \left(\frac{2\pi}{24 \times 60^2}\right)^2 \simeq 2.6 \times 10^{29}\,\text{J}. \quad \blacksquare$$

Exercise 3.3

A drum majorette's baton is modelled as a uniform cylindrical rod with spheres of equal mass at either end. The rod has mass 0.1 kg, length 0.8 m and diameter 0.04 m. Each sphere has diameter 0.1 m and mass 0.25 kg. The baton is rotated at 1 revolution per second about a fixed axis that is normal to the axis of the cylinder and through the centre of mass (see Figure 3.15). Determine the kinetic energy of the baton.

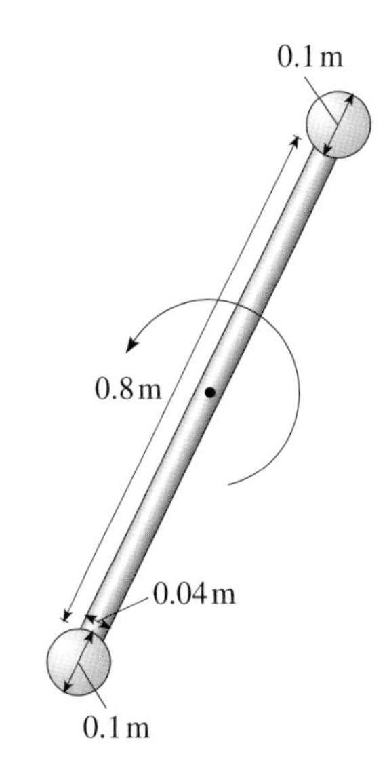

Figure 3.15

**Exercise 3.4*

(a) In the situation considered in Example 3.2, determine the total kinetic energy of the system (man plus roundabout) when the man is stationary at: (i) 0.2 m from the centre of the roundabout; (ii) 1 m from the centre. (Use the results found in the solution to Example 3.2, as needed.)

(b) In the reverse of the situation in Example 3.2, the man starts 1 m from the centre of the roundabout and moves inwards until he is 0.2 m from the centre. What happens to the kinetic energy of the system when he does this?

In a system such as that dealt with in Example 3.2 and Exercise 3.4, the angular momentum is constant because the total external torque is zero (both quantities being measured about the centre of the roundabout). However, the internal forces can change the kinetic energy of the system. This means that the kinetic energy is *not* necessarily constant, as you saw in Exercise 3.4(b), where the effort put in by the man in moving across the roundabout increased the total kinetic energy of that system.

**Exercise 3.5*

A rigid body of mass M is rotating about a fixed axis with angular speed ω. Suppose that the centre of mass is following a circle of radius R at speed v, and that I_G is the moment of inertia of the body about an axis parallel to the axis of rotation and through the centre of mass. Show that the kinetic energy of the body is

$$\tfrac{1}{2}I_G\omega^2 + \tfrac{1}{2}Mv^2.$$

The following exercise uses the principle of conservation of mechanical energy to analyse one of the situations that you saw in the video sequence.

Exercise 3.6

A diver begins a dive at rest and vertical in the handstand position. She starts to rotate from this position with negligible angular speed. She lets go of the diving board when her body makes an angle α with the vertical (where $0 < \alpha \leq \frac{\pi}{2}$), and she then starts the 'in-flight' part of the dive. Let ω be the angular speed of the diver at the moment of letting go of the board. Assume that, while in contact with the board at O, the diver is a rigid body able to rotate about an axis through O, normal to the plane of Figure 3.16. Use the principle of conservation of mechanical energy to obtain ω in terms of α and the following parameters: L, the distance from the diver's hands (in the handstand position) to her centre of mass; m, the mass of the diver; I_G, the moment of inertia of the diver about an axis through her centre of mass when her body is straight.

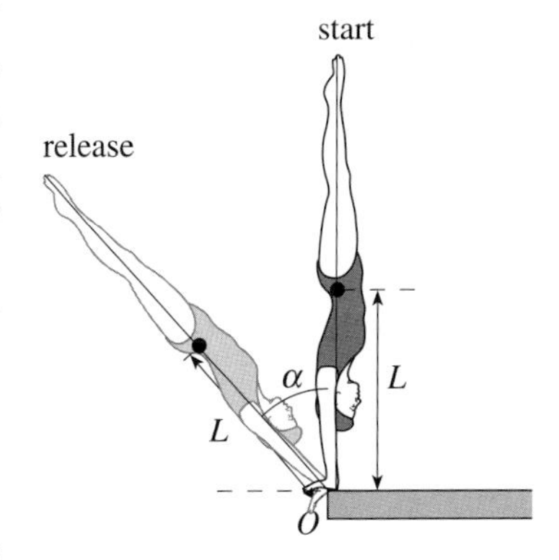

Figure 3.16

End-of-section Exercise

Exercise 3.7

Consider the diver from Exercise 3.6 when she is part way through her dive (as shown in Figure 3.17). Suppose that she has rotated through an angle θ ($\theta < \alpha$) in time t, and in that position the force exerted on her hands by the board has component vectors $R_1\mathbf{i}$ and $R_2\mathbf{j}$, as shown in the figure.

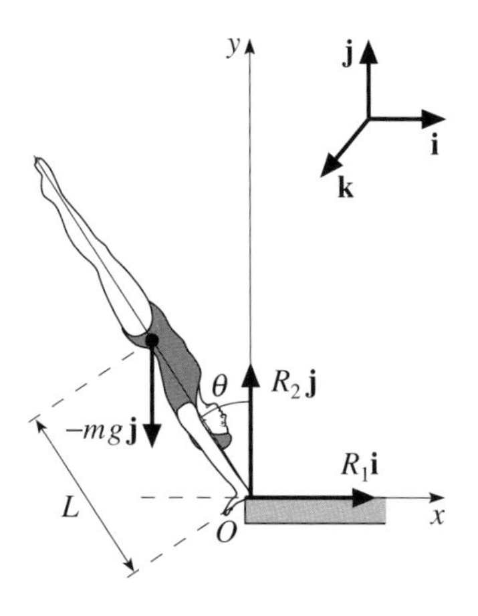

Figure 3.17

(a) With the origin and axes shown in Figure 3.17, let $x\mathbf{i} + y\mathbf{j}$ be the position of the diver's centre of mass. Express x and y in terms of θ. By differentiating, show that

$$\ddot{x} = L\dot{\theta}^2 \sin\theta - L\ddot{\theta}\cos\theta, \quad \ddot{y} = -L\dot{\theta}^2 \cos\theta - L\ddot{\theta}\sin\theta. \qquad (3.11)$$

(b) Let I_O be the diver's moment of inertia about an axis through O. Give the equation of rotational motion for the diver in terms of θ, I_O, m and L.

(c) Obtain another equation for the rotational motion by applying the principle of conservation of mechanical energy to the diver. Verify that differentiation of this equation leads to the equation of rotational motion that you found in part (b).

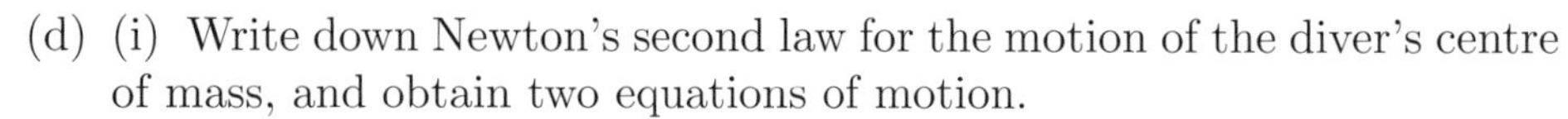

(d) (i) Write down Newton's second law for the motion of the diver's centre of mass, and obtain two equations of motion.

(ii) Use Equations (3.11) to substitute for $\ddot{x}$ and $\ddot{y}$ in these equations of motion.

(e) (i) Use the results of parts (b) and (c) to substitute for $\dot{\theta}^2$ and $\ddot{\theta}$ in your equation for R_1 in part (d)(ii). Hence show that

$$R_1 = mg\frac{mL^2}{I_O}\sin\theta(2 - 3\cos\theta).$$

(ii) Deduce that, for angles θ between 0 and $\pi/2$, the horizontal component of the force exerted by the diving board R_1 is zero when $\theta = 0$ or when $\theta = \arccos\frac{2}{3}$.

(f) Estimate I_O by modelling the diver as a uniform thin straight rod of length $2L$. Then estimate, as a multiple of the magnitude of her weight, the magnitude of the horizontal force that the diver would need to exert on the board to be able to remain in contact with it until $\theta = \frac{\pi}{2}$.

(g) At what point is the diver likely to lose contact with the board? Assume that there is nothing on the diving board on which the diver can grip, so she cannot pull on the board but can only push on it.

4 Rotation about a moving axis

The motion of an extended body may be much more complicated than that considered in Section 3, where we confined our attention to a *rigid* body rotating about a *fixed* axis. In this section we look at a more general situation where the axis of rotation is moving. The general case is considered in Subsection 4.1, and here we derive the result used in Section 1 that the motion can be decomposed into the motion of the centre of mass together with the rotation about the centre of mass. In Subsection 4.2, we consider the motion of a *rigid* body when the body is rotating about an axis whose *direction is fixed*, though the centre of mass may be moving. In Subsection 4.3 we look at the motion of rolling objects, such as the cans rolling down slopes which you saw in the video.

We shall not consider the motion of a rigid body when the direction of the axis of rotation varies.

4.1 The torque law relative to the centre of mass

In *Unit 19* we showed how Newton's second law of motion can be extended to an n-particle system. You saw there that the centre of mass of the system moves as if it were a single particle with the same mass as the whole system, and with all the external forces applied to this particle. The motion of the centre of mass is often referred to as the **linear motion** of the system, to distinguish it from the rotational motion of the system.

That is not to suggest that the centre of mass will always travel in a straight line!

In the video you saw that it was convenient to analyse complicated motion in two parts: the linear motion, and the motion relative to the centre of mass. Now, to apply the torque law as stated in Section 2, we need to work relative to a *fixed* origin. However, as you will now see, we can still use the torque law when these quantities are calculated relative to a point that is *moving*, so long as *that point is at the centre of mass.*

To demonstrate this, we need some notation. Throughout this subsection, we shall consider an extended body modelled as a system of n particles, with total mass M and centre of mass at a position $\mathbf{R}$ relative to some fixed point O. The ith particle of the system (for $i = 1, 2, \ldots, n$) has mass m_i and position relative to O given by

$$\mathbf{r}_i = \mathbf{R} + \mathbf{r}_i^{\text{rel}}, \tag{4.1}$$

where $\mathbf{r}_i^{\text{rel}}$ denotes the position of the particle relative to the centre of mass. In the following discussion it is also useful to obtain a relationship between the velocities of the particles relative to the different origins by differentiating Equation (4.1):

$$\dot{\mathbf{r}}_i = \dot{\mathbf{R}} + \dot{\mathbf{r}}_i^{\text{rel}}. \tag{4.2}$$

There is an additional equation involving $\mathbf{r}_i^{\text{rel}}$ that results from the fact that $\mathbf{R}$ is the centre of mass of the system. From *Unit 19*, we have

$$M\mathbf{R} = \sum_{i=1}^{n} m_i\mathbf{r}_i = \sum_{i=1}^{n} m_i\left(\mathbf{R} + \mathbf{r}_i^{\text{rel}}\right) = \sum_{i=1}^{n} m_i\mathbf{R} + \sum_{i=1}^{n} m_i\mathbf{r}_i^{\text{rel}}$$
$$= M\mathbf{R} + \sum_{i=1}^{n} m_i\mathbf{r}_i^{\text{rel}}.$$

This is where we use the fact that $\mathbf{R}$ is the centre of mass of the system.

Thus, as one would expect,

$$\sum_{i=1}^{n} m_i\mathbf{r}_i^{\text{rel}} = \mathbf{0}. \tag{4.3}$$

This equation states that if position vectors are taken relative to the centre of mass, then the centre of mass is at the origin.

The total external force on the ith particle is $\mathbf{F}_i$, and the total external force on the system is $\mathbf{F} = \sum_{i=1}^{n} \mathbf{F}_i$. Therefore the total external torque on the system relative to the centre of mass is

$$\mathbf{\Gamma}^{\text{rel}} = \sum_{i=1}^{n} \mathbf{r}_i^{\text{rel}} \times \mathbf{F}_i, \qquad (4.4)$$

and the total angular momentum relative to the centre of mass is

$$\boldsymbol{l}^{\text{rel}} = \sum_{i=1}^{n} \mathbf{r}_i^{\text{rel}} \times m_i \dot{\mathbf{r}}_i^{\text{rel}}. \qquad (4.5)$$

We aim to relate $\mathbf{\Gamma}^{\text{rel}}$ and $\boldsymbol{l}^{\text{rel}}$ to the corresponding quantities calculated relative to the fixed origin O, and start by looking at the total angular momentum relative to O, which is defined as

$$\boldsymbol{l} = \sum_{i=1}^{n} \mathbf{r}_i \times m_i \dot{\mathbf{r}}_i.$$

Substituting for $\mathbf{r}_i$ and $\dot{\mathbf{r}}_i$, using Equations (4.1) and (4.2), gives

$$\boldsymbol{l} = \sum_{i=1}^{n} (\mathbf{R} + \mathbf{r}_i^{\text{rel}}) \times m_i (\dot{\mathbf{R}} + \dot{\mathbf{r}}_i^{\text{rel}}).$$

Expanding the brackets gives

$$\boldsymbol{l} = \sum_{i=1}^{n} \left(\mathbf{R} \times m_i \dot{\mathbf{R}} + \mathbf{R} \times m_i \dot{\mathbf{r}}_i^{\text{rel}} + \mathbf{r}_i^{\text{rel}} \times m_i \dot{\mathbf{R}} + \mathbf{r}_i^{\text{rel}} \times m_i \dot{\mathbf{r}}_i^{\text{rel}} \right).$$

The last term can be recognized as the total angular momentum relative to the centre of mass (Equation (4.5)), so we have

$$\boldsymbol{l} = \sum_{i=1}^{n} \left(\mathbf{R} \times m_i \dot{\mathbf{R}} + \mathbf{R} \times m_i \dot{\mathbf{r}}_i^{\text{rel}} + \mathbf{r}_i^{\text{rel}} \times m_i \dot{\mathbf{R}} \right) + \boldsymbol{l}^{\text{rel}}.$$

As $\mathbf{R}$ is independent of i, this expression can be written as

$$\boldsymbol{l} = \mathbf{R} \times \left(\sum_{i=1}^{n} m_i \right) \dot{\mathbf{R}} + \mathbf{R} \times \left(\sum_{i=1}^{n} m_i \dot{\mathbf{r}}_i^{\text{rel}} \right) + \left(\sum_{i=1}^{n} m_i \mathbf{r}_i^{\text{rel}} \right) \times \dot{\mathbf{R}} + \boldsymbol{l}^{\text{rel}}.$$

The first bracketed term above is the total mass M of the system. The third bracketed term is zero by Equation (4.3) and the second bracketed term is zero by differentiating Equation (4.3). So we arrive at the result:

$$\boldsymbol{l} = \mathbf{R} \times M \dot{\mathbf{R}} + \boldsymbol{l}^{\text{rel}}. \qquad (4.6)$$

The next exercise asks you to derive a similar relationship that holds between the torque relative to the centre of mass and the torque relative to O.

*Exercise 4.1

Starting from the definition of $\mathbf{\Gamma}$, and using Equations (4.1) and (4.4), show that

$$\mathbf{\Gamma} = \mathbf{R} \times \mathbf{F} + \mathbf{\Gamma}^{\text{rel}}. \qquad (4.7)$$

The two results derived above are worth restating formally.

Decomposition theorems

Let $\mathbf{R}$ be the position vector of the centre of mass of a body relative to some fixed point O, M the total mass of the body and $\mathbf{F}$ the total external force on the body. If the total angular momentum of the body relative to the centre of mass is $\boldsymbol{l}^{\text{rel}}$, then the total angular momentum of the body relative to O is given by

$$\boldsymbol{l} = \mathbf{R} \times M\dot{\mathbf{R}} + \boldsymbol{l}^{\text{rel}}. \tag{4.6}$$

If $\boldsymbol{\Gamma}^{\text{rel}}$ is the total external torque on the body relative to the centre of mass, then the total external torque on the body about O is given by

$$\boldsymbol{\Gamma} = \mathbf{R} \times \mathbf{F} + \boldsymbol{\Gamma}^{\text{rel}}. \tag{4.7}$$

This states that both the total angular momentum and the total external torque of an n-particle system can be decomposed into the corresponding quantity for an equivalent particle located at the centre of mass plus the corresponding quantity for the rotational motion relative to the centre of mass.

Now we move on to derive the central result of this subsection, and one of the key results of the unit, which is the *torque law relative to the centre of mass*. To derive this result, we start by differentiating Equation (4.6) to obtain

$$\dot{\boldsymbol{l}} = \frac{d}{dt}\left(\mathbf{R} \times M\dot{\mathbf{R}}\right) + \dot{\boldsymbol{l}}^{\text{rel}}.$$

Using the torque law relative to a fixed origin O gives $\dot{\boldsymbol{l}} = \boldsymbol{\Gamma}$, so

$$\boldsymbol{\Gamma} = \frac{d}{dt}\left(\mathbf{R} \times M\dot{\mathbf{R}}\right) + \dot{\boldsymbol{l}}^{\text{rel}}.$$

Using the product rule for differentiating the cross product gives

See *Unit 20*.

$$\boldsymbol{\Gamma} = \dot{\mathbf{R}} \times M\dot{\mathbf{R}} + \mathbf{R} \times M\ddot{\mathbf{R}} + \dot{\boldsymbol{l}}^{\text{rel}}.$$

The first term on the right-hand side is zero, since $\dot{\mathbf{R}} \times \dot{\mathbf{R}} = \mathbf{0}$, so

$$\boldsymbol{\Gamma} - \mathbf{R} \times M\ddot{\mathbf{R}} = \dot{\boldsymbol{l}}^{\text{rel}}.$$

By Newton's second law $\mathbf{F} = M\ddot{\mathbf{R}}$, hence

$$\boldsymbol{\Gamma} - \mathbf{R} \times \mathbf{F} = \dot{\boldsymbol{l}}^{\text{rel}}.$$

Now we use Equation (4.7) to get the desired relationship between the torque and angular momentum relative to the centre of mass:

$$\boldsymbol{\Gamma}^{\text{rel}} = \dot{\boldsymbol{l}}^{\text{rel}}. \tag{4.8}$$

This is also worth stating formally.

Torque law relative to the centre of mass

The total external torque on an extended body relative to its centre of mass is equal to the rate of change of the total angular momentum relative to the centre of mass. So, if $\boldsymbol{\Gamma}^{\text{rel}}$ is the total external torque on the body relative to the centre of mass, and $\boldsymbol{l}^{\text{rel}}$ is the total angular momentum of the body relative to the centre of mass, as defined in Equations (4.4) and (4.5), then

$$\boldsymbol{\Gamma}^{\text{rel}} = \dot{\boldsymbol{l}}^{\text{rel}}. \tag{4.8}$$

Remember that we are modelling the extended body as a system of n particles.

This result shows that we can extend the torque law of Section 2 by considering torques and angular momentum *relative to the centre of mass*. Therefore, to model rotational motion, we can work in a frame of reference where the centre of mass is taken as the origin and thought of as fixed. We can then deal with motion of the centre of mass separately; this can be done by applying Newton's second law to an equivalent particle located at the centre of mass.

We can use the torque law relative to the centre of mass to justify an assumption we made in Section 1, that the angular momentum relative to the centre of mass is conserved for projectiles in flight.

Conservation of angular momentum: special case

Suppose that each particle in a system of n particles is subject to an external force of the form $cm_i\mathbf{k}$, where c is a constant, m_i is the mass of the ith particle and $\mathbf{k}$ is a fixed vector, and that there are no other external forces on the system. Then $\boldsymbol{\Gamma}^{\text{rel}} = \mathbf{0}$, and so $\boldsymbol{l}^{\text{rel}}$ is constant.

The next exercise asks you to establish this result.

Exercise 4.2

(a) Use Equation (4.4) and the torque law relative to the centre of mass to establish the boxed result above.

(b) Show that the boxed result applies to a body (such as a diver or gymnast) in flight and subject only to gravity.

**Exercise 4.3*

Suppose that all the external forces acting on a system of particles are directed towards the origin. Show that $\boldsymbol{\Gamma}^{\text{rel}} = -\mathbf{R} \times \mathbf{F}$.

We end this subsection with another decomposition theorem, this time for kinetic energy. This theorem is valuable if we wish to tackle a problem about rotational motion by using conservation of mechanical energy (rather than by using equations of motion). In terms of the vectors defined at the start of this subsection, the square of the speed of the ith particle is $\dot{\mathbf{r}}_i \cdot \dot{\mathbf{r}}_i$, so the total kinetic energy of the system is

Recall that $|\dot{\mathbf{r}}_i|^2 = \dot{\mathbf{r}}_i \cdot \dot{\mathbf{r}}_i$.

$$T = \sum_{i=1}^{n} \tfrac{1}{2} m_i \dot{\mathbf{r}}_i \cdot \dot{\mathbf{r}}_i.$$

Using Equation (4.2) gives

$$T = \sum_{i=1}^{n} \tfrac{1}{2} m_i \left(\dot{\mathbf{R}} + \dot{\mathbf{r}}_i^{\text{rel}}\right) \cdot \left(\dot{\mathbf{R}} + \dot{\mathbf{r}}_i^{\text{rel}}\right).$$

Expanding the brackets gives

$$T = \sum_{i=1}^{n} \tfrac{1}{2} m_i \left(\dot{\mathbf{R}} \cdot \dot{\mathbf{R}} + 2\dot{\mathbf{R}} \cdot \dot{\mathbf{r}}_i^{\text{rel}} + \dot{\mathbf{r}}_i^{\text{rel}} \cdot \dot{\mathbf{r}}_i^{\text{rel}}\right).$$

Here we have used $\mathbf{a} \cdot \mathbf{b} = \mathbf{b} \cdot \mathbf{a}$ to collect terms.

Using the fact that $\dot{\mathbf{R}}$ is independent of i allows us to rearrange to

$$T = \tfrac{1}{2} \left(\sum_{i=1}^{n} m_i\right) \dot{\mathbf{R}} \cdot \dot{\mathbf{R}} + \dot{\mathbf{R}} \cdot \left(\sum_{i=1}^{n} m_i \dot{\mathbf{r}}_i^{\text{rel}}\right) + \tfrac{1}{2} \sum_{i=1}^{n} m_i \dot{\mathbf{r}}_i^{\text{rel}} \cdot \dot{\mathbf{r}}_i^{\text{rel}}.$$

The first bracketed term in this equation is the total mass M of the system. Using Equation (4.3) we can show that the second bracketed term is zero. So the equation reduces to

$$T = \tfrac{1}{2} M \dot{\mathbf{R}} \cdot \dot{\mathbf{R}} + \tfrac{1}{2} \sum_{i=1}^{n} m_i \dot{\mathbf{r}}_i^{\text{rel}} \cdot \dot{\mathbf{r}}_i^{\text{rel}}. \tag{4.9}$$

This result can be stated in words as follows.

Kinetic energy decomposition theorem

The kinetic energy of an extended body is equal to the kinetic energy of an equivalent particle that has the velocity of the body's centre of mass, plus the sum of the kinetic energies due to the motion, relative to the centre of mass, of all the body's constituent particles.

The term 'equivalent particle' is used to mean a particle of the same mass as the body located at its centre of mass.

4.2 A rigid body rotating with fixed orientation

Consider a rigid body that is in motion, rotating about an axis which may itself move but which remains pointing in the same direction. A cylindrical can rolling down a slope, with its axis pointing in the same horizontal direction throughout, provides an example of such motion. In this situation, the centre of mass of the rigid body may be moving, but the motion *relative to the centre of mass* is of the type considered in Section 3. The position of each particle in the rigid body, relative to the centre of mass, is constrained in the same way that the position of each particle was in our discussion in Subsection 3.1. This means that arguments similar to those in Section 3 can be used to deduce expressions, in terms of the moment of inertia, for the angular momentum and kinetic energy of the rigid body, relative to its centre of mass.

To illustrate these points, take a rigid body of mass M that is rotating about an axis of fixed orientation through its centre of mass with angular velocity $\boldsymbol{\omega} = \omega\mathbf{k}$, where $\mathbf{k}$ is a fixed unit vector. Let I be the body's moment of inertia about that axis. Then, the $\mathbf{k}$-component of the angular momentum of the body relative to the centre of mass is $I\omega$, while the kinetic energy of the body relative to the centre of mass is $\frac{1}{2}I\omega^2$. Combining these results with the torque law relative to the centre of mass (Equation (4.8)) and the kinetic energy decomposition theorem (Equation (4.9)) leads to the following.

Rigid body rotating with fixed orientation

A rigid body of mass M is rotating about an axis of fixed orientation through its centre of mass, with angular velocity $\boldsymbol{\omega} = \omega\mathbf{k}$, where $\mathbf{k}$ is a fixed unit vector. Let I be the moment of inertia of the body about the axis of rotation.

The $\mathbf{k}$-component $l_{\text{a}}^{\text{rel}}$ $(= \boldsymbol{l}^{\text{rel}} \cdot \mathbf{k})$ of the angular momentum of the body relative to the centre of mass is given by

$$l_{\text{a}}^{\text{rel}} = I\omega. \qquad (4.10)$$

The **equation of relative rotational motion** of the body is

$$\Gamma_{\text{a}}^{\text{rel}} = I\dot{\omega}, \qquad (4.11)$$

where $\Gamma_{\text{a}}^{\text{rel}}$ $(= \boldsymbol{\Gamma}^{\text{rel}} \cdot \mathbf{k})$ is the $\mathbf{k}$-component of the total external torque relative to the centre of mass.

The kinetic energy T of the body is the sum of the kinetic energy of an equivalent particle at the centre of mass and the rotational kinetic energy relative to the centre of mass:

$$T = \tfrac{1}{2}M\left|\dot{\mathbf{R}}\right|^2 + \tfrac{1}{2}I\omega^2, \qquad (4.12)$$

where $\mathbf{R}$ is the position vector of the centre of mass.

*Exercise 4.4

A drum majorette's baton is modelled as a uniform cylindrical rod with spheres of equal mass at each end. The rod has mass 0.1 kg, length 0.8 m and diameter 0.04 m. Each sphere has diameter 0.1 m and mass 0.25 kg. The baton has been thrown upwards and is rotating at 1 revolution per second about a horizontal axis through its centre of mass and normal to the axis of the cylinder. Its centre of mass, which was initially at O, is moving vertically upwards at $5\,\mathrm{m\,s^{-1}}$.

You considered an identical baton in Exercise 3.3. Use any results from the solution to that exercise that you find useful.

(a) Find the kinetic energy of the baton.

(b) Find the **k**-component of the angular momentum of the baton, relative to O, where **k** is a unit vector in the direction of the axis of rotation.

In the video, you saw examples of the Highland sport of tossing the caber. We now consider one part of the motion of the caber: the moment at which it strikes the ground (see Figure 4.1). The aim of the toss is to ensure that the caber finishes lying on the ground with the end X, which was originally being held by the competitor, now furthest away from him. Even if the caber strikes the ground as shown in the figure, before it has rotated sufficiently for X to have moved to the right of Y, it may maintain sufficient rotation after impact for X to swing past Y, and for the caber to fall with X pointing away from the competitor. How might we model the effect of the caber hitting the ground on its rotational motion?

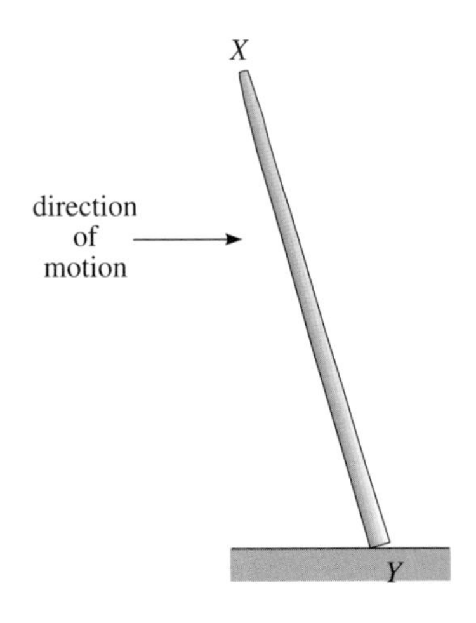

Figure 4.1

When an object hits the ground, there is an **impact**, during which the object is subject to forces of great magnitude over a short period of time. These forces drastically change the motion of the object. To model the impact, we shall assume that after hitting the ground the end Y of the caber is stationary, and that, during impact, all the forces on the caber are acting at the point Y. Take an origin at the point Y, and consider the torque and angular momentum about that point. Since we are assuming that all the external forces act at Y during the impact, the torque about Y is zero. Then, by the torque law, the *angular momentum about Y is conserved during the impact.*

We are assuming that during the impact the force due to gravity is negligible compared with the forces acting at Y.

You are asked to develop this model further in the following exercise.

Exercise 4.5

A caber is in flight, and its end Y is about to strike the ground at O at an angle θ from the vertical. Use the axes shown in Figure 4.2, and assume that the motion of the caber is confined to the (x, y)-plane throughout. The centre of mass G of the caber has velocity $v_x\mathbf{i} + v_y\mathbf{j}$, and the angular speed of the caber about G is ω (clockwise). Model the caber as a uniform thin straight rod of length $2L$ and mass m.

(a) Use a decomposition theorem to find the **k**-component of the angular momentum of the caber about O just before it hits the ground.

(b) Let ω_1 be the angular speed of rotation of the caber about O just after it hits the ground. Show that

$$\omega_1 = \tfrac{1}{4}\omega + \frac{3}{4L}(v_x \cos\theta + v_y \sin\theta).$$

(c) To rotate past the vertical, the caber must have sufficient kinetic energy after impact that it reaches the vertical with non-zero kinetic energy. Use this fact to obtain a condition (expressed in terms of ω_1 and the other parameters) that must be satisfied if the caber is to rotate past the vertical. (Do not substitute for ω_1 from part (b) — messy algebra!)

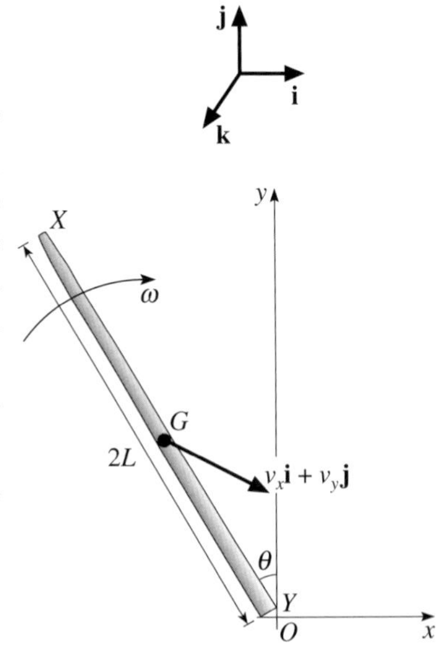

Figure 4.2

4.3 Rolling objects

In the video you saw solid and hollow cylindrical cans being 'raced' down an inclined plane. We are now in a position to model that situation quantitatively. To do so, we shall assume that there is no loss of mechanical energy when a cylinder rolls down a slope.

We discuss later why this assumption is justified.

Consider a cylinder of mass M and radius R rolling down a plane inclined at an angle ϕ to the horizontal (Figure 4.3). We shall first look at the behaviour of a uniform *solid* cylinder. Its moment of inertia I about an axis through its centre of mass is $\frac{1}{2}MR^2$ (from Table 3.1). The cylinder starts from rest at the origin O, and we want to find how long it will take to reach the point A, where the distance OA is L.

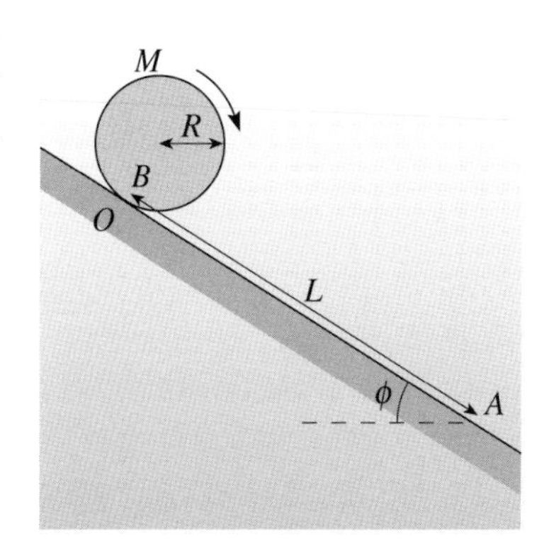

Figure 4.3

Take the situation where the cylinder has rolled as far as X (Figure 4.4), and choose Cartesian unit vectors $\mathbf{i}$ and $\mathbf{j}$ as shown in the figure. Let $OX = x$, and suppose that in rolling from O to X the cylinder has turned through an angle θ, without any slipping having occurred. The distance OX must be equal to the length of the circumference of the cylinder from B to X, where B is the point of contact between the cylinder and the slope at the outset, so

$$R\theta = x. \tag{4.13}$$

We refer to this equation as the **rolling condition**.

When the cylinder is at the point shown in Figure 4.4, its centre of mass has position $x\mathbf{i} + R\mathbf{j}$. Hence the velocity of the centre of mass is $\dot{x}\mathbf{i}$, since R is constant. The cylinder is rotating clockwise at an angular speed of $\dot{\theta}$. Therefore, by Equation (4.12), the cylinder has kinetic energy

$$T = \tfrac{1}{2}M\dot{x}^2 + \tfrac{1}{2}(\tfrac{1}{2}MR^2)\dot{\theta}^2. \tag{4.14}$$

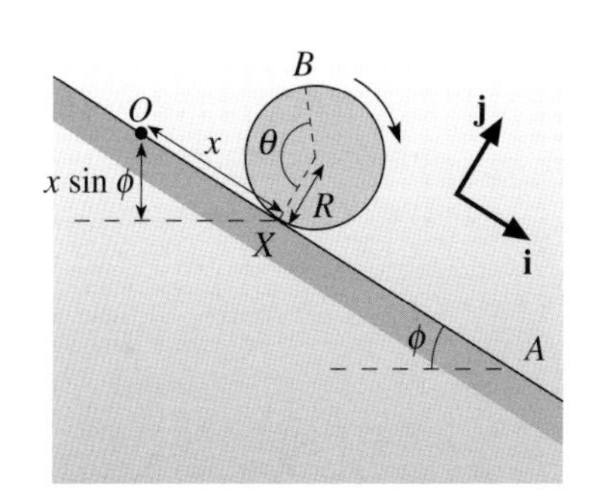

Figure 4.4

From Equation (4.13) we have $R\dot{\theta} = \dot{x}$, and so

$$T = \tfrac{1}{2}M\dot{x}^2 + \tfrac{1}{4}M\dot{x}^2 = \tfrac{3}{4}M\dot{x}^2.$$

Because the cylinder starts from rest at O, its initial kinetic energy is zero. In moving from O to X, the centre of mass of the cylinder descends a vertical distance $x\sin\phi$. So the potential energy of the cylinder is reduced by $Mgx\sin\phi$. Then, if mechanical energy is conserved, we have

$$\tfrac{3}{4}M\dot{x}^2 = Mgx\sin\phi. \tag{4.15}$$

By differentiating each side of this equation, we obtain

$$\tfrac{3}{2}M\dot{x}\ddot{x} = Mg\dot{x}\sin\phi. \tag{4.16}$$

On dividing by $M\dot{x}$ and rearranging, we obtain

The cylinder is not stationary, so $\dot{x}$ is not zero.

$$\ddot{x} = \tfrac{2}{3}g\sin\phi. \tag{4.17}$$

Now, if the cylinder were simply *sliding* down the slope (without friction) rather than rolling down, it would have acceleration $g\sin\phi$. But from Equation (4.17) we see that the rolling cylinder has a lower acceleration than if it were to slide down the slope. This is because, in the case of the rolling object, some of its potential energy has been converted into kinetic energy of rotation, while for a sliding object all the kinetic energy is associated with the linear motion of the centre of mass.

You saw this in *Unit 6*.

*Exercise 4.6

(a) Adapt the foregoing argument to obtain an expression for the acceleration of a hollow cylinder of mass M and radius R when it is rolling down the same slope as considered above. (Model the hollow cylinder as a thin cylindrical shell, all of whose mass is at a distance R from its axis.)

(b) In a 'race' over a distance of $2\,\mathrm{m}$ down a slope angled at $\frac{\pi}{6}$ to the horizontal, how much faster will a solid cylinder travel than a hollow one? Do the masses of the cylinders matter?

We shall now consider the forces on a cylinder as it rolls down a slope without slipping (see Figure 4.5). Since the cylinder starts from rest, it is gaining angular momentum about its centre of mass as it rolls, so there must be some force supplying a torque relative to the centre of mass. This cannot be the weight $\mathbf{W}$ — you saw in Exercise 4.2 that the force of gravity on a body gives a zero torque relative to the centre of mass. Another force on the cylinder is that from the slope: the normal reaction $\mathbf{N}$ of the slope acts through the centre of mass, so again it gives a zero torque about the centre of mass. That leaves only a force between the slope and the cylinder in the direction of the slope, which is supplied by friction. Therefore, we must include friction $\mathbf{F}$ in our model if the model is to have any hope of predicting the motion that is observed.

We shall assume that air resistance is negligible.

If there were no friction between the slope and the cylinder, the cylinder would simply slide down the slope without rolling.

*Exercise 4.7

(a) Use Newton's second law (for the motion of an equivalent particle at the centre of mass) and the equation of relative rotational motion (Equation (4.11)) to find an expression for the acceleration of a solid cylinder of mass M and radius R when it is rolling (without slipping) down a slope of angle ϕ to the horizontal, as in Figure 4.5.

(b) The condition for the cylinder to roll without slipping is $|\mathbf{F}| \leq \mu|\mathbf{N}|$, where μ is the coefficient of static friction. Obtain a condition relating ϕ and μ that must hold if only rolling is to occur.

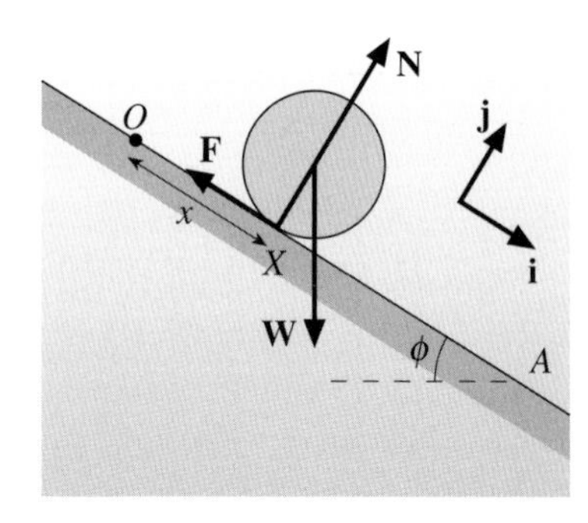

Figure 4.5

In a system where there is friction, you might reasonably expect there to be a loss of mechanical energy. However, this is not necessarily the case. A cornering car needs a sideways frictional force between each tyre and the road to avoid skidding, as you saw in *Unit 20*, but, so long as the car does not skid sideways, there is no loss of mechanical energy due to this force. The point of contact between the tyre and the road does not move in the direction of the frictional force, and thus no mechanical energy is lost to friction. The situation is similar for the rolling cylinder, though this is perhaps more difficult to see. The point on the cylinder that is in contact with the slope at any instant does not move relative to the slope (if it did, the cylinder would skid and the rolling condition would not hold). Hence there is no loss of mechanical energy due to the force $\mathbf{F}$. The truth of this assertion was demonstrated in Exercise 4.7(a), where you saw that the equation for the acceleration of the centre of mass obtained using Newton's second law, and making no assumption about the mechanical energy, is the same as that obtained earlier in this subsection using the assumption that mechanical energy is conserved.

That is, the force $\mathbf{F}$ is normal to the velocity $\dot{\mathbf{r}}$, and so $\mathbf{F} \cdot \dot{\mathbf{r}} = 0$. Therefore the work done by $\mathbf{F}$ is zero (see *Unit 24*).

End-of-section Exercises

Exercise 4.8

(a) During a caber-tossing competition, a competitor runs forward holding the caber (carrying the end X) and stops suddenly. While the competitor is running, the caber is vertical, and the whole caber has the same forward speed, v. When the competitor stops, a large force is exerted at X for a very short time, with the effect that the end X of the caber becomes stationary (see Figure 4.6). Model the caber as a uniform thin rod of length $2L$ and mass m, and assume that the motion of the caber is confined to two dimensions, in the (x, z)-plane in Figure 4.6.

(i) What will be the motion of the caber just after the competitor stops?

(ii) What will be the kinetic energy of the caber just after the competitor stops?

(b) Suppose that, after stopping, the competitor holds the end X of the caber stationary while the caber falls forward under gravity. Assuming that resistive forces are negligible, estimate the angular speed of the caber when it makes an angle θ with the vertical.

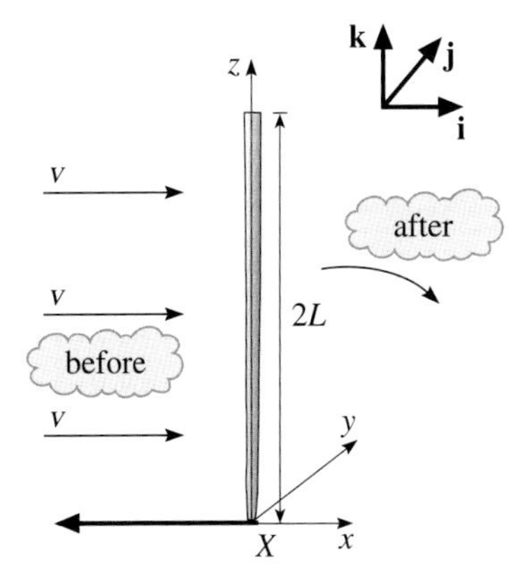

Figure 4.6 This represents the instant of change between the phases shown in Figure 1.6(i) and (ii).

**Exercise 4.9*

An object consists of two solid uniform cylinders, each of radius R and mass M, connected by a solid uniform cylindrical shaft of radius r and mass m. The object is suspended by a cord (of negligible thickness) wrapped around the shaft, and falls vertically under gravity (see Figure 4.7). Assume that the tension force due to the cord acts halfway along the shaft, that resistive forces are negligible, that the axis of rotation of the object is always horizontal, and that the cord unwinds from the shaft without slipping. Find the acceleration of the object in terms of r, R, m and M.

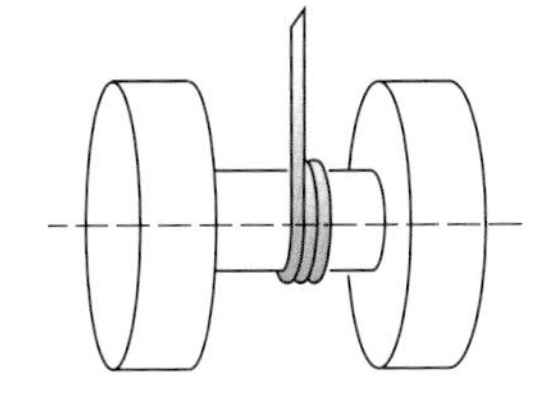

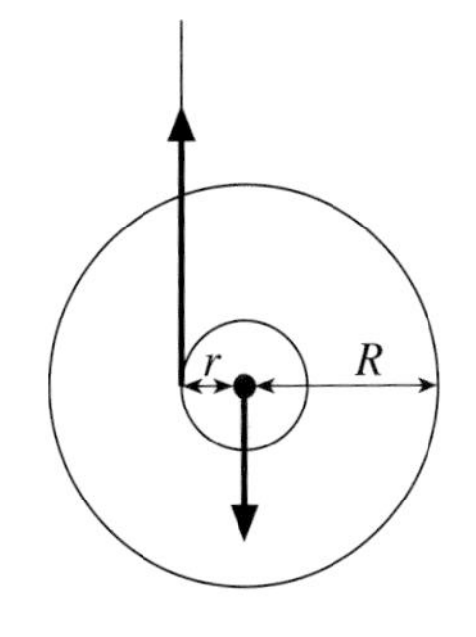

Figure 4.7

Outcomes

After studying this unit you should be able to:

- model the motion of an extended body as the motion of an equivalent particle at the centre of mass combined with the motion of the body relative to its centre of mass;
- find the moments of inertia of rigid bodies of common geometrical shapes about axes of symmetry by reference to Table 3.1, and use the parallel-axes theorem to find the moments of inertia of such bodies about other axes;
- determine the angular momentum and kinetic energy of a rigid body rotating about an axis whose direction is fixed, using the appropriate decomposition theorem if necessary;
- for an extended body subjected to an impact at a particular point, use conservation of angular momentum about that point to relate the motions of the body before and after the impact;
- give the equation of rotational motion for a rigid body rotating about a fixed axis, or the equation of relative rotational motion for a rigid body rotating about an axis whose direction is fixed;
- use the rolling condition to relate the translational and rotational motions of a body rolling across a plane surface without slipping;
- apply the various theoretical results established in this unit, including the torque law and the various decomposition theorems.

Solutions to the exercises

In all the solutions in this unit we work in SI units.

Section 1

1.1 **(a)** To determine the time of flight, t, we need only consider the vertical motion of the centre of mass. The centre of mass starts with an upward velocity component of $4\cos\frac{\pi}{6} = 2\sqrt{3}\,\text{m}\,\text{s}^{-1}$, but is subject to a constant acceleration of $g = 9.81\,\text{m}\,\text{s}^{-2}$ downwards, and it descends from an initial height (above ground level) of $3 - 1.2\cos\frac{\pi}{3} = 2.4\,\text{m}$ to a final height of $1.2\,\text{m}$. Hence, from the constant-acceleration equation,

$$-1.2 = 2\sqrt{3}t - \tfrac{1}{2} \times 9.81t^2.$$

Solving for t, and rejecting the negative root, we obtain $t = 0.96$. So the gymnast is in flight for about 0.96 s.

(b) The gymnast rotates through $\frac{5\pi}{3}$ (from Example 1.2(b)) in approximately 0.96 s, and therefore has an angular speed of $5\pi/(3 \times 0.96) \simeq 5.45\,\text{rad}\,\text{s}^{-1}$. Suppose his moment of inertia about an axis through his centre of mass is I_T in the tuck position, and I_E when fully extended. Just after leaving the bar, he is fully extended and has angular speed $\frac{10}{3}$ rad s^{-1} (from Example 1.2(a)). Now, angular momentum is given by $I\omega$, where I is the moment of inertia and ω is the angular speed. Since angular momentum is conserved, we have

$$I_E\tfrac{10}{3} = I_T 5.45.$$

Hence $I_T/I_E = 10/(3 \times 5.45) \simeq 0.61$. So adopting a tuck position must reduce the moment of inertia by at least 40%, if it is to allow the gymnast to complete the dismount. (In practice, the reduction in the moment of inertia would need to be greater than this, since the gymnast will need time to get into and out of the tuck position.)

1.2 **(a)** In the first phase, the whole caber gains a uniform horizontal speed. There is no rotation.

In the second phase, the bottom end of the caber is stationary. The upper part of the caber retains forward momentum. The result is to turn the forward motion into rotation about the bottom end of the caber. As the caber topples forwards, gravity supplies a torque about the hands, increasing the rate of rotation.

In the third phase, as the competitor pushes upwards, the resulting upward force applies a torque about the centre of mass, further increasing the rotation of the caber until the moment of release. (By waiting for the caber to rotate forward in the second phase before applying this force, the competitor increases the distance of the centre of mass from the line of action of the upward force that he applies, so increasing the torque.)

In the fourth phase, the centre of mass moves like a projectile. If resistive forces are ignored, it will follow a parabolic path and the angular speed about the centre of mass will be constant.

In the final phase, the end of the caber strikes the ground and becomes stationary (assuming that it does not skid or bounce). The caber will, however, retain some forward rotation about the end that hits the ground. If it lands as illustrated in Figure 1.6(v), with the upper end yet to reach the vertical, gravity will provide a torque that slows this rotation. Whether or not the caber will rotate past the vertical, ensuring the toss is successful, will depend on the angle at which the caber lands, and on how much angular momentum it has from the preceding phase.

(b) As the centre of mass of a tapered caber is nearer to the thicker end of the caber than to the thinner end being held by the competitor, in the third phase the centre of mass will be further from the line of action of the force (applied by the competitor) than if the caber was not tapered, so increasing the applied torque about the centre of mass.

For a tapered caber, the centre of mass will have further to fall during the fourth phase. This will increase the time of flight, and hence increase the angle through which the caber rotates while in flight.

Suppose that the caber strikes the ground, thicker end first, before it has rotated past the vertical. Then, in the fifth phase, the centre of mass will be closer to the ground than if the caber were symmetric, thereby reducing the torque that is slowing down the caber's rotation. Consequently the chances of a tapered caber reaching the vertical are greater.

Section 2

2.1 The pairs of forces shown in Figure 2.1(a), (b) and (c) satisfy Equation (2.1). Those in Figure 2.1(d) do not.

2.2 The pair of forces that satisfy Equation (2.1), but don't satisfy Newton's third law, is in Figure 2.1(c).

(The forces in Figures 2.1(a) and 2.1(b) satisfy Newton's third law: they are opposite in direction and act in the same straight line. Figure 2.1(d) does not show forces satisfying Newton's third law: although they act in the same straight line they are *not* in opposite directions.)

2.3 Differentiating the given expression for $\mathbf{r}$, we have

$$\dot{\mathbf{r}} = -6\sin(2t)\mathbf{i} + 8\cos(2t)\mathbf{j}.$$

Then at $t = 0$, the expressions for $\mathbf{r}$ and $\dot{\mathbf{r}}$ reduce to

$$\mathbf{r} = 3\mathbf{i} + 5\mathbf{k},$$
$$\dot{\mathbf{r}} = 8\mathbf{j}.$$

So the angular momentum of the particle about O at $t = 0$ is

$$\mathbf{r} \times m\dot{\mathbf{r}} = (3\mathbf{i} + 5\mathbf{k}) \times 20(8\mathbf{j}) = 160(3\mathbf{k} - 5\mathbf{i}).$$

2.4 **(a)** The angular speed ω of the particle is v/R, and the angular velocity $\boldsymbol{\omega}$ is $(v/R)\mathbf{k}$.

(b) By definition,

$$\boldsymbol{l} = \mathbf{r} \times m\dot{\mathbf{r}}. \tag{S.1}$$

Now, using ω as defined in part (a), we have

$$\mathbf{r} = R(\cos(\omega t)\mathbf{i} + \sin(\omega t)\mathbf{j}),$$

and therefore (since ω is constant)

$$\dot{\mathbf{r}} = R\omega(-\sin(\omega t)\mathbf{i} + \cos(\omega t)\mathbf{j}).$$

Then, substituting for $\mathbf{r}$ and $\dot{\mathbf{r}}$ in Equation (S.1), we find

$$\begin{aligned}\boldsymbol{l} &= R(\cos(\omega t)\mathbf{i} + \sin(\omega t)\mathbf{j}) \times mR\omega(-\sin(\omega t)\mathbf{i} + \cos(\omega t)\mathbf{j}) \\ &= mR^2\omega(\cos^2(\omega t)\mathbf{k} + \sin^2(\omega t)\mathbf{k}) \\ &= mR^2\omega\mathbf{k}. \end{aligned} \tag{S.2}$$

(c) For a single particle, the moment of inertia is mr^2 (from *Unit 25*), where r is the distance of the particle from the relevant axis. In this case, $r = R$, so

$$I = mR^2. \tag{S.3}$$

(d) Substituting into Equation (S.2) from Equation (S.3), and writing $\boldsymbol{\omega} = \omega\mathbf{k}$, we have

$$\boldsymbol{l} = mR^2\omega\mathbf{k} = I\boldsymbol{\omega}.$$

2.5 From the definition, the particle has angular momentum $\boldsymbol{l} = \mathbf{r} \times m\dot{\mathbf{r}}$, where $\mathbf{r}$ gives the particle's position relative to O. Since the velocity $\dot{\mathbf{r}}$ of the particle is constant, the particle will follow a straight line path, as illustrated in the figure below. The position vector $\mathbf{r}$ is varying, but wherever the particle is on the path, the vector $\mathbf{r} \times \dot{\mathbf{r}}$ will have magnitude $a|\dot{\mathbf{r}}|$, where a is the perpendicular distance from O to the particle's path, and direction normal to the plane shown in the figure (and out of the page in the case illustrated). Thus the angular momentum is constant, since both a and $|\dot{\mathbf{r}}|$ are constant and its direction is constant.

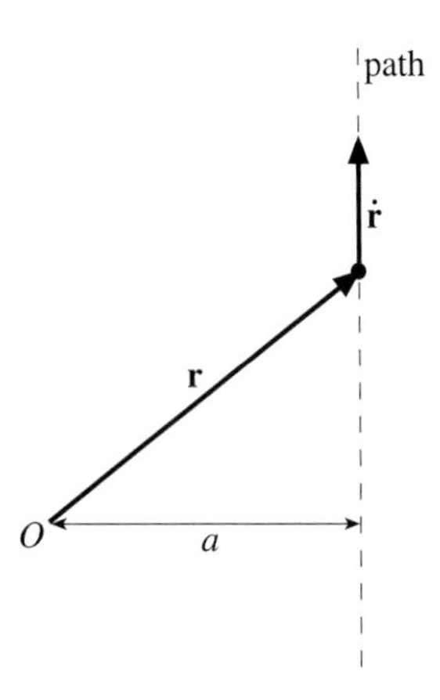

2.6 **(a)** As $\mathbf{r} = x\mathbf{i} + y\mathbf{j}$, it follows that

$$\begin{aligned}\mathbf{r} \times \dot{\mathbf{r}} &= (x\mathbf{i} + y\mathbf{j}) \times (\dot{x}\mathbf{i} + \dot{y}\mathbf{j}) \\ &= x\dot{y}\mathbf{k} - y\dot{x}\mathbf{k} = (x\dot{y} - y\dot{x})\mathbf{k}.\end{aligned}$$

(b) The angular momentum of the particle about O is given by

$$\begin{aligned}\boldsymbol{l} &= \mathbf{r} \times m\dot{\mathbf{r}} = m(\mathbf{r} \times \dot{\mathbf{r}}) \\ &= m(x\dot{y} - y\dot{x})\mathbf{k}, \end{aligned} \tag{S.4}$$

from part (a). But

$$x = r\cos\theta, \quad y = r\sin\theta.$$

Hence

$$\begin{aligned}\dot{x} &= \dot{r}\cos\theta - r\dot{\theta}\sin\theta, \\ \dot{y} &= \dot{r}\sin\theta + r\dot{\theta}\cos\theta.\end{aligned}$$

Then

$$\begin{aligned}x\dot{y} - y\dot{x} &= r\cos\theta(\dot{r}\sin\theta + r\dot{\theta}\cos\theta) \\ &\quad - r\sin\theta(\dot{r}\cos\theta - r\dot{\theta}\sin\theta) \\ &= r\dot{r}\cos\theta\sin\theta + r^2\dot{\theta}\cos^2\theta \\ &\quad - r\dot{r}\cos\theta\sin\theta + r^2\dot{\theta}\sin^2\theta \\ &= r^2\dot{\theta}. \end{aligned} \tag{S.5}$$

So, substituting from Equation (S.5) for $x\dot{y} - y\dot{x}$ in Equation (S.4), we find that the angular momentum of the particle about O is

$$\boldsymbol{l} = mr^2\dot{\theta}\mathbf{k}.$$

2.7 In Example 2.1(b)(i), we found

$$\dot{\mathbf{r}} = -R\omega\sin(\omega t)\mathbf{i} + R\omega\cos(\omega t)\mathbf{j}.$$

Differentiating this gives the acceleration

$$\ddot{\mathbf{r}} = -R\omega^2\cos(\omega t)\mathbf{i} - R\omega^2\sin(\omega t)\mathbf{j}. \tag{S.6}$$

The total force on the particle is $\mathbf{F} = m\ddot{\mathbf{r}}$. So, substituting for $\ddot{\mathbf{r}}$ from Equation (S.6), we have

$$\mathbf{F} = -mR\omega^2(\cos(\omega t)\mathbf{i} + \sin(\omega t)\mathbf{j}). \tag{S.7}$$

Now, $\boldsymbol{\Gamma} = \mathbf{r} \times \mathbf{F}$, which, on substituting for $\mathbf{r}$ from Equation (2.7) and for $\mathbf{F}$ from Equation (S.7), becomes

$$\begin{aligned}\boldsymbol{\Gamma} &= (R\cos(\omega t)\mathbf{i} + R\sin(\omega t)\mathbf{j} + h\mathbf{k}) \\ &\quad \times (-mR\omega^2)(\cos(\omega t)\mathbf{i} + \sin(\omega t)\mathbf{j}) \\ &= -mR^2\omega^2(\cos(\omega t)\sin(\omega t)\mathbf{k} - \cos(\omega t)\sin(\omega t)\mathbf{k}) \\ &\quad - mhR\omega^2(\cos(\omega t)\mathbf{j} - \sin(\omega t)\mathbf{i}) \\ &= mhR\omega^2(\sin(\omega t)\mathbf{i} - \cos(\omega t)\mathbf{j}).\end{aligned}$$

Comparing this with Equation (2.10), we see that we have obtained the same expression for $\boldsymbol{\Gamma}$.

2.8 **(a)** From Equation (S.2), the angular momentum, about O, of the particle at A is $m_1a^2\boldsymbol{\omega}$, while the angular momentum, about O, of the particle at B is $m_2b^2\boldsymbol{\omega}$. So the total angular momentum of the two-particle system modelling the roundabout is $m_1a^2\boldsymbol{\omega} + m_2b^2\boldsymbol{\omega} = I\boldsymbol{\omega}$, where $I = m_1a^2 + m_2b^2$.

(b) Since the force at C is applied in a horizontal direction at right angles to OC, it exerts a torque about O of $cF\mathbf{k}$. There are other external forces on the system that need to be taken into account: the force at O exerted by the fixed spindle, and the weight of each of the two particles. The force from the spindle has zero torque about O. Each weight exerts a non-zero torque about O, but the condition $m_1a = m_2b$ ensures that the torques exerted by the two weights are equal and opposite, so their sum is zero. Hence the total external torque on the two-particle system is $cF\mathbf{k}$.

Then, as the total angular momentum of the system is $I\boldsymbol{\omega}$ (from part (a)), the torque law applied to the system consisting of the two particles at A and B gives

$$\frac{d}{dt}(I\boldsymbol{\omega}) = cF\mathbf{k}.$$

Because I is a constant and $\boldsymbol{\omega} = \omega\mathbf{k}$, this equation can be rewritten as

$$I\dot{\omega}\mathbf{k} = cF\mathbf{k},$$

which simplifies to

$$I\dot{\omega} = cF. \quad \text{(S.8)}$$

(c) From Equation (S.8),

$$\dot{\omega} = \frac{cF}{I}.$$

Now $c = 1.5$, $F = 315$, and I can be calculated from

$$\begin{aligned} I &= m_1a^2 + m_2b^2 \\ &= (45 \times 1^2) + (60 \times 0.75^2) = 78.75. \end{aligned}$$

So, on substituting, we have

$$\dot{\omega} = \frac{1.5 \times 315}{78.75} = 6\,\text{rad}\,\text{s}^{-2}.$$

Rotations at 0.5 revolutions per second require an angular speed of $\pi\,\text{rad}\,\text{s}^{-1}$. A force of magnitude 315 N increases the angular speed from 0 to $6\,\text{rad}\,\text{s}^{-1}$ in one second, so to reach an angular speed of $\pi\,\text{rad}\,\text{s}^{-1}$ starting from rest will take $\frac{\pi}{6} \simeq 0.5\,\text{s}$.

2.9 The only force assumed to be acting on each star is the gravitational force due to the other star, which is an internal force. Hence the total external force acting upon the two-particle system is zero, and consequently so is the external torque. It follows from the torque law that the angular momentum of the system must be conserved, and so its magnitude l is constant.

Suppose that the distances of the stars from their common centre of mass, O, are d_1 and d_2, respectively, and that the angular velocity of each star about O is $\boldsymbol{\omega} = \omega\mathbf{k}$. (Since the two stars are rotating as though tied together by a rigid rod, their angular velocities must be the same.) Then, from Equation (2.6), the angular momentum of star 1 is $m_1d_1^2\omega\mathbf{k}$ and that of star 2 is $m_2d_2^2\omega\mathbf{k}$. The total angular momentum $\boldsymbol{l}$ of the system is

$$m_1d_1^2\omega\mathbf{k} + m_2d_2^2\omega\mathbf{k} = (m_1d_1^2 + m_2d_2^2)\omega\mathbf{k}.$$

By an argument similar to that used in Example 2.2, this must be equal to

$$\frac{m_1m_2}{m_1+m_2}d^2\omega\mathbf{k}.$$

Therefore

$$l = \frac{m_1m_2}{m_1+m_2}d^2\omega,$$

and this can be rearranged to give

$$\omega = \frac{m_1+m_2}{m_1m_2d^2}l.$$

Then, the period of rotation of the system is

$$\frac{2\pi}{\omega} = \frac{2\pi m_1m_2d^2}{(m_1+m_2)l}.$$

2.10 Apply the torque law about the point X. Since all the external forces are applied at X, the total external torque about X is zero. Hence the rate of change of angular momentum about X is zero, i.e. the angular momentum of the system *about* X is constant.

2.11 **(a)** From Equation (2.9), we have

$$\begin{aligned} \boldsymbol{l} &= mR^2\omega\mathbf{k} - mhR\omega(\sin(\omega t)\mathbf{j} + \cos(\omega t)\mathbf{i})) \\ &= mR^2\omega\mathbf{k} - mRh\omega\mathbf{e}_r. \end{aligned}$$

(b) (i) The angular momentum of the whole body is given by $\sum_{i=1}^{n}(m_iR^2\omega\mathbf{k} - m_iRh_i\omega\mathbf{e}_r)$, where m_i is the mass of particle i and h_i is its height above the (x,y)-plane. Now R and ω are the same for each particle in the body, so $\sum_{i=1}^{n} m_iR^2\omega\mathbf{k} = MR^2\omega\mathbf{k}$, where M is the sum of the masses m_i of all the particles forming the body, i.e. M is the mass of the body. Summing the terms $m_iRh_i\omega\mathbf{e}_r$ is less straightforward, because different particles in the body have different heights h_i, but we obtain $\omega\mathbf{e}_rR\sum_{i=1}^{n} m_ih_i$. Suppose $R\sum_{i=1}^{n} m_ih_i$ is denoted by A. Now R is positive, each m_i is positive and h_i is zero for a particle at the lowest point on the body, but is greater than zero everywhere else, so A is positive. Also R and each m_i and h_i are constant, and hence so is A. Therefore the angular momentum $\boldsymbol{l}$ of the whole body is

$$\boldsymbol{l} = MR^2\omega\mathbf{k} - A\omega\mathbf{e}_r, \quad \text{(S.9)}$$

where $A > 0$ is constant.

(ii) None of M, R, ω, $\mathbf{k}$ or A varies with time, but the vector $\mathbf{e}_r$ does (because its direction is changing). Hence, differentiating Equation (S.9) with respect to time yields

$$\dot{\boldsymbol{l}} = -A\omega\dot{\mathbf{e}}_r. \quad \text{(S.10)}$$

Now, $\mathbf{e}_r = \cos(\omega t)\mathbf{i} + \sin(\omega t)\mathbf{j}$, so

$$\dot{\mathbf{e}}_r = -\omega\sin(\omega t)\mathbf{i} + \omega\cos(\omega t)\mathbf{j},$$

which lies in the (x,y)-plane and is normal to $\mathbf{e}_r$ (since its dot product with $\mathbf{e}_r$ is 0). Also, for each particle the motion is circular, so $\dot{\mathbf{e}}_r$ is tangential to the motion, as you saw in *Unit 20*.

By the torque law, the total torque on the body is $\boldsymbol{\Gamma} = \dot{\boldsymbol{l}}$. Since each of A and ω is a positive constant, we see from Equation (S.10) that $\dot{\boldsymbol{l}}$, and therefore $\boldsymbol{\Gamma}$, is a non-zero (negative) multiple of $\dot{\mathbf{e}}_r$. Thus the body must be subject to a non-zero torque in a direction tangential to the motion.

(c) (i) Since the skater's centre of mass is following a circle at constant angular speed, its acceleration is towards the z-axis, i.e. in the direction of $-\mathbf{e}_r$. Thus, by Newton's second law, the total external force $\mathbf{F}$ on the skater must be in this direction.

(ii) Let $\mathbf{W}$ be the skater's weight, and let the force exerted on her skates by the ice have component forces $\mathbf{N}$ vertically upwards and $\mathbf{R}$ horizontally. So $\mathbf{F} = \mathbf{W} + \mathbf{N} + \mathbf{R}$. From part (c)(i), the vertical component of $\mathbf{F}$ is zero, so $\mathbf{W} + \mathbf{N} = \mathbf{0}$. If the skater is perfectly vertical, $\mathbf{N}$ and $\mathbf{W}$ have exactly the same line of action, so the sum of their torques must also be zero. Since $\mathbf{F}$ must be in the direction of $-\mathbf{e}_r$, the component of $\mathbf{R}$ normal to $\mathbf{e}_r$ must be zero. Therefore if O is the centre of the circle followed by the skater's feet, the line of action of $\mathbf{R}$ passes through O, and hence $\mathbf{R}$ has zero torque about O. This means that if the skater is vertical, the total torque about O will be zero. But part (b) showed that a system of this kind must be subject to a non-zero torque in the tangential direction! So it is impossible for the skater to follow a circle while remaining vertical.

To follow a circle, the skater needs to adopt a position in which there is a non-zero torque in the tangential direction. To do this, she must lean into the circle. This will mean that $\mathbf{W}$ and $\mathbf{N}$ do not have the same line of action, and so they provide a non-zero torque.

Section 3

3.1 **(a)** The z-component of the total torque on the roundabout is $1.5(100) - 0.1(c\omega)$.

The moment of inertia of the roundabout (from Example 3.1) is $\frac{1}{2}(250)(1.2)^2 = 180$, so, from Equation (3.4), the equation of rotational motion for the roundabout is

$$180\dot{\omega} = 150 - 0.1c\omega. \qquad \text{(S.11)}$$

(b) Employing methods from *Unit 2* (either separation of variables or the integrating factor method can be used in this case), we can obtain the general solution of Equation (S.11), which is

$$\omega = Ae^{-ct/1800} + \frac{1500}{c}.$$

Since the roundabout is at rest at the outset, we have $\omega = 0$ at $t = 0$. The particular solution satisfying this initial condition is

$$\omega = \frac{1500}{c}\left(1 - e^{-ct/1800}\right). \qquad \text{(S.12)}$$

(c) If pushing continues indefinitely, Equation (S.12) implies that the rotational speed will increase to almost $1500/c$ as the exponential term becomes negligible, and it will then become steady. For $c = 10$, this maximum angular speed is $150\,\text{rad}\,\text{s}^{-1}$. To follow the roundabout at that speed, the pusher would need to be travelling at $1.5(150) = 225\,\text{m}\,\text{s}^{-1}$. This is not very likely!

3.2 The moment of inertia, I_M, of the mace about AB is the sum of the moment of inertia, I_S, of the sphere about AB and the moment of inertia, I_R, of the rod about AB. Using Table 3.1, in conjunction with the parallel-axes theorem, we have

$$I_\text{S} = \tfrac{2}{5}Mr^2 + M(d+r)^2,$$

$$I_\text{R} = \tfrac{1}{4}mR^2 + \tfrac{1}{12}md^2 + m\left(\tfrac{1}{2}d\right)^2$$
$$= \tfrac{1}{4}mR^2 + \tfrac{1}{3}md^2,$$

and so

$$I_\text{M} = I_\text{S} + I_\text{R}$$
$$= \tfrac{2}{5}Mr^2 + M(d+r)^2 + \tfrac{1}{4}mR^2 + \tfrac{1}{3}md^2.$$

3.3 The kinetic energy of the baton is given by $\frac{1}{2}I\omega^2$, where I is the moment of inertia of the baton about the axis of rotation and ω is the angular speed. Now, the moment of inertia of the baton is the sum of those of the cylindrical rod and the two spheres. The cylinder is rotating about its centre of mass, and the moment of inertia (from Table 3.1) is

$$\tfrac{1}{4}(0.1)(0.02)^2 + \tfrac{1}{12}(0.1)(0.8)^2 \simeq 0.005\,34\,\text{kg}\,\text{m}^2.$$

Each sphere has its centre of mass 0.45 m from the centre of the baton. To find the moment of inertia of a sphere about the axis of rotation, we find the moment of inertia about its centre of mass from Table 3.1 and use the parallel-axes theorem, to obtain

$$\tfrac{2}{5}(0.25)(0.05)^2 + 0.25(0.45)^2 \simeq 0.0509\,\text{kg}\,\text{m}^2.$$

So the moment of inertia I of the baton is

$$0.005\,34 + 2(0.0509) \simeq 0.1071\,\text{kg}\,\text{m}^2.$$

The angular speed ω of the baton is $2\pi\,\text{rad}\,\text{s}^{-1}$. Hence the kinetic energy of the baton is

$$\tfrac{1}{2}I\omega^2 = \tfrac{1}{2}(0.1071)(2\pi)^2 \simeq 2.11\ \text{J}.$$

3.4 **(a)** **(i)** As you saw in Example 3.2, when the man is 0.2 m from the centre of the roundabout, the angular speed of the roundabout is $\omega_1 = \pi\,\text{rad}\,\text{s}^{-1}$. The moment of inertia of the combined system under these circumstances is $I_1 = 176\,\text{kg}\,\text{m}^2$. So the kinetic energy of the system is

$$\tfrac{1}{2}I_1\omega_1^2 = \tfrac{1}{2} \times 176\pi^2 \simeq 869\,\text{J}.$$

(ii) Similarly, when the man is 1 m from the centre, the angular speed is $\omega_2 \simeq 2.19\,\text{rad}\,\text{s}^{-1}$. The moment of inertia of the combined system is $I_2 = 252.8\,\text{kg}\,\text{m}^2$. So the kinetic energy of the system is

$$\tfrac{1}{2}I_2\omega_2^2 \simeq \tfrac{1}{2} \times 252.8(2.19)^2 \simeq 606\,\text{J}.$$

(b) When the man moves inwards, the kinetic energy of the system *increases*, from about 606 to about 869 joules.

3.5 The kinetic energy of the body is given by $\frac{1}{2}I\omega^2$, where I is the moment of inertia of the body about the axis of rotation. By the parallel-axes theorem,

$$I = I_G + MR^2.$$

The centre of mass is following a circle of radius R at angular speed ω, so $R\omega = v$, and hence the kinetic energy of the body is

$$\tfrac{1}{2}I\omega^2 = \tfrac{1}{2}(I_G + MR^2)\omega^2$$
$$= \tfrac{1}{2}I_G\omega^2 + \tfrac{1}{2}M(R\omega)^2$$
$$= \tfrac{1}{2}I_G\omega^2 + \tfrac{1}{2}Mv^2.$$

3.6 The diver's centre of mass starts at a height L above the board. In the position at which the diver lets go of the board, the vertical displacement (above the board) of her centre of mass is $L\cos\alpha$, so the potential energy has decreased by

$$mgL(1 - \cos\alpha).$$

Let I_O be the moment of inertia of the diver about O. Then the kinetic energy at the time of letting go of the board is $\frac{1}{2}I_O\omega^2$.

The kinetic energy at the outset is zero, as the diver is at rest, so by the conservation of mechanical energy, we have

$$\tfrac{1}{2}I_O\omega^2 = mgL(1-\cos\alpha).$$

The parallel-axes theorem gives

$$I_O = I_G + mL^2.$$

Hence

$$\omega = \sqrt{\frac{2mgL(1-\cos\alpha)}{I_G+mL^2}}.$$

3.7 **(a)** From Figure 3.17, we have

$$x = -L\sin\theta, \quad y = L\cos\theta.$$

Differentiating with respect to t (and remembering that θ is varying with t), we obtain

$$\dot{x} = -L\dot{\theta}\cos\theta, \quad \dot{y} = -L\dot{\theta}\sin\theta.$$

Differentiating again with respect to t gives

$$\begin{cases} \ddot{x} = L\dot{\theta}^2\sin\theta - L\ddot{\theta}\cos\theta, \\ \ddot{y} = -L\dot{\theta}^2\cos\theta - L\ddot{\theta}\sin\theta. \end{cases} \qquad \text{(S.13)}$$

(b) The diver is rotating about a fixed axis through O. The component of the total external torque about O in the direction of the axis of rotation (the $\mathbf{k}$-direction in Figure 3.17) is $mgL\sin\theta$. So, from Equation (3.4), the equation of rotational motion about O for the diver is

$$I_O\ddot{\theta} = mgL\sin\theta.$$

(c) As in Exercise 3.6, the principle of conservation of mechanical energy gives

$$\tfrac{1}{2}I_O\dot{\theta}^2 = mgL(1-\cos\theta).$$

Differentiating this equation with respect to t gives

$$\tfrac{1}{2}I_O(2\dot{\theta}\ddot{\theta}) = mgL\dot{\theta}\sin\theta,$$

which simplifies to

$$I_O\ddot{\theta} = mgL\sin\theta,$$

the equation of rotational motion derived in part (b).

(d) (i) By applying Newton's second law, we obtain

$$R_1\mathbf{i} + R_2\mathbf{j} - mg\mathbf{j} = m\ddot{\mathbf{r}} = m(\ddot{x}\mathbf{i} + \ddot{y}\mathbf{j}).$$

Resolving in the x- and y-directions gives

$$\begin{cases} R_1 = m\ddot{x}, \\ R_2 - mg = m\ddot{y}. \end{cases} \qquad \text{(S.14)}$$

(ii) Substituting from Equation (S.13) in Equation (S.14) for $\ddot{x}$ and $\ddot{y}$ gives

$$R_1 = m(L\dot{\theta}^2\sin\theta - L\ddot{\theta}\cos\theta), \qquad \text{(S.15)}$$

$$R_2 = mg + m(-L\dot{\theta}^2\cos\theta - L\ddot{\theta}\sin\theta).$$

(e) (i) From parts (b) and (c), we have

$$I_O\ddot{\theta} = mgL\sin\theta,$$

$$\tfrac{1}{2}I_O\dot{\theta}^2 = mgL(1-\cos\theta).$$

Then, from Equation (S.15), we obtain

$$\begin{aligned} R_1 &= mL(\dot{\theta}^2\sin\theta - \ddot{\theta}\cos\theta) \\ &= mL\left(\frac{2mgL}{I_O}(1-\cos\theta)\sin\theta - \frac{mgL}{I_O}\sin\theta\cos\theta\right) \\ &= mg\frac{mL^2}{I_O}\sin\theta(2-3\cos\theta). \end{aligned} \qquad \text{(S.16)}$$

(ii) From Equation (S.16) we have $R_1 = 0$ when $\sin\theta = 0$, with the only solution in the given range $0 \le \theta \le \frac{\pi}{2}$ being $\theta = 0$, or when $2 - 3\cos\theta = 0$, i.e. when $3\cos\theta = 2$, with the only solution in the given range being $\theta = \arccos\frac{2}{3}$ (which is 0.8411, or about 48°).

(f) From Table 3.1, the moment of inertia of a thin rod of length $2L$ and mass m about an axis through its centre of mass is $\frac{1}{12}m(2L)^2 = \frac{1}{3}mL^2$. So, for this model of the diver, using the parallel-axes theorem, $I_O = \frac{1}{3}mL^2 + mL^2 = \frac{4}{3}mL^2$.

Then, from Equation (S.16), we obtain

$$R_1 = \tfrac{3}{4}mg\sin\theta(2-3\cos\theta). \qquad \text{(S.17)}$$

At $\theta = \frac{\pi}{2}$, the right-hand side of Equation (S.17) is $\frac{3}{2}mg$. Therefore, if the diver were still in contact with the board when $\theta = \frac{\pi}{2}$, she would need to be exerting a horizontal force on the board equal in magnitude to R_1 (and opposite in direction), i.e. about 50% greater than the magnitude of her weight.

(g) Equation (S.16) shows that $R_1 < 0$ for small values of θ. The board is 'pushing' (horizontally) on the diver's hands, and, by Newton's third law, this corresponds to the diver pushing on the board. However, for $\theta > \arccos\frac{2}{3}$, we need $R_1 > 0$. We are assuming that the diver cannot pull on the board to provide a force in this direction, so the diver is unlikely to be able to rotate past $\arccos\frac{2}{3}$. The diver is therefore likely to lose contact with the board when θ is approximately $\arccos\frac{2}{3}$ (i.e. about 48°).

Section 4

4.1 Start from the definition of the total external torque relative to the fixed origin O:

$$\mathbf{\Gamma} = \sum_{i=1}^{n}\mathbf{r}_i \times \mathbf{F}_i.$$

Now use Equation (4.1) to substitute for $\mathbf{r}_i$, to yield

$$\mathbf{\Gamma} = \sum_{i=1}^{n}(\mathbf{R} + \mathbf{r}_i^{\text{rel}}) \times \mathbf{F}_i.$$

Expanding the bracket gives

$$\mathbf{\Gamma} = \sum_{i=1}^{n}\mathbf{R} \times \mathbf{F}_i + \sum_{i=1}^{n}\mathbf{r}_i^{\text{rel}} \times \mathbf{F}_i.$$

The first term on the right-hand side simplifies because $\mathbf{R}$ is independent of i, whilst the second term is by definition the torque relative to the centre of mass (Equation (4.4)), so

$$\mathbf{\Gamma} = \mathbf{R} \times \left(\sum_{i=1}^{n}\mathbf{F}_i\right) + \mathbf{\Gamma}^{\text{rel}}.$$

The bracketed term is the total force $\mathbf{F}$ acting on the system, so we obtain

$$\mathbf{\Gamma} = \mathbf{R} \times \mathbf{F} + \mathbf{\Gamma}^{\text{rel}},$$

as required.

4.2 **(a)** The total external force on the ith particle is $\mathbf{F}_i = cm_i\mathbf{k}$. Now, from Equation (4.4),

$$\boldsymbol{\Gamma}^{\text{rel}} = \sum_{i=1}^{n} \mathbf{r}_i^{\text{rel}} \times \mathbf{F}_i = \sum_{i=1}^{n} \mathbf{r}_i^{\text{rel}} \times cm_i\mathbf{k} = \left(\sum_{i=1}^{n} m_i\mathbf{r}_i^{\text{rel}}\right) \times c\mathbf{k};$$

but, from Equation (4.3), $\sum_{i=1}^{n} m_i\mathbf{r}_i^{\text{rel}} = \mathbf{0}$, so

$$\boldsymbol{\Gamma}^{\text{rel}} = \mathbf{0} \times c\mathbf{k} = \mathbf{0}.$$

Then, from the torque law relative to the centre of mass (Equation (4.8)), $\boldsymbol{l}^{\text{rel}}$ is constant.

(b) If we model the body in flight as a system of particles, then each particle of mass m_i is subject only to a force $\mathbf{F}_i = m_i g\mathbf{k}$, where $\mathbf{k}$ is a unit vector pointing vertically downwards. So the only external force on each particle has the form $cm_i\mathbf{k}$, where $c = g$ is a constant, and hence the boxed result applies, i.e. the angular momentum of the body relative to the centre of mass is conserved.

4.3 If the external force on the ith particle is acting towards the origin, it must act along the line of the position vector $\mathbf{r}_i$ of the particle, so $\mathbf{F}_i = c_i\mathbf{r}_i$, for some scalar c_i. The external torque on this particle about the origin is

$$\boldsymbol{\Gamma}_i = \mathbf{r}_i \times \mathbf{F}_i = \mathbf{r}_i \times c_i\mathbf{r}_i = \mathbf{0}.$$

Then, summing over all particles, $\boldsymbol{\Gamma} = \mathbf{0}$. Hence, from the torque decomposition theorem (Equation (4.7)),

$$\mathbf{R} \times \mathbf{F} + \boldsymbol{\Gamma}^{\text{rel}} = \boldsymbol{\Gamma} = \mathbf{0}.$$

Thus $\boldsymbol{\Gamma}^{\text{rel}} = -\mathbf{R} \times \mathbf{F}$, as required.

4.4 **(a)** The model of the baton is identical to that used in Exercise 3.3, and the angular speed (about the centre of mass) is the same as there. So the kinetic energy due to the rotation of the baton is 2.11 J as there. The total mass of the baton is 0.6 kg, and the speed of the centre of mass is $5\,\text{m}\,\text{s}^{-1}$. Hence the kinetic energy of an equivalent particle at the centre of mass is

$$\tfrac{1}{2}(0.6)5^2 = 7.5\,\text{J}.$$

Therefore, by Equation (4.12), the total kinetic energy of the baton is $7.5 + 2.11 = 9.61\,\text{J}$.

(b) An equivalent particle at the centre of mass of the baton would be moving vertically upwards. Since the centre of mass is vertically above O, this means that the position vector $\mathbf{R}$ of the centre of mass and the velocity $\dot{\mathbf{R}}$ of the centre of mass have the same direction. Hence $\mathbf{R} \times \dot{\mathbf{R}} = \mathbf{0}$. So the angular momentum of an equivalent particle at the centre of mass is

$$\mathbf{R} \times M\dot{\mathbf{R}} = M(\mathbf{R} \times \dot{\mathbf{R}}) = \mathbf{0}.$$

Therefore, by the angular momentum decomposition theorem (Equation (4.6)), the angular momentum of the baton about O is equal to its angular momentum relative to the centre of mass. By Equation (4.10), the $\mathbf{k}$-component of this is $I\omega$, where $I = 0.1071$ (from Exercise 3.3) and $\omega = 2\pi$, so

$$I\omega = 0.1071(2\pi) \simeq 0.6729.$$

So the angular momentum of the baton, relative to O, has a $\mathbf{k}$-component of approximately $0.67\,\text{kg}\,\text{m}^2\,\text{s}^{-1}$.

4.5 **(a)** From the angular momentum decomposition theorem, the angular momentum, $\boldsymbol{l}$, of the caber about O just prior to impact is the sum of the angular momentum, $\boldsymbol{l}_G$, of an equivalent particle at the centre of mass and the angular momentum, $\boldsymbol{l}^{\text{rel}}$, relative to the centre of mass. Now

$$\boldsymbol{l}_G = \mathbf{R} \times m\dot{\mathbf{R}},$$

where $\mathbf{R} = (-L\sin\theta)\mathbf{i} + (L\cos\theta)\mathbf{j}$ and $\dot{\mathbf{R}} = v_x\mathbf{i} + v_y\mathbf{j}$. So

$$\begin{aligned}\boldsymbol{l}_G &= ((-L\sin\theta)\mathbf{i} + (L\cos\theta)\mathbf{j}) \times m(v_x\mathbf{i} + v_y\mathbf{j})\\ &= mL(-(v_y\sin\theta)\mathbf{k} - (v_x\cos\theta)\mathbf{k})\\ &= -mL(v_x\cos\theta + v_y\sin\theta)\mathbf{k}.\end{aligned}$$

From Table 3.1, the moment of inertia I of the caber (modelled as a thin rod of length $2L$) about an axis through its centre of mass is $\frac{1}{12}m(2L)^2 = \frac{1}{3}mL^2$. Now, since the angular speed ω is measured clockwise, the angular velocity is $\boldsymbol{\omega} = -\omega\mathbf{k}$. So, using Equation (4.10), the $\mathbf{k}$-component of the angular momentum of the caber relative to the centre of mass is $l_{\text{a}}^{\text{rel}} = I(-\omega) = -\frac{1}{3}mL^2\omega$.

The $\mathbf{k}$-component of the angular momentum $\boldsymbol{l}$ just before the caber hits the ground is the sum of the $\mathbf{k}$-component of $\boldsymbol{l}^{\text{rel}}$ and the $\mathbf{k}$-component of $\boldsymbol{l}_G$, and thus is

$$-mL\left(\tfrac{1}{3}L\omega + v_x\cos\theta + v_y\sin\theta\right).$$

(b) From the parallel-axes theorem, the moment of inertia of the caber about an axis through O is

$$\tfrac{1}{3}mL^2 + mL^2 = \tfrac{4}{3}mL^2.$$

Assuming that the angular momentum about O is unchanged by the impact, we have, on equating $\mathbf{k}$-components of the angular momentum just before impact (from part (a)) and just after impact,

$$-mL\left(\tfrac{1}{3}L\omega + v_x\cos\theta + v_y\sin\theta\right) = -\tfrac{4}{3}mL^2\omega_1.$$

Hence

$$\begin{aligned}\omega_1 &= \frac{3}{4L}\left(\tfrac{1}{3}L\omega + v_x\cos\theta + v_y\sin\theta\right)\\ &= \tfrac{1}{4}\omega + \frac{3}{4L}(v_x\cos\theta + v_y\sin\theta).\end{aligned} \tag{S.18}$$

(c) After impact, the caber is rotating about its end O at an angular speed ω_1, so its kinetic energy is

$$\tfrac{1}{2}I\omega_1^2 = \tfrac{1}{2}\left(\tfrac{4}{3}mL^2\right)\omega_1^2 = \tfrac{2}{3}mL^2\omega_1^2.$$

To reach the vertical, its gain in potential energy must be

$$mgL(1 - \cos\theta).$$

To pass the vertical, the caber must reach the vertical while still retaining some kinetic energy, so we need

$$\tfrac{2}{3}mL^2\omega_1^2 - mgL(1 - \cos\theta) > 0,$$

i.e. (as $m > 0$ and $L > 0$)

$$\tfrac{2}{3}L\omega_1^2 - g(1 - \cos\theta) > 0. \tag{S.19}$$

The values of θ, v_x, v_y and ω when the caber strikes the ground will be determined by the way that the competitor launches the caber. If we know these values and the length $2L$ of the caber, we can calculate ω_1 from Equation (S.18). Then condition (S.19) enables us to determine whether or not the caber will pass the vertical.

4.6 **(a)** For a cylindrical shell with all its mass at a distance R from its axis, the moment of inertia about the centre of mass is MR^2. Then the total kinetic energy T of the cylinder is

$$T = \tfrac{1}{2}M\dot{x}^2 + \tfrac{1}{2}(MR^2)\dot{\theta}^2 = M\dot{x}^2$$

(compare with Equation (4.14)).

The assumption of conservation of mechanical energy then gives

$$M\dot{x}^2 = Mgx\sin\phi$$

(compare with Equation (4.15)). Differentiating with respect to time, we have

$$2M\dot{x}\ddot{x} = Mg\dot{x}\sin\phi,$$

(compare with Equation (4.16)) and so

$$\ddot{x} = \tfrac{1}{2}g\sin\phi \qquad \text{(S.20)}$$

(compare with Equation (4.17)).

(We see that a hollow cylinder has a smaller acceleration than a solid one. This agrees with the result of the 'race' conducted in the video. A higher proportion of the potential energy lost goes into rotational kinetic energy in the case of a hollow cylinder.)

(b) From Equations (4.17) and (S.20), we can see that the acceleration is independent of the mass in each case. With $\phi = \frac{\pi}{6}$, $\sin\phi = \frac{1}{2}$, and substituting in Equations (4.17) and (S.20), we obtain

$$\ddot{x}_{\text{solid}} = \tfrac{1}{3}g; \qquad \text{(S.21)}$$

$$\ddot{x}_{\text{hollow}} = \tfrac{1}{4}g. \qquad \text{(S.22)}$$

To find the time T to move 2 m down the slope at constant acceleration a_0, starting from rest, we can use the formula $x = v_0t + \frac{1}{2}a_0t^2$ from *Unit 6* to obtain $\frac{1}{2}a_0T^2 = 2$. So $T = 2/\sqrt{a_0}$, and substituting for a_0 from Equation (S.21) and Equation (S.22) the times are

$$T_{\text{solid}} = 1.11\,\text{s};$$

$$T_{\text{hollow}} = 1.28\,\text{s}.$$

Therefore the solid cylinder is 0.17 s faster.

4.7 **(a)** The centre of mass has acceleration $\ddot{x}\mathbf{i}$, where x is displacement down the slope. So Newton's second law applied to an equivalent particle at the centre of mass gives

$$\begin{aligned} M\ddot{x}\mathbf{i} &= \mathbf{W} + \mathbf{N} + \mathbf{F} \\ &= Mg(\sin\phi\mathbf{i} - \cos\phi\mathbf{j}) + |\mathbf{N}|\mathbf{j} - |\mathbf{F}|\mathbf{i}. \end{aligned}$$

Resolving in the **i**- and **j**-directions, we obtain

$$M\ddot{x} = Mg\sin\phi - |\mathbf{F}|, \qquad \text{(S.23)}$$

$$0 = -Mg\cos\phi + |\mathbf{N}|. \qquad \text{(S.24)}$$

The (clockwise) rotational acceleration of the cylinder about its centre of mass is $\ddot{\theta}$, where $x = R\theta$ (from Equation (4.13)), so $\ddot{x} = R\ddot{\theta}$. The moment of inertia of a solid cylinder of mass M about an axis in the **k**-direction through its centre of mass is $\frac{1}{2}MR^2$ (see Table 3.1). Hence the equation of relative rotational motion is

$$-R|\mathbf{F}| = -\tfrac{1}{2}MR^2\ddot{\theta} = -\tfrac{1}{2}MR\ddot{x}.$$

So, we have

$$|\mathbf{F}| = \tfrac{1}{2}M\ddot{x}. \qquad \text{(S.25)}$$

Substituting this into Equation (S.23) gives

$$Mg\sin\phi - \tfrac{1}{2}M\ddot{x} = M\ddot{x},$$

hence

$$g\sin\phi = \tfrac{3}{2}\ddot{x},$$

which can be rearranged as

$$\ddot{x} = \tfrac{2}{3}g\sin\phi. \qquad \text{(S.26)}$$

This is the same as Equation (4.17), which was obtained under the assumption of conservation of mechanical energy.

(b) We have, from Equation (S.24),

$$|\mathbf{N}| = Mg\cos\phi,$$

and, from Equations (S.25) and (S.26),

$$|\mathbf{F}| = \tfrac{1}{2}M\ddot{x} = \tfrac{1}{2}M\left(\tfrac{2}{3}g\sin\phi\right) = \tfrac{1}{3}Mg\sin\phi.$$

So

$$\frac{|\mathbf{F}|}{|\mathbf{N}|} = \frac{Mg\sin\phi}{3Mg\cos\phi} = \tfrac{1}{3}\tan\phi,$$

or equivalently,

$$|\mathbf{F}| = \tfrac{1}{3}\tan\phi|\mathbf{N}|.$$

The condition that the cylinder rolls without slipping is $|\mathbf{F}| \leq \mu|\mathbf{N}|$, i.e. $\frac{1}{3}\tan\phi|\mathbf{N}| \leq \mu|\mathbf{N}|$, so that

$$\tan\phi \leq 3\mu.$$

4.8 **(a) (i)** During the brief period that the competitor is in the act of stopping, the large force exerted at X has zero torque about X. We would be justified in regarding the effect of the torque exerted by the weight of the caber during this short period as negligible, but since the caber is vertically above X, the line of action of its weight passes through X, and so will have zero torque about X anyway. Hence, while the competitor is in the act of stopping, angular momentum about X is constant. Thus the angular momentum of the caber about X is the same just before and just after the competitor stops.

Before the competitor stops, the whole caber is moving forward in the **i**-direction at speed v. We now use the angular momentum decomposition theorem to find the angular momentum of the caber about X. The angular momentum relative to the centre of mass is zero, since the caber is stationary relative to the centre of mass. The angular momentum (about X) of an equivalent particle of mass m and velocity $v\mathbf{i}$ at the centre of mass is

$$L\mathbf{k} \times mv\mathbf{i} = mvL\mathbf{j}.$$

Therefore, the total angular momentum of the caber about X is $mvL\mathbf{j}$.

Just after the competitor stops, the caber will be rotating about an axis through X (in the **j**-direction).

Suppose that its angular speed is ω, and its moment of inertia about X is I_X. Now angular momentum about X is the same just before and just after the competitor stops, so equating **j**-components gives

$$I_X\omega = mvL. \qquad \text{(S.27)}$$

Using Table 3.1 and the parallel-axes theorem, we have

$$I_X = mL^2 + \tfrac{1}{12}m(2L)^2 = \tfrac{4}{3}mL^2. \qquad \text{(S.28)}$$

Hence, on substituting into Equation (S.27) and rearranging, we obtain $\omega = \frac{3}{4}v/L$.

So, just after the competitor stops, the caber will be rotating forwards (clockwise) at an angular speed of $\frac{3}{4}v/L$.

(ii) The kinetic energy of the caber just after the competitor stops is

$$\tfrac{1}{2}I_X\omega^2 = \tfrac{1}{2}(\tfrac{4}{3}mL^2)\left(\frac{3v}{4L}\right)^2 = \tfrac{3}{8}mv^2.$$

(b) Suppose that the caber has angular speed ω_1 about X when its angle with the vertical is θ. Then, by the conservation of mechanical energy, we have

$$\tfrac{1}{2}I_X\omega^2 + mgL = \tfrac{1}{2}I_X\omega_1^2 + mgL\cos\theta.$$

Rearranging gives

$$\omega_1^2 = \omega^2 + \frac{2mgL}{I_X}(1-\cos\theta),$$

which, on substituting for $\omega = 3v/(4L)$ and I_X (from Equation (S.28)), yields

$$\omega_1^2 = \frac{9v^2}{16L^2} + \frac{3g}{2L}(1-\cos\theta).$$

So, when the caber makes an angle θ with the vertical, its (clockwise) angular speed is

$$\omega_1 = \sqrt{\frac{9v^2}{16L^2} + \frac{3g}{2L}(1-\cos\theta)}.$$

4.9 Suppose that the object has fallen a (vertical) distance x since the start of the motion, and has turned through an angle θ. Then the amount of cord that has unwound from the shaft is $r\theta$, so $x = r\theta$.

Let T be the magnitude of the tension force in the cord. From Newton's second law, the equation of motion (in the vertical direction) of an equivalent particle at the centre of mass is

$$(2M+m)g - T = (2M+m)\ddot{x}. \qquad \text{(S.29)}$$

Let I be the moment of inertia of the object about a horizontal axis along the axes of the cylinders, and hence through the centre of mass. Then the equation of relative rotational motion is

$$rT = I\ddot{\theta}. \qquad \text{(S.30)}$$

The moment of inertia of the object is the sum of those of its three parts:

$$I = 2\left(\tfrac{1}{2}MR^2\right) + \tfrac{1}{2}mr^2 = MR^2 + \tfrac{1}{2}mr^2. \qquad \text{(S.31)}$$

From Equation (S.29), the downward acceleration of the object is

$$\ddot{x} = g - \frac{T}{2M+m}.$$

Substituting for T from Equation (S.30), and then for $\ddot{\theta}$ using $x = r\theta$, we have

$$\ddot{x} = g - \frac{I}{(2M+m)r}\ddot{\theta} = g - \frac{I}{(2M+m)r^2}\ddot{x}.$$

Hence, on gathering terms and using Equation (S.31), we obtain

$$\ddot{x} = \frac{g(2M+m)r^2}{I+(2M+m)r^2} = \frac{g(2M+m)r^2}{M(R^2+2r^2)+\frac{3}{2}mr^2}.$$

UNIT 28 Planetary orbits

Study guide for Unit 28

In this unit you will see how Newton's laws of motion and Newton's law of universal gravitation can be used to predict the orbits of planets around the Sun. In particular, we will show that Kepler's laws of planetary motion can be derived using Newtonian mechanics. This unit builds on ideas and results from many of the earlier units of this course, principally:

- the use of energy diagrams to find turning points (*Unit 8*);
- the expressions for velocity and acceleration for circular motion in plane polar coordinates (*Unit 20*);
- the concept of conservative fields (*Unit 24*);
- the concept of the angular momentum of a particle (*Unit 20*);
- Newton's law of universal gravitation (*Unit 20*).

The main focus of this unit is contained in Sections 4 and 5; Sections 1–3 are introductory in nature. However, we suggest that you study the sections in the order in which they are presented, although Section 3 could be studied at any time before Section 4.

Sections 2, 4 and 5 are of average length and will each take about one study session to complete. However Sections 1 and 3 are shorter and should only take half a study session to complete.

You will not need access to your computer while studying this unit.

Introduction

> I offer this work as the mathematical principles of philosophy, for the whole burden of philosophy seems to consist in this — from the phenomena of motions to investigate the forces of nature, and then from these forces to demonstrate the other phenomena; and to this end the general propositions in the first and second Books are directed. In the third Book I ... derive from celestial phenomena the forces of gravity with which bodies tend to the Sun and the several planets. Then from these forces, by other propositions which are also mathematical, I deduce the motions of the planets, the comets, the Moon, and the sea.
>
> Sir Isaac Newton, from the Preface to the First Edition of *Principia*.

Astronomers have attempted to describe and explain the orbits of the planets since ancient times. However, early attempts were usually based on the assumption that the Sun and the planets move in orbits round the Earth. It was not until the Polish astronomer Nicolaus Copernicus (1473–1543) postulated in *De Revolutionibus Orbium Celestium* (1543) that the Earth and the other planets orbit round the Sun that the foundations were laid for our present understanding of planetary orbits. Copernicus also proposed circular orbits for the planets, however, which observation quickly showed not to be the case.

It was when the German astronomer Johannes Kepler (1571–1630) went to work with the Danish astronomer Tycho Brahe (1546–1601) in Prague in 1600 that the next major advances in the understanding of planetary orbits were made. Brahe had been collecting astronomical data for almost 40 years. Based on this data, Kepler arrived at three laws that describe planetary orbits with unprecedented accuracy. Kepler's first law states that each planet moves in an elliptical orbit with the Sun at one of the foci of the ellipse. Kepler's second law states that the line joining a planet to the Sun sweeps out equal areas in equal times as the planet describes its orbit. Both laws were published in *Astronomia Nova* (1609), but they were not widely accepted at the time. Kepler's third law, which states that the square of the orbital period of a planet is proportional to the cube of the semi-major axis of its elliptical orbit, was published in *Harmonica Mundi* (1619). The publication of these three laws preceded Newton's mathematical derivation of them by a lifetime.

We will discuss Kepler's three laws in more detail in Section 2.

The third book of Sir Isaac Newton's monumental work *Principia*, entitled *The System of the World*, was published in 1687, some 20 years after he had discovered many of its results. In the book Newton establishes his law of universal gravitation and uses his three laws of motion to predict the character of the orbits of planets and their moons. Tradition has it that the astronomer Halley, the physicist Hooke, and the architect Wren, had discussed at various times in 1684 the problem of determining the orbit of a planet around the Sun if the force between them varied as the inverse square of the distance. Unable to succeed with the problem, they took it to Newton, only to find that he had already solved it, together with other problems of planetary motion. Encouraged constantly by Halley, Newton finally published *Principia*. The theory which it expounded was extraordinarily successful. Only in the twentieth century, with the theories of relativity and quantum mechanics, did it become evident that there are natural processes not explained accurately by the Newtonian world-view.

Newton's law of universal gravitation is described in Section 3.

Newtonian mechanics is used to derive the equation for planetary orbits in Sections 4 and 5.

The main aim of this unit is to apply Newtonian mechanics in order to derive Kepler's three laws of planetary orbits. In deriving the laws of planetary motion we shall use modern notation and methods, although it must be said that the calculus in its original form was the innovation of Newton and his contemporary, Leibniz. In summary, then, there is little new mathematics introduced in this unit. Instead we utilize the methods of calculus, vector analysis and Newtonian mechanics developed earlier in the course to describe one of the great scientific advances of the last four centuries.

In *Unit 20* we derived expressions for the velocity and acceleration of the *circular* motion of a particle using polar coordinates. In Section 1 of this unit we generalize these expressions to the *general* motion of a particle in a plane. Kepler's laws for planetary orbits are stated and explained in Section 2. We also derive the equation of an ellipse in polar coordinates. In Section 3 we introduce Newton's law of universal gravitation.

In Sections 4 and 5 the equation of gravitational orbits is derived and we show how Kepler's laws follow as a consequence of Newtonian mechanics. The gravitational attraction between a planet and the Sun is a *central* force in that it is directed from the planet to the Sun. In Section 4 we concentrate on the consequences of a force being central. In particular, we demonstrate that the motion takes place in a plane and that Kepler's second law is valid. In order to do this we use the concept of *angular momentum*. You will also see that the fact that central forces are *conservative* leads to a potential energy function and to the conservation of total mechanical energy. In Section 4 you will also see how qualitative information about central forces can be used to predict whether the motion is *bound* or *unbound*. In order to do this we extend the use of *energy diagrams*, which were introduced in *Unit 8* for one-dimensional motion.

Angular momentum was introduced in Section 4 of *Unit 20*. Conservative fields were introduced in *Unit 24*.

Finally, in Section 5, you will see how Newton's law of universal gravitation predicts elliptical orbits and explains Kepler's third law. In particular, we show how the size and shape of the elliptical orbit is connected to the angular momentum and mechanical energy of the planet.

1 Kinematics of planar motion using polar coordinates

The ultimate goal of this unit is to model the motion of planets, satellites and comets. In order to do this, we assume that the only force acting on such a body is a gravitational attraction due to a second much more massive body. For example, to predict the orbit of a planet, we assume that the only force acting on it is the gravitational attraction of the Sun (see Figure 1.1).

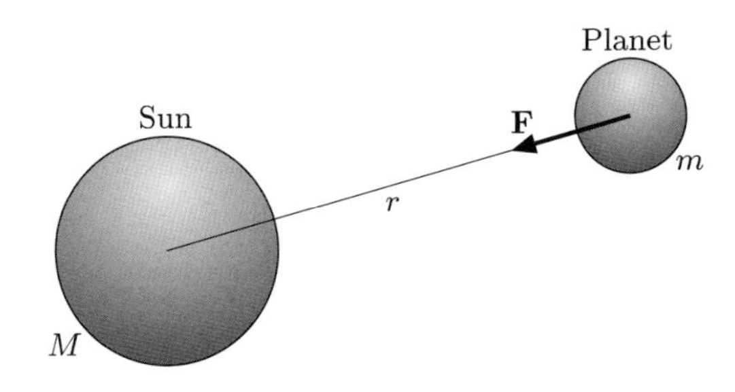

Figure 1.1

We discuss this force in detail in Section 3, where you will see that it is a function of the distance between the two bodies (as well as their masses). So it would seem sensible to use spherical polar coordinates to describe the motion. However, because the force is also directed along the line of separation of the two bodies, as shown in Figure 1.1, it turns out that the motion is confined to a plane, as we will show in Section 4. Hence we are able to use *plane polar coordinates* $\langle r, \theta \rangle$ to describe the motion. You saw circular motion expressed in this way in *Unit 20*, but here we consider the case where the radial distance r is not constant.

In *Unit 20* we showed that, using polar coordinates $\langle r, \theta \rangle$ and the corresponding orthogonal *unit polar vectors* $\mathbf{e}_r$ and $\mathbf{e}_\theta$ (see Figure 1.2) the polar form of the position vector is

$$\mathbf{r} = r\mathbf{e}_r, \tag{1.1}$$

where $r = |\mathbf{r}|$ is the distance of the particle from the origin. This equation is not as simple as it looks because, for general motion in the plane, *both* r and $\mathbf{e}_r$ depend on time, as do the polar angle θ and its associated unit vector $\mathbf{e}_\theta$.

Unit 20 Subsection 1.3

The polar coordinates $\langle r, \theta \rangle$ are defined in terms of the Cartesian coordinates (x, y) by the equations

$$x = r\cos\theta, \quad y = r\sin\theta.$$

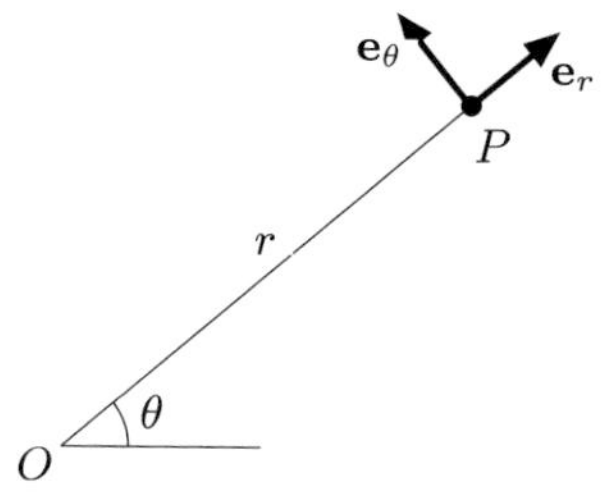

Figure 1.2

In order to study the motion of a particle in plane polar coordinates, it is necessary to have expressions for its velocity and acceleration vectors in terms of $r, \theta, \mathbf{e}_r$ and $\mathbf{e}_\theta$. In the course of deriving these equations, we need to express the time derivatives $\dot{\mathbf{e}}_r, \dot{\mathbf{e}}_\theta$ in terms of $\mathbf{e}_r, \mathbf{e}_\theta$. The required relations for achieving this are

$$\dot{\mathbf{e}}_r = \dot{\theta}\mathbf{e}_\theta \quad \text{and} \quad \dot{\mathbf{e}}_\theta = -\dot{\theta}\mathbf{e}_r. \tag{1.2}$$

These equations were derived in *Unit 20* Subsection 1.3. Although attention was restricted there to circular motion, the derivations apply also in the general case.

We shall now apply Equations (1.2) to obtain expressions for the velocity $\mathbf{v} = \dot{\mathbf{r}}$ and acceleration $\mathbf{a} = \ddot{\mathbf{r}}$ in terms of polar coordinates and unit polar vectors. As pointed out above, the position vector $\mathbf{r}$ is given by

$$\mathbf{r} = r\mathbf{e}_r. \tag{1.1}$$

Differentiating this equation by using the product rule, we have

$$\dot{\mathbf{r}} = \dot{r}\mathbf{e}_r + r\dot{\mathbf{e}}_r,$$

which, by the first of Equations (1.2), may be written as

$$\dot{\mathbf{r}} = \dot{r}\mathbf{e}_r + r\dot{\theta}\mathbf{e}_\theta. \tag{1.3}$$

Note that $\dot{r} = d|\mathbf{r}|/dt$, the rate of change of the radial coordinate, is *not* in general the same as the speed $|\dot{\mathbf{r}}|$ of the particle.

Exercise 1.1

By differentiating Equation (1.3) with respect to time, remembering that r, θ, $\mathbf{e}_r$ and $\mathbf{e}_\theta$ are all functions of time, show that the acceleration of a particle moving in the (x, y)-plane is

$$\ddot{\mathbf{r}} = (\ddot{r} - r\dot{\theta}^2)\mathbf{e}_r + (2\dot{r}\dot{\theta} + r\ddot{\theta})\mathbf{e}_\theta.$$

In Exercise 1.1 you saw that, in plane polar coordinates, the acceleration is

$$\ddot{\mathbf{r}} = (\ddot{r} - r\dot{\theta}^2)\mathbf{e}_r + (2\dot{r}\dot{\theta} + r\ddot{\theta})\mathbf{e}_\theta.$$

Recognizing that

$$\frac{1}{r}\frac{d}{dt}(r^2\dot{\theta}) = 2\dot{r}\dot{\theta} + r\ddot{\theta},$$

we can write the expression for the acceleration as

$$\ddot{\mathbf{r}} = (\ddot{r} - r\dot{\theta}^2)\mathbf{e}_r + \frac{1}{r}\frac{d}{dt}(r^2\dot{\theta})\mathbf{e}_\theta. \tag{1.4}$$

The following box summarizes the results that we have obtained so far.

Position, velocity and acceleration in plane polar coordinates

In terms of r, θ, $\mathbf{e}_r$ and $\mathbf{e}_\theta$, the position $\mathbf{r}$, velocity $\dot{\mathbf{r}}$ and acceleration $\ddot{\mathbf{r}}$ of a particle moving in the (x, y)-plane are given by the equations

$$\mathbf{r} = r\mathbf{e}_r, \tag{1.1}$$

$$\dot{\mathbf{r}} = \dot{r}\mathbf{e}_r + r\dot{\theta}\mathbf{e}_\theta, \tag{1.3}$$

$$\ddot{\mathbf{r}} = (\ddot{r} - r\dot{\theta}^2)\mathbf{e}_r + \frac{1}{r}\frac{d}{dt}(r^2\dot{\theta})\mathbf{e}_\theta. \tag{1.4}$$

Exercise 1.2

Show that the above expressions for the velocity and acceleration (Equations (1.3) and (1.4)) reduce to the equivalent expressions derived in *Unit 20* for the case $r = R$, where R is a constant.

Of the following two exercises, the first will give you practice in expressing a particle's velocity and acceleration in plane polar coordinates. The second asks you to express the kinetic energy of a particle in polar coordinates. The result of Exercise 1.4 will be applied later in the unit.

Exercise 1.3

A particle moves in the (x, y)-plane with radial coordinate $r(t) = at^2$ and angle $\theta(t) = bt$, where a and b are positive constants. Find the velocity and acceleration in terms of t, $\mathbf{e}_r$ and $\mathbf{e}_\theta$.

**Exercise 1.4*

Show that if the motion of a particle takes place in the (x, y)-plane then the kinetic energy T of the particle may be written as

$$T = \tfrac{1}{2}m(\dot{r}^2 + r^2\dot{\theta}^2).$$

So far we have derived kinematical formulae for the planar motion of a particle, using polar coordinates. Before proceeding to the subject of planetary orbits we shall derive the corresponding equations of motion. The starting point is, as usual, Newton's second law.

In plane Cartesian coordinates, Newton's second law $m\ddot{\mathbf{r}} = \mathbf{F}$ takes the form

$$m(\ddot{x}\mathbf{i} + \ddot{y}\mathbf{j}) = F_x\mathbf{i} + F_y\mathbf{j},$$

Here, F_x and F_y are respectively the x- and y-components of the force $\mathbf{F}$.

leading to the two scalar equations

$$m\ddot{x} = F_x \quad \text{and} \quad m\ddot{y} = F_y.$$

Similarly, Newton's second law $m\ddot{\mathbf{r}} = \mathbf{F}$ may be expressed in plane polar coordinates, using Equation (1.4), as

$$m\left((\ddot{r} - r\dot{\theta}^2)\mathbf{e}_r + \frac{1}{r}\frac{d}{dt}(r^2\dot{\theta})\mathbf{e}_\theta\right) = F_r\mathbf{e}_r + F_\theta\mathbf{e}_\theta,$$

Here, F_r and F_θ are respectively the *radial* and *transverse* components of the force $\mathbf{F}$.

leading to the pair of scalar equations

$$m(\ddot{r} - r\dot{\theta}^2) = F_r \quad \text{and} \quad \frac{m}{r}\frac{d}{dt}(r^2\dot{\theta}) = F_\theta. \tag{1.5}$$

It is these equations of motion that are used in the following exercise, which represents a situation in which it is appropriate to use polar rather than Cartesian coordinates.

*Exercise 1.5

A puck P of mass m moves without friction around the origin O on a horizontal table (see Figure 1.3). It is fixed to a light, inextensible string OP, which is reeled in steadily so that the puck's distance from the origin is given by

$$r(t) = r(0) - kt \qquad (t < r(0)/k),$$

where k is a positive constant. The string remains taut throughout.

The upper bound on the time t is included because $r(t)$ must always be non-negative. The puck would reach the origin at time $t = r(0)/k$ if the situation remained as described until that time.

(a) Show that the equations of motion for the particle which represents the puck are

$$mr\dot{\theta}^2 = T \quad \text{and} \quad \frac{d}{dt}(r^2\dot{\theta}) = 0,$$

where $T = |\mathbf{T}|$ is the magnitude of the tension $\mathbf{T}$ in the string.

(b) Show that at time t the magnitude of the tension is given by

$$T(t) = \frac{mr^4(0)\dot{\theta}^2(0)}{r^3(t)} = \frac{mr^4(0)\dot{\theta}^2(0)}{(r(0) - kt)^3}.$$

(c) Suppose that $m = 0.1\,\text{kg}$, $k = \frac{1}{60}\,\text{m}\,\text{s}^{-1}$, the initial distance is $r(0) = 1\,\text{m}$ and the initial angular speed is $\dot{\theta}(0) = 1\,\text{rad}\,\text{s}^{-1}$. Suppose further that the string will break when it experiences a tension of magnitude 500 N. Find the distance r and the time t at which the string breaks.

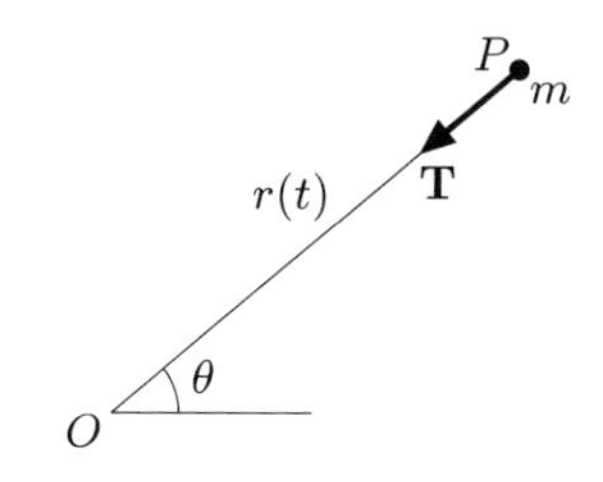

Figure 1.3

End-of-section Exercises

Exercise 1.6

A particle is constrained to move along a path whose polar coordinates are given by

$$r = e^{kt}, \quad \theta = \omega t \quad (t > 0),$$

where k and ω are positive constants. Find expressions for the velocity and acceleration of the particle in terms of $\mathbf{e}_r$ and $\mathbf{e}_\theta$.

Exercise 1.7

A particle of mass m is constrained to move in a planar path with equation

$$\frac{l}{r} = 1 + e\cos\theta, \tag{1.6}$$

Note that in this exercise e is *not* the base of the natural logarithm function.

where l and e are constants such that $l > 0$ and $e \geq 0$, in such a manner that the angular momentum component

$$L_z = mr^2\dot{\theta} \tag{1.7}$$

is constant.

Equation (1.6) is the equation of a circle if $e = 0$, an ellipse if $0 < e < 1$, a parabola if $e = 1$ and a hyperbola if $e > 1$.

(a) By differentiating Equation (1.6) with respect to time and using Equation (1.7), show that

$$\dot{r} = \frac{eL_z}{ml}\sin\theta.$$

By differentiating this equation with respect to time, show further that

$$\ddot{r} = \frac{eL_z^2}{m^2 l}\frac{\cos\theta}{r^2}.$$

(b) Hence find an expression for the total force acting on the particle in terms of r, $\mathbf{e}_r$, $\mathbf{e}_\theta$, m, l, e and L_z.

---

2 Kepler's laws of planetary motion

The Earth is an ordinary-sized planet that orbits a middle-aged star of rather small size near the outer fringes of a typical spiral galaxy some 10^5 light-years across. This galaxy contains between 10^{11} and 10^{12} visible stars, together with much other matter, and is one member of a rough association, or cluster, of some thousand galaxies of various shapes and sizes.

One light-year is the distance travelled by light in one year: approximately 9.461×10^{15} m.

Located in this myriad of astronomical objects is our solar system. It consists of a relatively massive Sun encircled by nine planets, some of which themselves possess one or more satellite moons, and a number of smaller bodies such as comets and asteroids. Every member of the solar system interacts via the gravitational force with all the others and, indeed, with all other heavenly bodies. But distances between stars are measured in light-years; since the force of gravity between two bodies decreases rapidly in magnitude as their separation increases, gravitational interactions with objects beyond the solar system can mostly be neglected.

The gravitational influence of a body increases with its mass, and within the solar system there is a rough hierarchy of size. The Sun is by far the largest object, followed by the planets and then by their moons. The Earth's mass is only about 3×10^{-6} that of the Sun; the Moon's mass is about 10^{-2} that of the Earth. Jupiter, the largest planet, is roughly 300 times more massive than the Earth, but its distance from the Sun is over five times greater than the distance of the Earth from the Sun. So the major gravitational force on the Earth is that due to the Sun. In fact, the gravitational influence of a planet upon any other body is of little significance compared with the gravitational influence of the Sun, unless the body acted upon is relatively close to the planet. To a good first approximation, then, we can think of the planets as orbiting the Sun singly, and the moons as singly orbiting their planets. This is the model adopted by Newton, who considered the problem of only *two* bodies orbiting one another. We shall assume in addition that one of the bodies is very much more massive than the other.

In a more advanced treatment, the effects of the other planets can be added as perturbations.

An analysis of the motion of one relatively light body moving under the gravitational attraction of a second, relatively massive, body is the overall goal of this unit. In this section we introduce the topic of planetary motion by describing the features of their orbits that were established by Kepler from experimental observation and stated in the form of three laws. These laws will be derived in Sections 4 and 5 as a *consequence* of Newton's law of universal gravitation, which we consider in Section 3.

As they are worded, Kepler's three laws refer specifically to the orbits of planets around the Sun, but they apply also to the orbit of any relatively light body about another much more massive body. The laws were established by Kepler from experimental observations of the motion of several of the planets.

Johannes Kepler (1571–1630) (Courtesy of Science Museum Science & Society Picture Library)

Kepler's laws of planetary motion

Law I Each planet moves in an ellipse, with the Sun at one focus of the ellipse.

Law II The line joining a planet to the Sun sweeps out equal areas in equal times.

Law III The square of the orbital period of a planet is proportional to the cube of the semi-major axis of its orbit.

Kepler's first law specifies the *shape* of a planetary orbit. Since the law refers to an *ellipse* and to a *focus*, we start by considering the mathematics of ellipses.

An **ellipse** is a symmetrical plane figure such as that drawn in Figure 2.1. One of the implications of this first law, then, is that the orbit of a planet about the Sun *lies in a plane*. An ellipse is usually defined as a set of points (X, Y) which, with a suitable choice of origin and axes, satisfy the equation

$$\frac{X^2}{a^2} + \frac{Y^2}{b^2} = 1, \tag{2.1}$$

where a and b are positive constants with $a \geq b$. The constants a and b are called respectively the *semi-major axis* and *semi-minor axis* of the ellipse. Their geometrical significance is shown in Figure 2.1.

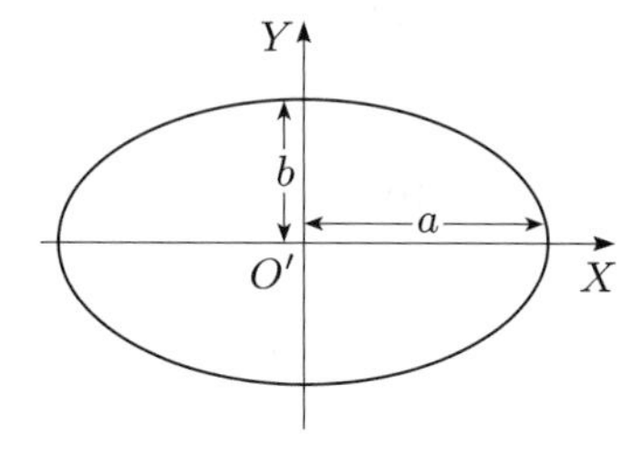

Figure 2.1

Exercise 2.1

What can be said about an ellipse in the special case $a = b$?

Exercise 2.2

(a) Show that the area A of an ellipse can be expressed as

$$A = 2b \int_{-a}^{a} \sqrt{1 - (X/a)^2}\, dX.$$

(b) By using the substitution $X = a\cos u$, show that $A = \pi ab$.

To understand Kepler's first law, it remains to explain where a focus of an ellipse is located, and then to express the equation of the ellipse relative to this point. We shall express the equation with respect to a new set of axes Oxy, shown in Figure 2.2 on the facing page. These axes are obtained from the set $O'XY$ of Figure 2.1 by a translation of the axes to the right by a distance q, where

$$q = \sqrt{a^2 - b^2}. \tag{2.2}$$

We could also shift axes to the left by the distance q, but our choice represents no loss of generality since this configuration is just the other rotated by an angle π.

The points F and O of Figure 2.2, which are located a distance q to the left and to the right of the centre of the ellipse, are called the *foci* of the ellipse.

'Foci' is the plural of 'focus'.

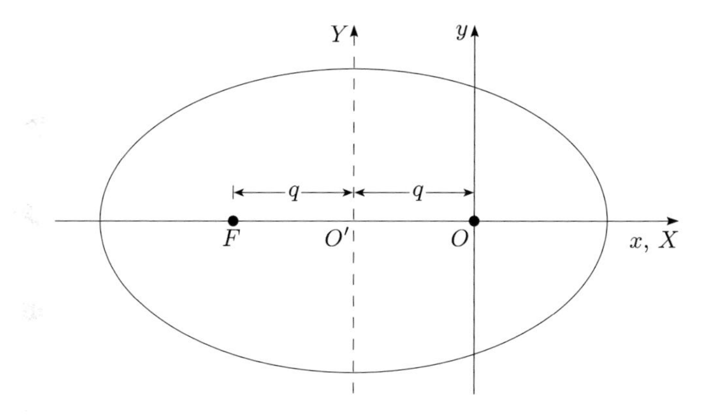

Figure 2.2

Exercise 2.3

Where are the foci of a circle?

Since the translation is along the coincident x- and X-axes, the new coordinates (x, y) are related to the original ones (X, Y) by

$$X = x + q, \qquad Y = y.$$

Then, from Equation (2.1), the equation of the ellipse takes the form

$$\frac{(x+q)^2}{a^2} + \frac{y^2}{b^2} = 1.$$

We shall now re-express this equation in plane polar coordinates. After multiplying the equation by b^2 and rearranging, we obtain

$$y^2 = b^2 - \frac{b^2}{a^2}(x+q)^2 = b^2 - \frac{b^2}{a^2}(x^2 + 2qx + q^2).$$

Adding x^2 to both sides and collecting terms gives

$$x^2 + y^2 = \left(b^2 - \frac{b^2}{a^2}q^2\right) - \frac{2b^2q}{a^2}x + \left(1 - \frac{b^2}{a^2}\right)x^2.$$

The left-hand side of the above equation is r^2, the square of the radial distance, so that, on using Equation (2.2) to express q in terms of a, b, we have

$$r^2 = \frac{b^4}{a^2} - 2\frac{b^2x}{a}\sqrt{1 - \frac{b^2}{a^2}} + \left(1 - \frac{b^2}{a^2}\right)x^2. \qquad (2.3)$$

This rather cumbersome expression is made neater by employing two new quantities defined in terms of a and b. These quantities are the *eccentricity*

This usage of the symbol e should not be confused with its use as the base of natural logarithms, 2.718 28....

$$e = \frac{q}{a} = \sqrt{1 - \frac{b^2}{a^2}} \qquad (2.4)$$

and the *semi-latus rectum*

$$l = \frac{b^2}{a}. \qquad (2.5)$$

Note that, since $b \leq a$, we have $0 \leq e < 1$. This is a condition on the eccentricity for ellipses.

The eccentricity of the Earth's orbit is about 0.02.

Exercise 2.4

Find e when

(a) $b = a$ (a circle); (b) $b = \frac{1}{2}a$; (c) $b = \frac{1}{3}a$.

Comment on the relationship between the eccentricity and shape of an ellipse.

*Exercise 2.5

Show that the semi-latus rectum l is given in terms of the semi-major axis a and the eccentricity e by

$$l = a(1 - e^2). \tag{2.6}$$

From Equations (2.3)–(2.5), we now have

$$r^2 = l^2 - 2lex + e^2x^2$$

or

$$r^2 = (l - ex)^2.$$

Putting $x = 0$ into this equation gives $r = l$, showing that the semi-latus rectum l is the distance from the origin to the ellipse's intercepts on the y-axis. This is illustrated in Figure 2.3 below.

Then taking the square root of both sides gives

$$r = \pm(l - ex). \tag{2.7}$$

We must now decide on the choice of sign for the right-hand side of Equation (2.7), to be consistent with the fact that r is never negative. We shall show that, for all points x on the ellipse, the quantity $l - ex$ is positive. From Figure 2.2, the largest value of x on the ellipse is $x = a - q$. Thus we have, for all points on the curve,

$$l - ex \geq l - e(a - q).$$

But we also have $q = \sqrt{a^2 - b^2}$, $l = b^2/a$ and $e = q/a$, so the right-hand side of this inequality is

$$\begin{aligned} l - e(a - q) &= \frac{b^2}{a} - \frac{\sqrt{a^2 - b^2}}{a}\left(a - \sqrt{a^2 - b^2}\right) \\ &= \frac{b^2}{a} - \sqrt{a^2 - b^2} + \frac{a^2 - b^2}{a} \\ &= a - \sqrt{a^2 - b^2}, \end{aligned}$$

which is never negative. Hence $l - ex$ itself is never negative. Thus the positive sign is appropriate in Equation (2.7), and the equation for an ellipse with respect to the axes Oxy of Figure 2.2 is

$$r = l - ex \quad \text{or} \quad \frac{l}{r} = 1 + e\frac{x}{r}.$$

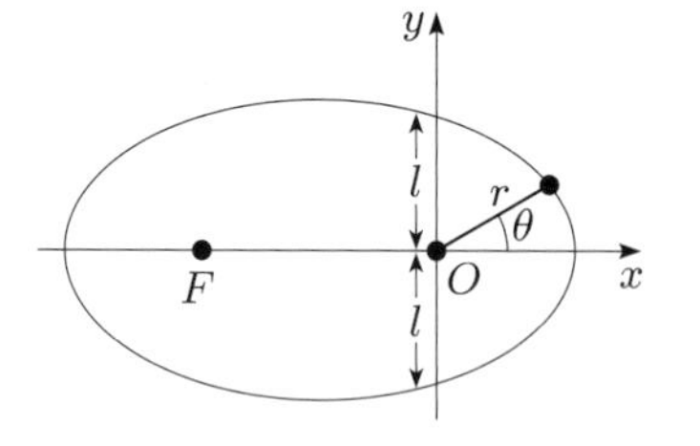

Figure 2.3

Since $x = r\cos\theta$ (see Figure 2.3), we have the convenient form

$$\frac{l}{r} = 1 + e\cos\theta \tag{2.8}$$

for the equation of an ellipse in polar coordinates with origin at a focus of the ellipse.

Kepler's first law therefore says that if the origin of coordinates is located at the Sun, then the orbit of each planet lies in a plane containing that origin, and is described by Equation (2.8) once the axes have been appropriately oriented. With a different orientation for the axes (but the same origin), Equation (2.8) becomes

$$\frac{l}{r} = 1 + e\cos(\theta - \theta_0), \tag{2.9}$$

where θ_0 is the clockwise angle through which the axes have been rotated from their position in Figure 2.3. The major axis of the ellipse then lies along the direction specified by $\theta = \theta_0$.

The equation of an ellipse in polar coordinates

The equation of an ellipse in polar coordinates with origin at a focus of the ellipse is

$$\frac{l}{r} = 1 + e\cos\theta, \tag{2.8}$$

where $l > 0$ and $0 \leq e < 1$. The *semi-latus rectum* l and the *eccentricity* e of the ellipse are related to its *semi-major axis* a and *semi-minor axis* b by

$$e = \sqrt{1 - \frac{b^2}{a^2}}, \tag{2.4}$$

$$l = \frac{b^2}{a} = a(1 - e^2). \tag{2.5, 2.6}$$

The area of the ellipse is

$$A = \pi ab. \tag{2.10}$$

If $e = 0$, the ellipse is a circle.

This result was derived in Exercise 2.2(b).

Kepler's second law says that the line joining a planet to the Sun sweeps out equal areas in equal times. This law can be used to specify the *rate* at which a planet moves in its particular elliptical orbit.

Suppose, without loss of generality, that the planet moves in an anticlockwise sense, as shown in Figure 2.4. In Figure 2.4 the two shaded regions represent the areas swept out by the planet between times t_1 and t_2, and between times t_3 and t_4. Assuming that the two time intervals are of equal duration, Kepler's second law says that these areas are equal. If $A(t)$ is the total area swept out since some initial time, $t = 0$ say, this law can be expressed as

$$A(t_4) - A(t_3) = A(t_2) - A(t_1) \quad \text{whenever} \quad t_4 - t_3 = t_2 - t_1.$$

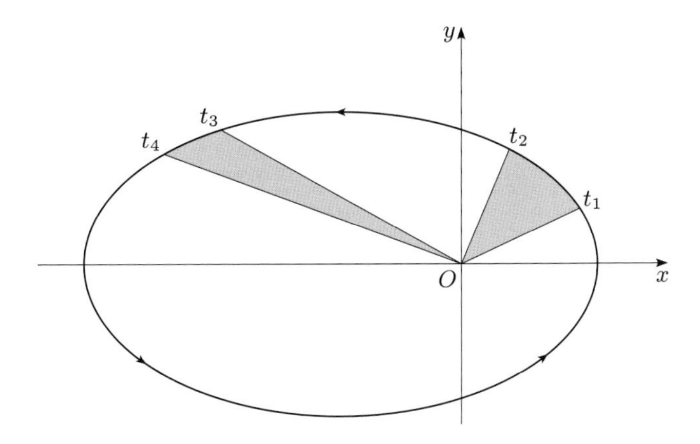

Figure 2.4

A more concise way of stating Kepler's second law is that the *rate* at which area is swept out is constant, that is, $\dot{A}$ is constant.

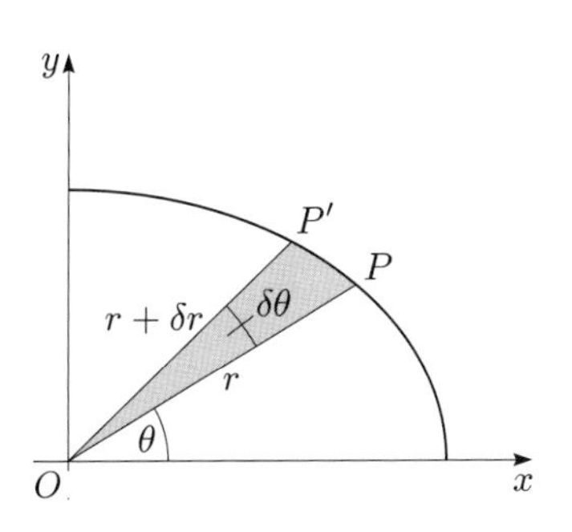

Figure 2.5

It is possible also to state the law in a form that relates the radial coordinate r to the rate of change $\dot{\theta}$ of the angular coordinate. Figure 2.5 shows a close-up of part of the planetary orbit, where we consider the area δA swept out during a small time interval of duration δt. Over this interval the planet moves from point P at time t to point P' at time $t + \delta t$, traversing an angle $\delta\theta$ and changing its radius from r to $r + \delta r$. If δt is sufficiently small then the area δA will lie between the areas of two circular sectors with angle $\delta\theta$, one having radius r and the other radius $r + \delta r$. Now the area of a sector of a circle of radius R is $\frac{1}{2}R^2\phi$, where ϕ is the angle between the radii bounding the sector. So, if $r(t)$ is increasing in the part of the curve under consideration then this gives

If $r(t)$ is decreasing then the expressions for the upper and lower bounds in this inequality are reversed, leading to the same outcome.

$$\tfrac{1}{2}r^2\delta\theta \leq \delta A \leq \tfrac{1}{2}(r + \delta r)^2\delta\theta.$$

On dividing through by δt, and then taking the limit as δt tends to zero, we obtain

$$\dot{A} = \tfrac{1}{2}r^2\dot{\theta}. \tag{2.11}$$

Since $\dot{A}$ is constant according to Kepler's second law, this law may also be interpreted as saying that

$$r^2\dot{\theta} = \text{constant}. \tag{2.12}$$

Exercise 2.6

Compare the average speeds of the orbiting planet during the two equal intervals $t_1 \leq t \leq t_2$ and $t_3 \leq t \leq t_4$ in Figure 2.4. Your answer should consist of a few sentences only.

Kepler's third law gives a relation between the period of a planetary orbit and the lateral extent (semi-major axis) of the orbit. If T is the period then, by definition, the planet will take this time to make one full circuit of the ellipse. If the particular orbit has semi-major axis a, then Kepler's third law says that T^2 is proportional to a^3, that is,

$$T^2 = ka^3, \tag{2.13}$$

where k is a constant. This law, then, makes a statement connecting the overall rate of motion of the planet to a geometrical property of its orbit. We shall prove this result in Section 5.

This result was proved for circular orbits in *Unit 20* Exercise 2.5.

Exercise 2.7

The semi-major axis of the orbit around the Sun of the planet Mars is 1.524 times as large as that of the Earth. The Earth's period for its orbit around the Sun is 365.256 days. Find the period (in Earth days) for the orbit of Mars around the Sun.

End-of-section Exercises

Exercise 2.8

An *ellipse* can be defined as the path in the plane of a point P such that the sum of the distances of P from two distinct fixed points F and F' is constant, that is

$$FP + F'P = 2a,, \tag{2.14}$$

where a is a positive constant.

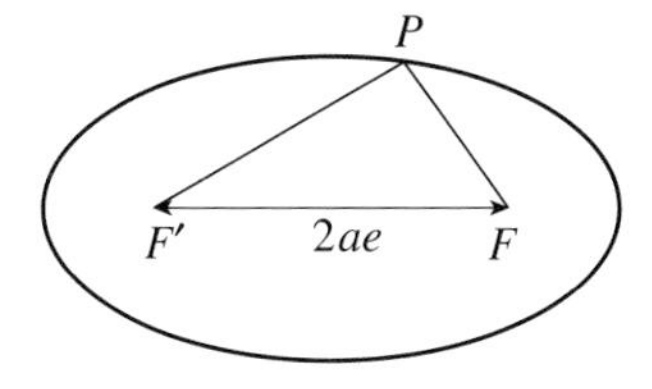

Figure 2.6

The points F and F' are the *foci* of the ellipse, and the distance between them is $2ae$, where $0 < e < 1$ and e is the *eccentricity* of the ellipse, as shown in Figure 2.6.

(a) Explain why the distance between F and F' must be less than $2a$, unless P lies on the line segment FF'.

(b) Show that Equation (2.14) can be written as

$$|\mathbf{r} + 2ae\mathbf{i}| = 2a - |\mathbf{r}|, \tag{2.15}$$

where $\mathbf{r}$ is the position vector of P with respect to F, and $\mathbf{i}$ is a unit vector in the direction from F' to F.

(c) Square both sides of Equation (2.15), and hence obtain

$$\frac{l}{r} = 1 + e\cos\theta,$$

where r and θ are the polar coordinates of P relative to F and the direction of $\mathbf{i}$, and $l = a(1 - e^2)$ is the *semi-latus rectum* of the ellipse.

Exercise 2.9

In Cartesian coordinates, the equation of an ellipse is

$$\frac{X^2}{13^2} + \frac{Y^2}{12^2} = 1.$$

Find the eccentricity e and semi-latus rectum l of this ellipse. Hence write down a polar equation of the ellipse, using one of the foci of the ellipse as the origin.

*Exercise 2.10

(a) Show that Equations (2.5) and (2.6) can be rearranged into the form

$$a = \frac{l}{1 - e^2} \tag{2.16}$$

and

$$b = \frac{l}{\sqrt{1 - e^2}}. \tag{2.17}$$

(b) Hence find the Cartesian equation for the ellipse

$$\frac{1}{r} = \tfrac{1}{9}(5 + 4\cos\theta)$$

with respect to the coordinates (X, Y) shown in Figure 2.1.

3 Newton's law of universal gravitation

> I began to think of gravity extending to ye orb of the Moon, and ... from Kepler's Rule ... I deduced that the forces which keep the Planets in their Orbs must [vary] reciprocally as the square of their distances from the centres about which they revolve: and thereby compared the force requisite to keep the Moon in her Orb with the force of gravity at the surface of the Earth, and found them to answer pretty nearly. All this was in the two plague years of 1665 and 1666, for in those days I was in the prime of my age for invention, and minded Mathematics and Philosophy more than at any time since.
>
> *Isaac Newton's account of his discovery of the law of universal gravitation.*

Newton's law of universal gravitation describes the nature of the gravitational force between pairs of particles. It gives the attractive force between them as a function of the masses of the particles and of their separation. It is *universal* in the sense that it is hypothesized to hold between the particles comprising all bodies in the universe, and not just between those comprising the Earth and an apple, or the Earth and the Moon. In words, the law can be stated as follows.

You met Newton's law of universal gravitation in *Unit 20*.

Newton's law of universal gravitation

The force of gravity between two particles is attractive, directed along the line between them, proportional to the product of their masses, and inversely proportional to the square of their separation.

Let us write this mathematically, using the vector notation which was unavailable to Newton. We write the position vectors of the two particles as $\mathbf{r}_i, \mathbf{r}_j$ and their masses as m_i, m_j. The gravitational force on the particle of mass m_i due to the presence of the particle of mass m_j is denoted by $\mathbf{F}_{ij}$. From the verbal statement of Newton's law above, we know the following.

(i) $\mathbf{F}_{ij}$ is directed from the particle of mass m_i to the particle of mass m_j, hence its direction is defined by the unit vector

$$\frac{\mathbf{r}_j - \mathbf{r}_i}{|\mathbf{r}_j - \mathbf{r}_i|} = -\frac{\mathbf{r}_i - \mathbf{r}_j}{|\mathbf{r}_i - \mathbf{r}_j|}$$

(see Figure 3.1).

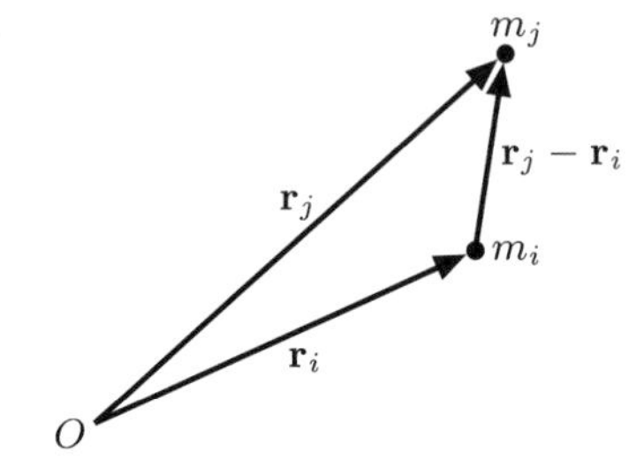

Figure 3.1

(ii) The magnitude of $\mathbf{F}_{ij}$ is proportional to $m_i m_j$, and to $\dfrac{1}{|\mathbf{r}_i - \mathbf{r}_j|^2}$.

Putting these elements together gives the following.

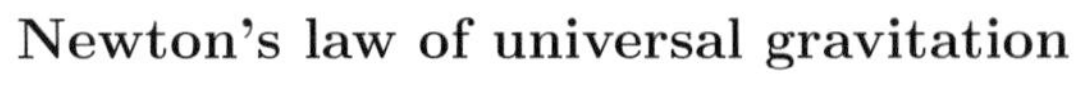

Newton's law of universal gravitation

The gravitational force of attraction exerted on a particle of mass m_i at position $\mathbf{r}_i$ by a particle of mass m_j at position $\mathbf{r}_j$ is

$$\mathbf{F}_{ij} = -\frac{G m_i m_j}{|\mathbf{r}_i - \mathbf{r}_j|^3}(\mathbf{r}_i - \mathbf{r}_j). \qquad (3.1)$$

Here G is a constant of proportionality, called the universal constant of gravitation, or the *gravitational constant*. Its value, in SI units, is

$$G \simeq 6.673 \times 10^{-11}\,\mathrm{m^3\,kg^{-1}\,s^{-2}}.$$

The constant G is one of the least precisely measured physical constants.

Exercise 3.1

Gravitation is an inter-particle force. By Newton's third law the force exerted upon a particle of mass m_i by a particle of mass m_j should be equal in magnitude, but opposite in direction, to the force exerted upon the particle of mass m_j by the particle of mass m_i. Show that the universal law of gravitation is consistent with this, so that $\mathbf{F}_{ij} + \mathbf{F}_{ji} = \mathbf{0}$.

Using Equation (3.1) it is possible to calculate the force of attraction between any two objects, provided that they are sufficiently small to be modelled by particles. In many cases, however, it is far from the truth to claim that both objects are 'small' relative to the situation being considered. For example, Figure 3.2(a) shows a satellite of mass m, in orbit around the Earth at a height approximately equal to the Earth's own radius. At first sight it seems unreasonable here to model the Earth by a particle, although it appears sensible (for most purposes) to use a particle model for the satellite.

In fact, it can be shown that if the Earth's mass is assumed to be distributed in a *spherically symmetric* manner, then its attraction on the satellite is the *same* as if all its mass were concentrated in a particle at its centre (see Figure 3.2(b)). Indeed this result can be extended to show that the gravitational attraction between *two* spherically symmetric bodies is the same as if the masses of the two bodies were concentrated at their centres.

It took Newton 20 years to prove this result!

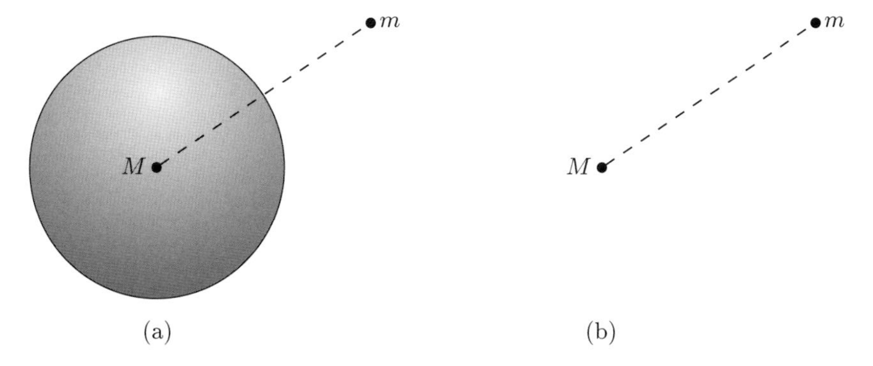

Figure 3.2

The gravitational force is often called an *inverse square* law. The reason for this is clear if we consider the force $\mathbf{F}(\mathbf{r})$ on a particle of mass m at position $\mathbf{r}$ due to a spherically symmetric mass distribution of mass M with its centre at the origin, which is

$$\mathbf{F}(\mathbf{r}) = -\frac{GmM}{r^3}\mathbf{r} = -\frac{GmM}{r^2}\mathbf{e}_r, \tag{3.2}$$

where $r = |\mathbf{r}|$ is the distance of the particle from the centre of the spherically symmetric mass distribution and $\mathbf{e}_r = \mathbf{r}/r$. It is the inverse square of the distance r, which appears in this last expression.

To end this section, we examine how Newton's law of universal gravitation matches up with the simpler model used previously in this course for motion near the surface of the Earth. When modelling motion close to the Earth it is customary to assume, as we have done in earlier units, that the force on a particle of mass m is directed vertically downwards and has the constant magnitude mg, where $g = 9.81\,\mathrm{m\,s^{-2}}$. More generally, under the assumption that the Earth is a spherically symmetric distribution of mass M, at any point $\mathbf{r}$ on or above the Earth's surface the gravitational force is

$$\mathbf{F}(\mathbf{r}) = -\frac{GmM}{r^2}\mathbf{e}_r,$$

using the centre of the Earth as the origin.

Clearly the two descriptions agree as to the direction of the gravitational force, since $-\mathbf{e}_r$, being directed towards the centre of the Earth, is always 'vertically downwards' from a local point of view. It remains then to compare the two expressions for the magnitude.

*Exercise 3.2

(a) Show that $g = GM/R^2$, where R is the radius of the Earth.

(b) Estimate the mass M of the Earth, given that $R = 6.371 \times 10^6$ m, $g = 9.81\,\mathrm{m\,s^{-2}}$ and $G = 6.673 \times 10^{-11}\,\mathrm{m^3\,kg^{-1}\,s^{-2}}$.

Exercise 3.3

Given that the acceleration due to gravity is $9.81\,\mathrm{m\,s^{-2}}$ at the Earth's surface, and that the radius of the Earth is 6.371×10^6 m, find the acceleration due to gravity at a height of 10^4 m above the Earth's surface.

It can be shown that the model of a constant gravitational force is a reasonable model for heights of a few kilometres above the Earth's surface. Consider two points P_1 and P_2 lying on the same radial line, with P_1 on the surface and P_2 at a distance h above it (see Figure 3.3). We wish to compare the force of gravity at points P_1 and P_2 on a particle of mass m.

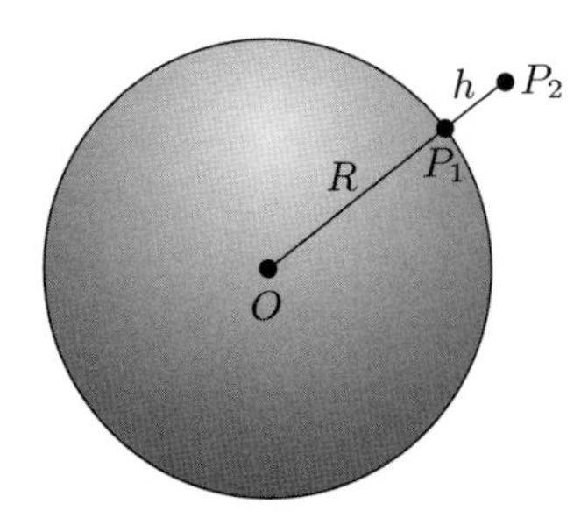

Figure 3.3

At both points the force on the particle m is 'downward', along the direction of $-\mathbf{e}_r$. The magnitude of the force at P_1 on the Earth's surface (at radius R) is

$$F_1 = \frac{GmM}{R^2}.$$

At the point P_2, which is a height h above P_1, the force has magnitude

$$F_2 = \frac{GmM}{(R+h)^2}.$$

The ratio of these two magnitudes is

$$\frac{F_2}{F_1} = \frac{R^2}{(R+h)^2} = \frac{1}{(1+h/R)^2} \simeq 1 - \frac{2h}{R}.$$

Here we have taken the first two terms of the binomial expansion for $(1+h/R)^{-2}$.

Provided that h is small compared to R, the force of gravity at point P_2 is nearly equal to that at P_1.

End-of-section Exercise

Exercise 3.4

The Moon has radius 1.738×10^6 m and mass 7.353×10^{22} kg.

(a) Find the magnitude of the acceleration due to gravity on the surface of the Moon.

(b) At what height above the surface of the Moon will the magnitude of the acceleration due to gravity be 90% of its value at the surface?

---

4 Motion under a central force

In Section 3 we introduced Newton's law of universal gravitation. In this section and the next we shall develop a mathematical model to describe the orbit of a body under the gravitational attraction of a much larger body. To a reasonably good approximation, this model applies to the orbits of a planet around the Sun, of a moon around a planet, of an artificial satellite around a planet or around the Sun, and of comets around the Sun. The model will enable us to derive Kepler's three laws of planetary motion, which were stated and explained in Section 2.

The modelling assumptions that suffice to yield these laws are as follows.

Assumptions for gravitational orbits

(1) Newtonian mechanics, including Newton's three laws of mechanics and his law of universal gravitation, is applicable.
(2) All forces other than the gravitational attraction between the two bodies may be neglected. (In particular, the gravitational effect of other celestial objects is ignored.)
(3) One body is much more massive than the other.
(4) Both bodies have a spherically symmetric distribution of mass.

Of these assumptions, (1) is the hardest to improve upon and (3) is the easiest, while (2) and (4) are intermediate. It was only with Einstein's general theory of relativity in the early twentieth century that small corrections to Newton's laws (Assumption (1)) were introduced. This was done in order to explain small departures from the Newtonian prediction that had been observed in the orbit of the planet Mercury. We could (but will not!) improve upon Assumption (3) using the mathematics developed in the course. (It turns out that both bodies move in elliptical orbits about their common centre of mass.) This improvement is required, for example, to describe the orbits of two stars of comparable mass under their mutual gravitational attraction.

In this section we shall concentrate on the consequences of the direction of the gravitational forces between two particles being along their line of separation and the magnitude of the forces being a function of their separation. We will leave the consequences of this force being an inverse square law until the next section.

4.1 Central forces and angular momentum

By Assumption (3) above, we suppose that the more massive body (of mass M) does not move at all under the gravitational action of the lighter body (of mass m). The centre of mass of the more massive body coincides with its geometric centre, by Assumption (4). For convenience, we choose the origin of coordinates to be at this centre, as shown in Figure 4.1 overleaf.

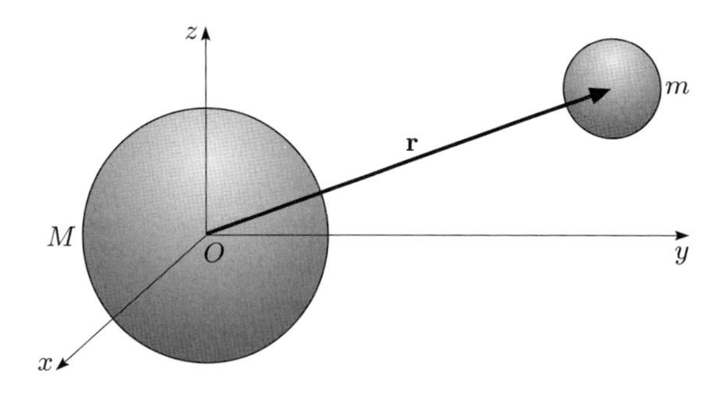

Figure 4.1

It was shown in *Unit 19* that the centre of mass of a system of particles acted upon by external forces moves as if all the mass of the system were concentrated there. We may therefore treat the motion of the centre of mass of the lighter body as if it were a particle. Again, by Assumption (4), the centre of mass of the lighter body coincides with its geometric centre. Furthermore, since both bodies are assumed to be spherically symmetric (Assumption (4)), we can apply the result stated in Section 3, which equates the gravitational forces exerted by two spherically symmetric bodies with those between two particles of masses M and m. The resulting two-particle view is shown in Figure 4.2, where $\mathbf{r}$ is the position vector of the lighter particle.

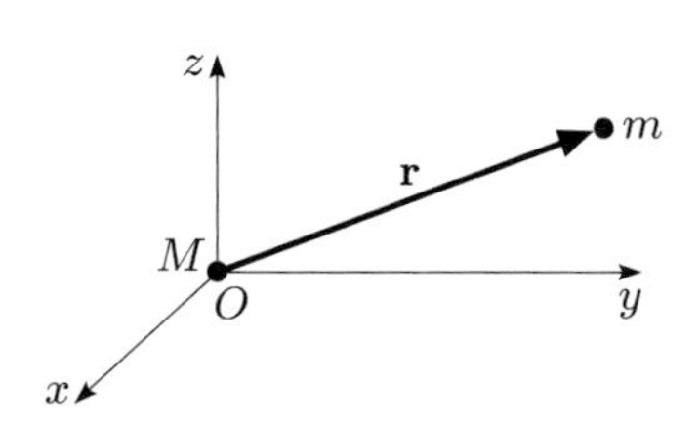

Figure 4.2

There is a simplifying feature of this model which can be shown at the outset: *the motion of the particle of mass m occurs in a plane.* The proof of this statement rests on the fact that the gravitational force exerted on the particle of mass m is a *central force.* In general, this term describes a force whose direction is from the source of the force directly towards (or away from) the particle. If the source is at the origin, this means that a central force has the direction of $\mathbf{r}$ or of $-\mathbf{r}$. The definition is as follows.

Definition of a central force

A **central force F**, acting from the origin on a particle with position vector $\mathbf{r}$, has the form

$$\mathbf{F}(\mathbf{r}) = g(\mathbf{r})\mathbf{r}, \tag{4.1}$$

where $g(\mathbf{r}) = g(x, y, z)$ is a scalar function of position.

Exercise 4.1

Which of the following are central forces (where K is a constant)?

(i) $\mathbf{F}(\mathbf{r}) = K\mathbf{r}$

(ii) $\mathbf{F}(\mathbf{r}) = \dfrac{K}{r^2}\mathbf{r}$

(iii) $\mathbf{F}(\mathbf{r}) = \dfrac{Kx}{r^2}\mathbf{r}$

(iv) $\mathbf{F}(\mathbf{r}) = \dfrac{Ky}{r^2}\mathbf{j}$

(v) $\mathbf{F}(\mathbf{r}) = \dfrac{K}{r^2}(\mathbf{i} + \mathbf{j} + \mathbf{k})$

(vi) $\mathbf{F}(\mathbf{r}) = \dfrac{K}{r}(x\mathbf{i} + y\mathbf{j} + z\mathbf{k})$

Exercise 4.2

What is the scalar function $g(\mathbf{r})$ for the gravitational force given by Equation (3.2)?

If the force is in the direction of $\mathbf{r}$, it is said to be **repulsive**, whereas if it is in the direction of $-\mathbf{r}$, it is said to be **attractive**. So the gravitational force is attractive.

The angular momentum $\mathbf{L}$ of a particle with mass m and position vector $\mathbf{r}$ relative to the origin is, as defined in *Unit 20* Section 4,

$$\mathbf{L} = \mathbf{r} \times m\dot{\mathbf{r}}. \tag{4.2}$$

In *Units 20* and *27* we used the symbol $\boldsymbol{l}$ for angular momentum. Throughout this unit we use the symbol $\mathbf{L}$ for angular momentum to avoid any confusion with the symbol l used to represent the semi-latus rectum of an ellipse.

This definition is not confined to two-dimensional motion, though the main application in *Unit 20* was to motion in a circle. However, it is a consequence of the results of Exercise 4.3 below that if the particle is acted upon by a *central* force then its motion *does* lie in a plane.

*Exercise 4.3

Consider a particle with position $\mathbf{r} \neq \mathbf{0}$ and velocity $\dot{\mathbf{r}} \neq \mathbf{0}$, acted upon solely by a central force.

(a) Use the torque law $\dot{\mathbf{L}} = \mathbf{\Gamma}$ (*Unit 20* Section 4) to show that $\mathbf{L}$ is a constant vector.

(b) If $\mathbf{L} \neq \mathbf{0}$, show that the position vector $\mathbf{r}$ is perpendicular to the angular momentum $\mathbf{L}$.

(c) If $\mathbf{L} = \mathbf{0}$, show that the position vector $\mathbf{r}$ and the velocity $\dot{\mathbf{r}}$ are parallel or anti-parallel.

In part (a) of Exercise 4.3 you saw that the angular momentum $\mathbf{L}$ of the particle is a constant and so, as long as $\mathbf{L} \neq \mathbf{0}$, has a fixed direction. Furthermore, using part (b) of this exercise, the position vector $\mathbf{r}$ of the particle is always perpendicular to this fixed direction. Hence, when $\mathbf{L}$ is non-zero, the particle acted upon by a central force moves in the plane perpendicular to the fixed direction of $\mathbf{L}$, as shown in Figure 4.3. Also (from part (c) of the above exercise), in the event that $\mathbf{L}$ is zero, the position vector $\mathbf{r}$ and the velocity $\dot{\mathbf{r}}$ of the particle are parallel or anti-parallel. So the particle is moving along the line joining it to the origin and, as the total force is central, it must continue to move along this line. So, in this case too, the particle always lies in a fixed plane (in fact, on a fixed line). In general, a particle that is acted on by a cental force moves in a fixed plane and its angular momentum $\mathbf{L}$ is a constant. In particular, these results apply to a particle in a gravitational orbit. These conclusions arise from the fact that the gravitational force is *central* and not from any other detail of its form.

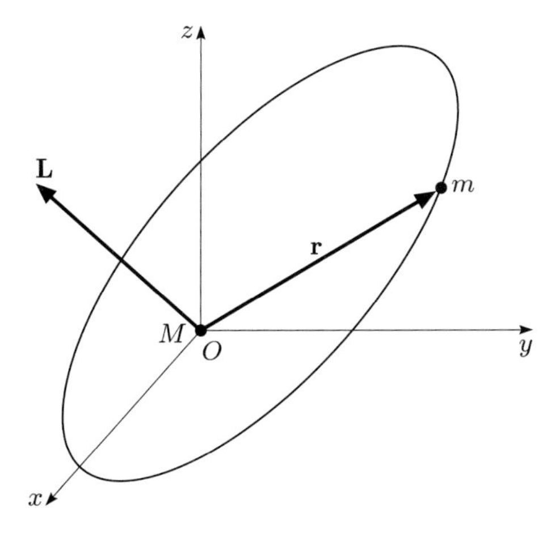

Figure 4.3

Motion under a central force

A particle with mass m and position vector $\mathbf{r}$, which moves solely under the action of a central force, has constant angular momentum

$$\mathbf{L} = \mathbf{r} \times m\dot{\mathbf{r}}. \tag{4.2}$$

Its motion is confined to the plane perpendicular to the direction of $\mathbf{L}$ when $\mathbf{L}$ is non-zero, and to a straight line if $\mathbf{L} = \mathbf{0}$.

As the motion under the action of a central force is planar, we can now choose to orient the coordinate axes so that the motion lies in the (x, y)-plane, as indicated in Figure 4.4. This will permit us to apply the apparatus of plane polar coordinates, which was developed in Section 1.

It has yet to be established that the planar motion of a particle in gravitational orbit is as simple as that depicted here. For example, some other central forces lead to spiralling motions.

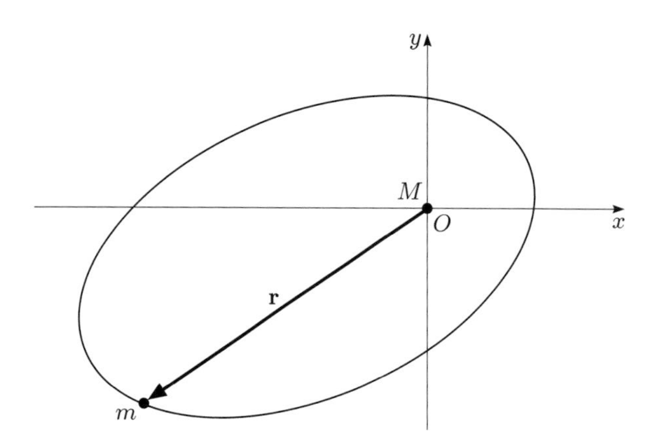

Figure 4.4

Since the angular momentum $\mathbf{L}$ is a constant vector, both its direction and magnitude are constant. The constancy of its *direction* sufficed above to show that the orbit always lies in a plane. This is actually *part* of the content of Kepler's first law, which asserts that the orbits are ellipses and therefore plane figures.

We have not yet used the additional information that the *magnitude* of $\mathbf{L}$ is constant, and this is actually sufficient to prove Kepler's second law. As you may recall from Section 2, this law relates to the rate at which area A is swept out by the line joining a planet to the Sun (which corresponds here to the line of the position vector $\mathbf{r}$). We showed that dA/dt was related to the radial distance r and the angular velocity $\dot{\theta}$ by the equation $dA/dt = \frac{1}{2}r^2\dot{\theta}$ (Equation (2.11)).

Kepler's second law states that dA/dt is constant, which from above is equivalent to the condition

$$r^2\dot{\theta} = \text{constant}. \tag{4.3}$$

In the following exercise you are asked to show that Kepler's second law is a consequence of the constancy of angular momentum.

*Exercise 4.4

By expressing $\mathbf{r}$ and $\dot{\mathbf{r}}$ in terms of the plane polar unit vectors $\mathbf{e}_r$ and $\mathbf{e}_\theta$, show that the angular momentum of a particle moving in the (x, y)-plane is $\mathbf{L} = L_z\mathbf{k}$, where

$$L_z = mr^2\dot{\theta}.$$

Using the result of Exercise 4.4, we can deduce that, for a particle moving solely under the action of a central force, the constancy of the angular momentum, and hence its magnitude, implies that $r^2\dot{\theta}$ = constant and Kepler's second law is valid.

In summary, thus far, we can say the following.

Central forces and Kepler's second law

Kepler's second law, and the fact that each planet moves in a plane, are consequences only of the fact that the gravitational force between a planet and the Sun is a central force; taken together, they amount to a statement of the conservation of angular momentum.

4.2 Isotropic central forces

With the force of gravity in mind as the ultimate target, we now specialize from central forces to the more restricted case of *isotropic* central forces. These are central forces for which the magnitude depends only on the radial distance from the origin.

Isotropic means 'the same in all directions'.

Definition of an isotropic central force

An **isotropic central force F**, acting from the origin on a particle with position vector $\mathbf{r}$, has the form

$$\mathbf{F}(\mathbf{r}) = f(r)\mathbf{e}_r, \qquad (4.4)$$

where r is the distance from the origin, and $\mathbf{e}_r = \mathbf{r}/r$.

A central force was defined by $\mathbf{F}(\mathbf{r}) = g(\mathbf{r})\mathbf{r}$, which is equivalent to

$$\mathbf{F}(\mathbf{r}) = g(\mathbf{r})r\mathbf{e}_r.$$

This force is also isotropic if $g(\mathbf{r}) = g(r)$.

Exercise 4.5

(a) Which of the forces listed in Exercise 4.1 are isotropic central forces?

(b) Show that the gravitational force is isotropic, and find the function $f(r)$ for this case.

One important property of isotropic central forces is that they are *conservative.*

Exercise 4.6

Use the curl test (*Block 6* page 151) to show that for a sufficiently simple domain if $\mathbf{F}(\mathbf{r})$ is an isotropic central force then it is conservative.

You showed that this was true for $f(r) = kr^n$ in *Unit 24* Exercise 4.4(b).

Now every conservative field $\mathbf{F}(\mathbf{r})$ has a potential function $U(\mathbf{r})$ such that $\mathbf{F} = -\mathbf{grad}\, U$.

Exercise 4.7

(a) If $\mathbf{F}(\mathbf{r}) = f(r)\mathbf{e}_r$, what is the potential function U in terms of f?

(b) Use the result of part (a) to find the potential function $U(\mathbf{r})$ for the gravitational force.

The potential function for isotropic central forces

The isotropic central force $\mathbf{F}(\mathbf{r}) = f(r)\mathbf{e}_r$ has a potential function $U(r)$ such that

$$U(r) = -\int f(r)dr, \tag{4.5}$$

or

$$f(r) = -\frac{dU}{dr}.$$

(Note that U is determined only up to the addition of a constant.)

In particular, for the gravitational force,

$$U(r) = -\frac{GmM}{r}. \tag{4.6}$$

So far as mechanics is concerned, the importance of conservative force fields is that the law of conservation of mechanical energy holds for them. Although this is true for *any* conservative force, we will derive this law for the special case of an isotropic central force. In order to do this, we start with Newton's second law for the motion of a particle of mass m acted upon by an isotropic central force.

Choosing our axes as in Figure 4.4, so that the orbit lies in the (x, y)-plane, Newton's second law gives

$$m\ddot{\mathbf{r}} = f(r)\mathbf{e}_r.$$

Since the right-hand side of this equation is directed along the unit vector $\mathbf{e}_r$, it makes sense to express the acceleration $\ddot{\mathbf{r}}$ in terms of plane polar coordinates, using Equation (1.4). The particle's equation of motion in the plane can then be written as

$$m(\ddot{r} - r\dot{\theta}^2)\mathbf{e}_r + \frac{m}{r}\frac{d}{dt}(r^2\dot{\theta})\mathbf{e}_\theta = f(r)\mathbf{e}_r,$$

from which we have

$$m(\ddot{r} - r\dot{\theta}^2) = f(r) \tag{4.7}$$

and

$$\frac{m}{r}\frac{d}{dt}(r^2\dot{\theta}) = 0.$$

The second equation can be integrated directly to give

$$mr^2\dot{\theta} = \text{constant} = L_z. \tag{4.8}$$

This is the *conservation of angular momentum*, which was shown in the previous subsection (Equation (4.3)) to be valid for any central force. This can be exploited to eliminate the variable $\dot{\theta}$ in Equation (4.7). Thus on putting $\dot{\theta} = L_z/(mr^2)$ into Equation (4.7), we obtain

$$m\ddot{r} - mr\left(\frac{L_z}{mr^2}\right)^2 = f(r)$$

or

$$m\ddot{r} = f(r) + \frac{L_z^2}{mr^3}. \tag{4.9}$$

Equations (4.8) and (4.9) contain, between them, the possibility of a complete solution to the problem of finding the orbit of a particle of mass m under the action of any isotropic central force. The procedure to do this would be as follows.

1. The initial conditions are the values of $\langle r, \theta \rangle$ and $\langle \dot{r}, \dot{\theta} \rangle$ at some initial time, say $t = 0$.
2. Since L_z is a constant, these initial conditions determine the value of L_z for all subsequent times, from Equation (4.8).
3. Equation (4.9) may be solved, either analytically if possible or numerically, to obtain an expression or values for $r(t)$, where $t > 0$.
4. This solution may be substituted into Equation (4.8) to obtain an expression for $\dot{\theta}(t)$, from which $\theta(t)$ can be found by integration.

In order to integrate Equation (4.9), we first multiply it by $\dot{r}$ to obtain

$$m\dot{r}\ddot{r} = \left(f(r) + \frac{L_z^2}{mr^3} \right) \dot{r}. \tag{4.10}$$

Writing $z = \dot{r}$ for clarity, we note that

$$\frac{d}{dt}(\tfrac{1}{2}m\dot{r}^2) = \frac{d}{dt}(\tfrac{1}{2}mz^2) = mz\frac{d}{dt}(z) = m\dot{r}\frac{d}{dt}(\dot{r}) = m\dot{r}\ddot{r}.$$

So Equation (4.10) can be written in the form

$$\frac{d}{dt}(\tfrac{1}{2}m\dot{r}^2) = \left(f(r) + \frac{L_z^2}{mr^3} \right) \frac{dr}{dt},$$

which can be integrated with respect to t to give

$$\tfrac{1}{2}m\dot{r}^2 = \int \left(f(r) + \frac{L_z^2}{mr^3} \right) \frac{dr}{dt} dt = \int \left(f(r) + \frac{L_z^2}{mr^3} \right) dr.$$

Now, using Equation (4.5), we have

$$\int f(r) dr = -U(r)$$

and

$$\int \frac{L_z^2}{mr^3} dr = -\frac{L_z^2}{2mr^2} \text{ (+ constant).}$$

Hence the integral of Equation (4.9) can be written as

$$\tfrac{1}{2}m\dot{r}^2 + \frac{L_z^2}{2mr^2} + U(r) = E, \tag{4.11}$$

Note that the energy E can be negative.

where E is a constant. In the next exercise you will see that this equation shows that the *total mechanical energy is conserved* for a particle moving under the action of an isotropic central force.

Exercise 4.8

Show that the conservation of total mechanical energy is equivalent to Equation (4.11) for a particle moving under the action of an isotropic central force.

Hint: You found an expression for the kinetic energy of a particle using polar coordinates in Exercise 1.4.

The equations of motion for a particle moving under the action of an isotropic central force

The equations of motion for a particle of mass m moving under an isotropic central force $\mathbf{F}(\mathbf{r}) = f(r)\mathbf{e}_r$ are

$$\frac{m}{r}\frac{d}{dt}(r^2\dot{\theta}) = 0$$

and

$$m\ddot{r} = f(r) + \frac{L_z^2}{mr^3}. \qquad (4.9)$$

Equivalently, the motion of the particle can be determined from the conservation of angular momentum,

$$mr^2\dot{\theta} = L_z, \quad \text{(a constant)} \qquad (4.8)$$

and the conservation of total mechanical energy,

$$\tfrac{1}{2}m\dot{r}^2 + \frac{L_z^2}{2mr^2} + U(r) = E, \qquad (4.11)$$

where

$$U(r) = -\int f(r)dr. \qquad (4.5)$$

We cannot proceed further with Step 3 of our procedure for finding the orbit of a particle without knowing the precise form of $f(r)$ (or equivalently $U(r)$). We will do this for the gravitational force in the next section. But we can obtain a great deal of qualitative information about the orbit from the shape of the graph of the potential function $U(r)$. Now, Equation (4.11) has the appearance of an energy equation for a particle moving in *one dimension.* The first term, $\frac{1}{2}m\dot{r}^2$, resembles the one-dimensional kinetic energy. Since the terms $L_z^2/(2mr^2) + U(r)$ in Equation (4.11) occupy the position of a one-dimensional potential energy function, we shall call this the **effective potential energy** and denote it by $U^{\text{eff}}(r)$. This gives

$$E = \tfrac{1}{2}m\dot{r}^2 + U^{\text{eff}}(r),$$

where the effective potential energy is

$$U^{\text{eff}}(r) = \frac{L_z^2}{2mr^2} + U(r). \qquad (4.12)$$

In summary, the *radial* motion of the particle is as if it were moving in one dimension, with $r > 0$, under the influence of a one-dimensional conservative force having potential energy function $U^{\text{eff}}(r)$. We analysed this type of motion in *Unit 8* Section 2, by using an energy diagram and finding the turning points of the motion. As the 'kinetic energy' $\frac{1}{2}m\dot{r}^2$ is non-negative, motion is only possible in regions where

$$E - U^{\text{eff}}(r) \geq 0, \qquad (4.13)$$

and the 'turning points' of the motion occur when

$$E - U^{\text{eff}}(r) = 0.$$

Looking at the graph of the function U^{eff}, and using the constancy of E, allows us to see whether there are any turning points for the radial motion. At turning points $\dot{r}$ vanishes, and the radial motion (usually) reverses direction. The details depend upon the precise form of the potential energy function U and the value of E.

If there are two turning points then these are the closest and furthest distances from the origin reached by the particle at the given value of energy E. If there is only one turning point then the motion is *unbound*, and the turning point is the distance of closest approach.

Consider, for example, a potential energy function that has the shape shown in Figure 4.5(a), which is the form of the gravitational potential energy with $k = GmM$. The resulting effective potential energy function $U^{\text{eff}}(r)$ is shown in Figure 4.5(b).

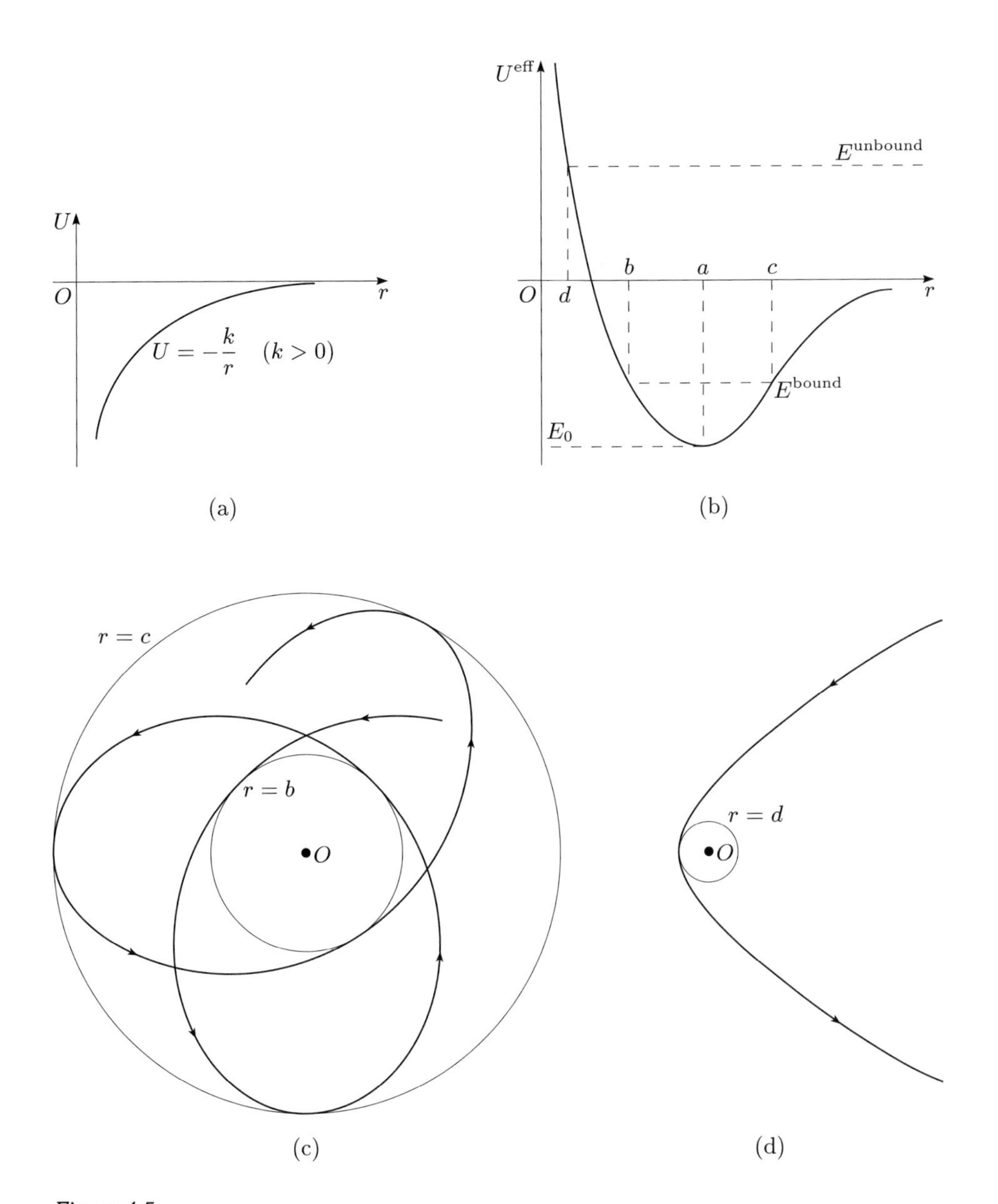

Figure 4.5

If $E < E_0$, $E - U^{\text{eff}}(r) < 0$ for all values of r and consequently no motion is possible.

If $E_0 < E < 0$, on the other hand, there are two turning points at $r = b$ and at $r = c$. The particle has inner and outer bounding radii, which are called *radial turning points*, at $r = b$ and $r = c$, and the motion is confined to the region $b \leq r \leq c$. Obviously, the particle is not really moving in a single dimension, since as r varies with time the angle θ is changing too. The type of motion for this case is illustrated in Figure 4.5(c).

If $E \geq 0$, from Figure 4.5(b) we see that there is only one radial turning point at $r = d$ and motion is confined to the region $r \geq d$, as shown in Figure 4.5(d), and all the orbits are unbounded.

Finally, if $E = E_0$, there is only one value of r for which $E - U^{\text{eff}}(r) \geq 0$, namely $r = a$, for which $E - U^{\text{eff}}(a) = 0$. So the orbit of the particle is the circle $r = a$.

Summarizing, we have shown the following.

- For $E < E_0$, no motion is possible.
- For $E = E_0$, the orbit is a circle of radius a centred on the origin.
- For $E_0 < E < 0$, there are two radial turning points at $r = b$ and $r = c$. The orbit is bound in the region $b \leq r \leq c$, as shown in Figure 4.5(c).
- For $E \geq 0$, there is only one turning point at $r = d$. The orbit is unbound in the region $r \geq d$, as illustrated in Figure 4.5(d).

Exercise 4.9

Consider a particle moving under the action of an isotropic central force whose potential energy function is

$$U(r) = -\frac{k}{r},$$

This is the form of the potential energy function for the gravitational force, with $k = GmM$.

where $k > 0$, so that its *effective* potential energy function is

$$U^{\text{eff}}(r) = \frac{L_z^2}{2mr^2} - \frac{k}{r}.$$

(a) Find the value $r = a$ for which the function $U^{\text{eff}}(r)$ has a minimum.

(b) Hence calculate the corresponding minimum value $E_0 = U^{\text{eff}}(a)$.

The gravitational potential energy has precisely the form shown in Figure 4.5(a). This means that bodies moving in a gravitational field can have either *bound* or *unbound* orbits. You will see in Section 5 that the bound orbits are *ellipses* and the unbound orbits are *parabolas* or *hyperbolas*, but we cannot conclude this without explicitly integrating Equation (4.11). At this stage, using Figure 4.5 and the result of Exercise 4.9, all we can conclude is that:

- for $E < -G^2m^3M^2/(2L_z^2)$, no motion is possible;
- for $E = -G^2m^3M^2/(2L_z^2)$, the orbit is a circle of radius $L_z^2/(Gm^2M)$;
- for $-G^2m^3M^2/(2L_z^2) < E < 0$, the orbit is bound;
- for $E \geq 0$, the orbit is unbound.

In this section, you have seen that particles moving under the action of an isotropic central force have planar orbits and satisfy the conservation of angular momentum and total mechanical energy. These two conservation laws can be used to predict whether the orbit is bound or unbound and to find the radial turning points. This is illustrated in the following exercise.

*Exercise 4.10

A particle of mass 3 kg is moving under the action of an attractive central force (measured in newtons)

$$\mathbf{F}(\mathbf{r}) = -\frac{45}{r^2}\mathbf{e}_r.$$

Initially its position (in metres) and velocity (in m s^{-1}) are

$$\mathbf{r}(0) = 2\mathbf{i} \quad \text{and} \quad \dot{\mathbf{r}}(0) = 3\mathbf{j}.$$

(a) What is the potential energy function for the particle's motion?

(b) Use the initial conditions to find the particle's angular momentum about the origin and also its total mechanical energy.

(c) Use the conservation of mechanical energy to show that in its motion the particle satisfies the equation

$$\dot{r}^2 = -6 + \frac{30}{r} - \frac{36}{r^2}.$$

(d) Hence find the minimum and maximum distances of the particle from the origin during its motion.

End-of-section Exercises

Exercise 4.11

A particle of mass m is launched with speed u perpendicular to the line that joins it to a spherically symmetric body of much larger mass M which is centred on the origin. At the instant of launch, the distance between the particle of mass m and the centre of the body of mass M is R. The only force acting on the particle is the gravitational force,

$$\mathbf{F}(\mathbf{r}) = -\frac{GmM}{r^2}\mathbf{e}_r.$$

(a) Find the magnitude L_z of the angular momentum of the particle.

(b) Find the total mechanical energy of the particle.

(c) Show that the motion will be bound provided that $u^2 < 2GM/R$.

The particle's speed of launch u and distance of launch R are related by the condition $u^2 = GM/(2R)$.

(d) Find the total mechanical energy, and show that the resulting orbit is bound.

(e) Find r_{min} and r_{max}, the respective smallest and largest distances of the particle from the centre of the attracting body of mass M.

Exercise 4.12

A particle of mass 1 kg moves in a planar orbit under the influence of an attractive central force (in newtons)

$$\mathbf{F}(\mathbf{r}) = -4r\mathbf{e}_r$$

at distance r metres from the origin.

(a) Find a potential energy function $U(r)$ for the particle's motion.

(b) If the initial position (in metres) and velocity (in m s^{-1}) of the particle are $\mathbf{r}(0) = \mathbf{i}$ and $\dot{\mathbf{r}}(0) = 4\mathbf{j}$ respectively, show that

$$\dot{r}^2 = 20 - 4r^2 - 16r^{-2}.$$

(c) Hence find the maximum and minimum distances from the origin of the particle in its orbit.

5 Planetary orbits

5.1 The equation of gravitational orbits

In this final section, we achieve our goal of finding the equation of the orbit of a body moving under the gravitational attraction of a second much more massive body. For an isotropic central force

$$\mathbf{F}(\mathbf{r}) = f(r)\mathbf{e}_r,$$

you saw in the previous section that, using the conservation of angular momentum

$$mr^2\dot{\theta} = L_z \quad \text{(a constant)} \tag{4.8}$$

the radial equation of motion

$$m(\ddot{r} - r\dot{\theta}^2) = f(r) \tag{4.7}$$

could be rewritten in the form

$$m\ddot{r} = f(r) + \frac{L_z^2}{mr^3}. \tag{4.9}$$

We integrated this once to obtain

$$\tfrac{1}{2}m\dot{r}^2 + \frac{L_z^2}{2mr^2} + U(r) = E, \tag{4.11}$$

where the potential energy function $U(r)$ is given by

$$U(r) = -\int f(r)dr. \tag{4.5}$$

This equation is equivalent to the conservation of total mechanical energy.

Knowing the function $f(r)$ (or equivalently $U(r)$), we can now, in principle, integrate Equation (4.11) to find $r(t)$. This solution can be substituted into Equation (4.8) to obtain a differential equation for $\theta(t)$, which can, in its turn, be integrated. We will then have completed Steps 3 and 4 of the procedure on page 155 of Section 4 for finding the equations of the orbits of an isotropic central force.

However, in the case of the gravitational force, for which

$$f(r) = -\frac{GmM}{r^2},$$

it turns out that it is simpler to revert to consideration of the radial equation

$$m\ddot{r} = \frac{L_z^2}{mr^3} - \frac{GmM}{r^2} \tag{5.1}$$

and to seek to obtain from this equation a relation of the form $r = r(\theta)$ to describe gravitational orbits. To do so, we apply the chain rule of differentiation to convert Equation (5.1), which specifies a function $r(t)$, to an equation for $r(\theta)$. For the first derivative, $\dot{r}$, we have

$$\dot{r} = \frac{dr}{dt} = \frac{d\theta}{dt}\frac{dr}{d\theta} = \dot{\theta}\frac{dr}{d\theta}.$$

From Equation (4.8), $\dot{\theta}$ can be replaced by $L_z/(mr^2)$, where L_z is a constant. The previous equation can then be expressed as

$$\dot{r} = \frac{L_z}{mr^2}\frac{dr}{d\theta}$$

or, in a form which will shortly be convenient, as

$$\dot{r} = -\frac{L_z}{m}\frac{d}{d\theta}\left(\frac{1}{r}\right). \tag{5.2}$$

The equation of motion contains $\ddot{r}$, which may be written in terms of a derivative with respect to θ by a further application of the chain rule. Thus, we obtain

$$\ddot{r} = \frac{d}{dt}(\dot{r}) = \frac{d\theta}{dt}\frac{d}{d\theta}(\dot{r}) = \dot{\theta}\frac{d}{d\theta}(\dot{r})$$

which, after another use of the relation $\dot{\theta} = L_z/(mr^2)$ and substitution for $\dot{r}$ from Equation (5.2), becomes

$$\ddot{r} = -\frac{L_z^2}{m^2r^2}\frac{d^2}{d\theta^2}\left(\frac{1}{r}\right). \tag{5.3}$$

Equation (5.1) can now be written as

$$-\frac{L_z^2}{mr^2}\frac{d^2}{d\theta^2}\left(\frac{1}{r}\right) = \frac{L_z^2}{mr^3} - \frac{GmM}{r^2}.$$

Defining

$$u(\theta) = \frac{1}{r(\theta)} \tag{5.4}$$

gives, after some rearrangement,

$$\frac{d^2u}{d\theta^2} + u(\theta) = \frac{Gm^2M}{L_z^2}. \tag{5.5}$$

Equations (5.4) and (5.5) contain the information necessary to deduce the orbit $r = r(\theta)$. You have met equations like Equation (5.5) many times. It is a second-order, constant-coefficient, inhomogeneous differential equation, whose general solution has two arbitrary constants. One way of writing the solution is

For example, in *Unit 7* Exercises 4.3 and 4.5 a similar equation was derived when modelling the motion of a particle suspended from a model spring in a uniform gravitational field.

$$u(\theta) = B\cos(\theta - \theta_0) + \frac{Gm^2M}{L_z^2}. \tag{5.6}$$

The two arbitrary constants in this solution are the amplitude B and the phase θ_0. We can assume that B is non-negative. This represents no loss of generality, since the sign of the term $B\cos(\theta - \theta_0)$ may be changed by adding π to the arbitrary phase θ_0. The orbital equation is obtained from Equation (5.6) on using Equation (5.4) to replace u by $1/r$. After multiplying through by

$$l = \frac{L_z^2}{Gm^2M} \tag{5.7}$$

and putting $e = Bl$, the orbital equation can be written as

$$\frac{l}{r(\theta)} = 1 + e\cos(\theta - \theta_0). \tag{5.8}$$

Here B is a non-negative but otherwise arbitrary constant, so the same is true of e.

Equations (5.7) and (5.8), together with the knowledge that L_z (or, equivalently, l) and e are constants, provide the required mathematical description of gravitational orbits for the model outlined at the beginning of Section 4. The remainder of this section will be spent in examining the implications of these results.

Note first that the introduction of the symbols l and e has permitted us to write the orbital equation in a form which is identical to Equation (2.9). Provided that $e < 1$, therefore, Equation (5.8) represents an *ellipse* with eccentricity e and semi-latus rectum l.

The terms 'eccentricity' and 'semi-latus rectum' are used to describe e and l whether or not the orbit is an ellipse.

*Exercise 5.1

Equation (5.8), with $l > 0$ and $e \geq 0$, describes a general gravitational orbit.

(a) By considering the possible values of the right-hand side of this equation, show that the distance of closest approach of the particle of mass m to the origin occurs at the angle $\theta = \theta_0$, and has the value

$$r_{\text{min}} = \frac{l}{1+e}.$$

(b) Show that, when $e < 1$, the maximum distance of the particle of mass m from the origin occurs at the angle $\theta = \theta_0 + \pi$, and has the value

$$r_{\text{max}} = \frac{l}{1-e}.$$

(c) Show that, when $e \geq 1$, there is no maximum value of r.

(d) From parts (a)–(c), give conditions on the eccentricity e which characterize bound and unbound orbits.

From the results of Exercise 5.1 we can sketch the possible types of orbit that Equation (5.8) represents. This is done in Figure 5.1. When $0 \leq e < 1$, the orbits are closed (ellipses) with closest and furthest distances r_{min} and r_{max}, respectively. When $e \geq 1$, the orbits are unbound (hyperbolas or parabolas), and only the distance of closest approach r_{min} is defined. In either case, the orbit is symmetrical about the line $\theta = \theta_0$.

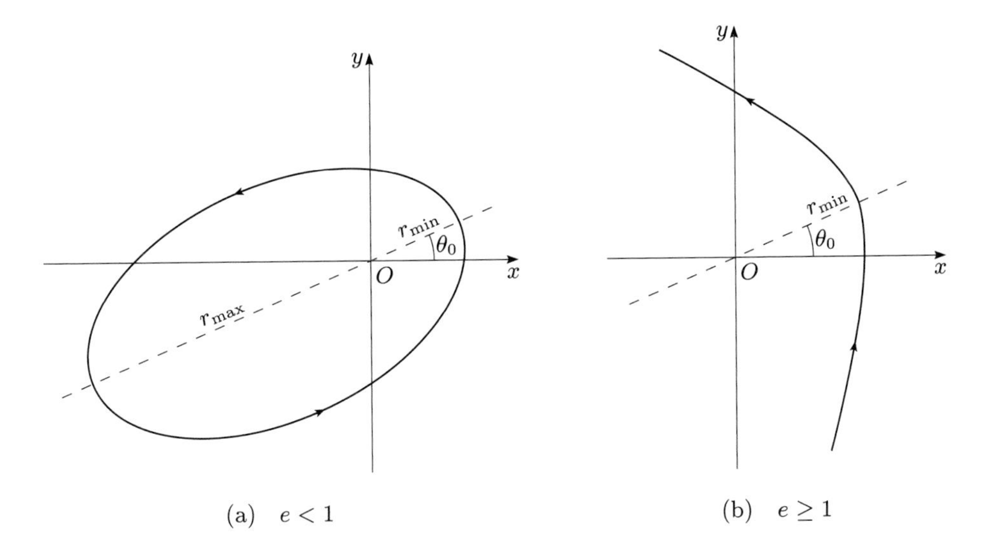

Figure 5.1

It is convenient to consider the gravitational orbits with respect to a set of axes that are rotated anticlockwise by an angle θ_0 from those of Figure 5.1. This is equivalent to choosing $\theta_0 = 0$ in the orbital equation, or to choosing the x-axis to coincide with an orbital symmetry, and represents no loss of generality. In place of Equation (5.8) we then have

$$\frac{l}{r} = 1 + e\cos\theta, \tag{5.9}$$

where the semi-latus rectum l is given as before by Equation (5.7). The corresponding pictures for the orbits are shown in Figure 5.2.

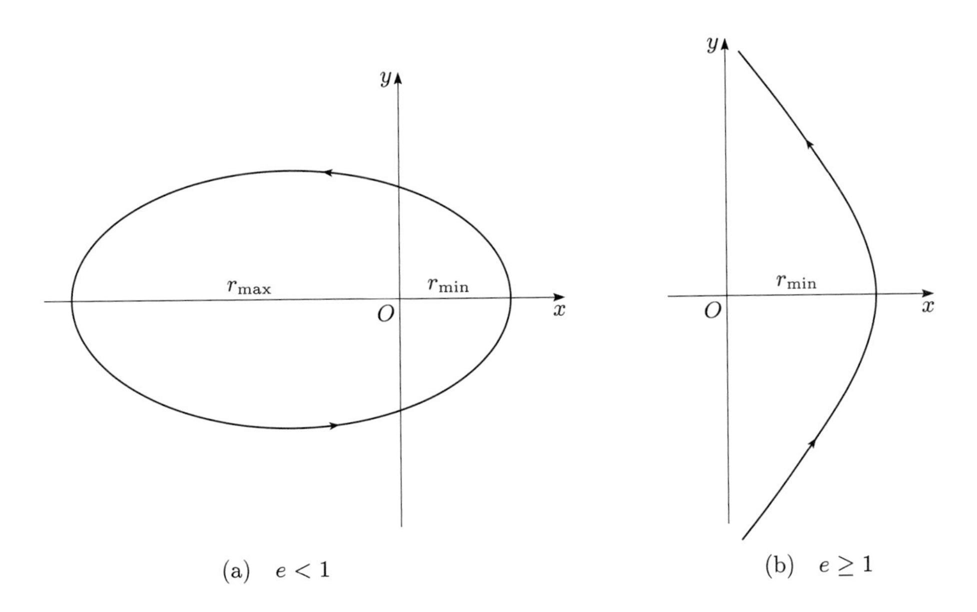

Figure 5.2

Values for the constants l and e in Equation (5.9) can be calculated in a specific case from experimental observations, and this can be done in various ways. For example, suppose that the distance of closest approach r_{min} and the corresponding angular velocity $\dot{\theta}$ have been measured, and that the value of the central mass M is known. Then a value for L_z/m can be obtained from Equation (4.8). This leads in turn to a value for l from Equation (5.7) and a value for e from the result of Exercise 5.1(a).

The energy analysis carried out in Section 4 predicted that gravitational motion will be bound if the total mechanical energy E satisfies the inequality $U^{\text{eff}}_{\text{min}} \le E < 0$, and unbound if $E \ge 0$. It is to be expected that these predictions are related to those obtained in terms of the eccentricity e in Exercise 5.1, namely, that an orbit is bound if $e < 1$ and unbound if $e \ge 1$. We consider this relationship in the example below.

This analysis was based on Equations (4.11) and (4.12), together with Figure 4.5(b).

Example 5.1

Show that the total mechanical energy can be written as

$$E = \frac{GmM}{2l}(e^2 - 1). \tag{5.10}$$

Hence verify that the condition $E \ge 0$ for unbound orbits is equivalent to $e \ge 1$, and that the condition $E < 0$ for bound orbits is equivalent to $e < 1$ (given that $e \ge 0$).

Solution

From Equation (4.11), E can be written as

$$E = \tfrac{1}{2}m\dot{r}^2 + \frac{L_z^2}{2mr^2} - \frac{GmM}{r}.$$

Using Equation (5.2) for $\dot{r}$, this becomes

$$E = \tfrac{1}{2}m\frac{L_z^2}{m^2}\left[\frac{d}{d\theta}\left(\frac{1}{r}\right)\right]^2 + \frac{L_z^2}{2mr^2} - \frac{GmM}{r}.$$

From Equation (5.7) for l, this is

$$E = \frac{GmM}{2l}\left\{\left[\frac{d}{d\theta}\left(\frac{l}{r}\right)\right]^2 + \left(\frac{l}{r}\right)^2 - 2\left(\frac{l}{r}\right)\right\}.$$

But l/r is given in terms of θ by Equation (5.9), so that

$$E = \frac{GmM}{2l}[e^2\sin^2\theta + (1 + e\cos\theta)^2 - 2(1 + e\cos\theta)].$$

On simplifying, this gives

$$E = \frac{GmM}{2l}(e^2 - 1).$$

So the condition $E \ge 0$ for unbound orbits corresponds to $e \ge 1$, and the condition $E < 0$ for bound orbits corresponds to $e < 1$. (Although this outcome is expected, it represents a useful cross-check on the results achieved.) ■

Equation of gravitational orbits

The Newtonian model for the gravitational orbit of a spherically symmetric body of mass m around a spherically symmetric body of much larger mass M located at the origin leads to the orbital equation

$$\frac{l}{r} = 1 + e\cos\theta, \tag{5.9}$$

where the eccentricity e is non-negative and the semi-latus rectum l is given by

$$l = \frac{L_z^2}{Gm^2M}. \tag{5.7}$$

Here L_z is the constant magnitude of the angular momentum of the orbiting body.

The eccentricity e of the orbit is related to the energy E of the particle by

$$E = \frac{GmM}{2l}(e^2 - 1). \tag{5.10}$$

If $0 \leq e < 1$ then Equation (5.9) describes an ellipse.

5.2 Planets and comets

In this final subsection we shall verify the statement made at the beginning of Section 4 that Kepler's laws of planetary motion are consequences of our model based on Newton's laws. Following this there is a short discussion about the orbits of comets.

Kepler's first law says that each planetary orbit is an ellipse, with the Sun at one focus. You showed in Exercise 4.3 that a planet's orbit lies in a plane because gravity is a *central* force. According to the model, you saw in the previous subsection that a gravitational orbit within this plane has an equation of the form

$$\frac{l}{r} = 1 + e\cos\theta, \tag{5.9}$$

where the semi-latus rectum l and the eccentricity e are positive constants for a particular planet.

Planetary orbits are clearly bound, and you established in Exercise 5.1 that $e < 1$ is a necessary and sufficient condition for bound motion. But for $e < 1$, Equation (5.9) is the equation developed in Section 2 to describe an ellipse with one focus at the origin. In our Newtonian model of planetary motion, the Sun is located at this focus. Thus Kepler's first law is a consequence of the model.

Equation (2.8).

Kepler's second law says that the line joining a planet to the Sun sweeps out equal areas in equal times. We showed in Section 4 that this is equivalent to the equation

$$r^2\dot{\theta} = \text{constant},$$

which expresses the constancy of the planet's angular momentum. This is again a consequence of gravity being a central force.

Kepler's third law is a relation between the period of a (bound) orbit and its lateral extent. It says that if T is the period and a is the semi-major axis of the elliptical orbit, then

$$T^2 = ka^3, \tag{5.11}$$

where k is a constant not depending on T or on a. In Exercise 2.5 of *Unit 20* you saw that Equation (5.11) holds for the special case of a circular orbit, where the eccentricity e is zero. In this case the semi-major and semi-minor axes both equal the radius of the circle. In Exercise 5.2 you are asked to establish Kepler's third law for any elliptical orbit.

*Exercise 5.2

Consider an elliptical orbit with semi-major axis a and semi-minor axis b. Then it is known from Exercise 2.2 that the area of the ellipse is πab. Also, the semi-latus rectum is

$$l = \frac{b^2}{a} = \frac{L_z^2}{Gm^2M}$$

(from Equations (2.5) and (5.7)), and the rate at which area is swept out is

$$\dot{A} = \tfrac{1}{2}r^2\dot{\theta} = \frac{L_z}{2m}$$

(from Equations (2.11) and (4.8)). Here L_z is the (constant) magnitude of the orbital angular momentum.

(a) From these facts, show that the orbital period, T, and the semi-major axis, a, are related by Kepler's third law, in the form

$$T^2 = ka^3, \quad \text{where} \quad k = \frac{4\pi^2}{GM}.$$

(b) Given that the orbital period of the Earth about the Sun is 365.256 days and the semi-major axis of its orbit is 149.6×10^6 km, use Kepler's third law to calculate the mass of the Sun.

Kepler's laws were formulated to describe the bound orbits of planets, so there is no reason to suppose that they should have significance for unbound orbits. The first and third laws can by their very nature apply only to the bound case. However, Kepler's second law applies even for unbound orbits since, as you have seen, it depends only upon the fact that gravity is a central force.

The Newtonian model that led to Equation (5.9) for gravitational orbits makes no assumption as to whether the motion is bound (with eccentricity $e < 1$) or unbound (with $e \geq 1$). As shown in Example 5.1, these conditions for the eccentricity are related to similar conditions on the total mechanical energy E of an orbit. If $E < 0$ for a body moving under the gravitational influence of the Sun, then the body has insufficient energy to 'escape' from the Sun's gravitational field and is confined to bound and periodic motion. Bodies with energy $E \geq 0$ may approach the Sun once, but are not 'captured' by it. These unbound orbits are called *parabolic* when $e = 1$ $(E = 0)$ and *hyperbolic* when $e > 1$ $(E > 0)$.

At any particular time there are millions of bodies in the solar system moving in nearly or actually unbound orbits under the Sun's gravity. These are the *comets*. Precise details of cometary orbits are not easily obtained, but it appears that most comets are in weakly bound orbits, with values of eccentricity e just less than unity. These comets therefore have highly eccentric, or flattened, orbits, as illustrated in Figure 5.3.

You investigated the connection between the eccentricity and shape of an ellipse in Exercise 2.4.

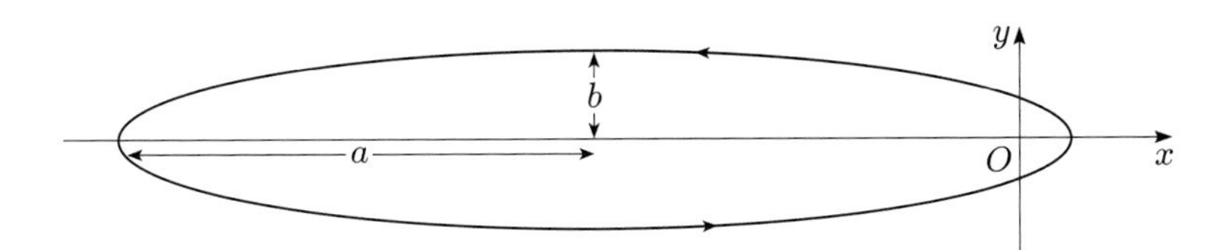

Figure 5.3

As a first approximation, the orbits of these bound comets obey Kepler's laws, but as they follow their elongated trajectories through the solar system they occasionally pass close to a planet. In these circumstances the gravitational effect of this third body can alter their orbits, even to the extent of raising their energies to positive values. Owing to its relatively large mass, Jupiter is a particular offender in this regard. The most famous bound comet is Halley's comet, which has a period of about 76 years and last passed close to the Sun in early 1986. Its orbit has eccentricity $e \simeq 0.97$ and a semi-major axis of about 18 times the distance from the Earth to the Sun. Comparable data for the planets and the Moon are given in the table below.

For each body except the Earth, the values given in the table for mass, period and semi-major axis are multiples of the corresponding values for the Earth.

Name	Mass	Period of revolution around Sun	Semi-major axis of orbit	Eccentricity of orbit
Sun	332 948.0			
Moon	0.012			0.055
Mercury	0.055	0.241	0.387	0.206
Venus	0.815	0.615	0.723	0.007
Earth	5.977×10^{24} kg	365.256 days	149.6×10^6 km	0.017
Mars	0.107	1.88	1.524	0.093
Jupiter	317.9	11.86	5.203	0.048
Saturn	95.1	29.46	9.539	0.056
Uranus	14.6	84.00	19.182	0.047
Neptune	17.2	164.79	30.058	0.009
Pluto	0.17	247.70	39.44	0.254

At any time there are comets in the solar system that are pursuing unbound trajectories. These bodies come in from distant places, pass partly around the Sun to a distance of closest approach and then recede, never to return to our solar system.

End-of-section Exercises

Exercise 5.3

For a gravitational orbit, it was shown in Example 5.1 that the total mechanical energy is

$$E = \frac{GmM}{2l}(e^2 - 1),$$

where m is the mass of the orbiting body, M is the mass of the central body, G is the gravitational constant, and e is the eccentricity of the orbit.

(a) For a bound orbit, show that

$$E = -\frac{GmM}{2a},$$

where a is the semi-major axis of the elliptical orbit.

(b) For any orbit, show that

$$E = \frac{GmM}{2r_{\text{min}}}(e - 1),$$

where r_{min} is the distance of closest approach of the orbiting body to the origin.

Exercise 5.4

A particle of mass m is launched with speed u at right angles to the line that joins it to a spherically symmetric body of much larger mass M. At the instant of launch, the distance between m and the centre of M is R. You showed in Exercise 4.11 that, for the subsequent motion, the angular momentum has magnitude

$$L_z = muR,$$

the total mechanical energy is

$$E = \tfrac{1}{2}mu^2 - \frac{GmM}{R},$$

and the motion is bound if

$$u^2 < \frac{2GM}{R}.$$

(a) For bound motion, show that the semi-major axis of the orbit is

$$a = \left(\frac{2}{R} - \frac{u^2}{GM}\right)^{-1}.$$

(b) For bound motion, find an expression for the eccentricity e in terms of u, R, M and G.

*Exercise 5.5

A particle of mass m moves under the action of a repulsive central force

$$\mathbf{F} = \frac{k}{r^3}\mathbf{e}_r,$$

where k is a positive constant.

(a) Show that the equation of radial motion of the particle is

$$m\ddot{r} = \left(k + \frac{L_z^2}{m}\right)\frac{1}{r^3}.$$

(b) Show that, in terms of $u = 1/r$, this can be rewritten in the form

$$\frac{d^2u}{d\theta^2} + \omega^2 u = 0,$$

where

$$\omega^2 = 1 + \frac{mk}{L_z^2}.$$

(c) Hence find the equation of the path of the particle.

Outcomes

After studying this unit you should be able to:

- calculate the semi-latus rectum and eccentricity of an ellipse from its semi-major and semi-minor axes;
- calculate the semi-major and semi-minor axes of an ellipse from its semi-latus rectum and eccentricity;
- understand and use the expressions for the position, velocity and acceleration in plane polar coordinates;
- understand the concepts of a central force and an isotropic central force;
- use the conservation of angular momentum and of mechanical energy to find the radial turning points of the motion of a particle moving under the action of an isotropic central force;
- understand and use Newton's law of universal gravitation;
- understand the assumptions underlying Newton's model for gravitational orbits;
- calculate the semi-latus rectum and eccentricity of the gravitational orbit of a particle from its angular momentum and energy;
- understand how Kepler's three laws of planetary motion can be derived from Newton's law of universal gravitation.

Solutions to the exercises

Section 1

1.1 From Equation (1.3), the velocity is

$$\dot{\mathbf{r}} = \dot{r}\mathbf{e}_r + r\dot{\theta}\mathbf{e}_\theta.$$

Differentiating this with respect to time, remembering that r, θ, $\mathbf{e}_r$ and $\mathbf{e}_\theta$ are all functions of time, and using the product rule, we obtain

$$\ddot{\mathbf{r}} = (\ddot{r}\mathbf{e}_r + \dot{r}\dot{\mathbf{e}}_r) + (\dot{r}\dot{\theta}\mathbf{e}_\theta + r\ddot{\theta}\mathbf{e}_\theta + r\dot{\theta}\dot{\mathbf{e}}_\theta).$$

Using Equations (1.2), this may be written as

$$\begin{aligned}\ddot{\mathbf{r}} &= (\ddot{r}\mathbf{e}_r + \dot{r}\dot{\theta}\mathbf{e}_\theta) + (\dot{r}\dot{\theta}\mathbf{e}_\theta + r\ddot{\theta}\mathbf{e}_\theta - r\dot{\theta}^2\mathbf{e}_r)\\ &= (\ddot{r} - r\dot{\theta}^2)\mathbf{e}_r + (2\dot{r}\dot{\theta} + r\ddot{\theta})\mathbf{e}_\theta,\end{aligned}$$

as required.

1.2 In the case $r = R$, where R is a constant, we have

$$\dot{r} = 0 \quad \text{and} \quad \ddot{r} = 0.$$

So the velocity is

$$\begin{aligned}\dot{\mathbf{r}} &= \dot{r}\mathbf{e}_r + r\dot{\theta}\mathbf{e}_\theta \qquad (1.3)\\ &= R\dot{\theta}\mathbf{e}_\theta,\end{aligned}$$

and the acceleration is

$$\begin{aligned}\ddot{\mathbf{r}} &= (\ddot{r} - r\dot{\theta}^2)\mathbf{e}_r + \frac{1}{r}\frac{d}{dt}(r^2\dot{\theta})\mathbf{e}_\theta \qquad (1.4)\\ &= -R\dot{\theta}^2\mathbf{e}_r + \frac{1}{R}\frac{d}{dt}(R^2\dot{\theta})\mathbf{e}_\theta\\ &= -R\dot{\theta}^2\mathbf{e}_r + R\ddot{\theta}\mathbf{e}_\theta.\end{aligned}$$

These two expressions agree with Equations (1.13) and (1.14) of *Unit 20*, which are the equations for the velocity and acceleration for circular motion.

1.3 We have

$$r = at^2, \quad \dot{r} = 2at, \quad \ddot{r} = 2a,$$
$$\theta = bt, \quad \dot{\theta} = b,$$

so that the velocity and acceleration are given by

$$\begin{aligned}\dot{\mathbf{r}} &= \dot{r}\mathbf{e}_r + r\dot{\theta}\mathbf{e}_\theta \qquad (1.3)\\ &= 2at\mathbf{e}_r + abt^2\mathbf{e}_\theta\end{aligned}$$

and

$$\begin{aligned}\ddot{\mathbf{r}} &= (\ddot{r} - r\dot{\theta}^2)\mathbf{e}_r + \frac{1}{r}\frac{d}{dt}(r^2\dot{\theta})\mathbf{e}_\theta \qquad (1.4)\\ &= (2a - ab^2t^2)\mathbf{e}_r + \frac{1}{at^2}\frac{d}{dt}(a^2bt^4)\mathbf{e}_\theta\\ &= a(2 - b^2t^2)\mathbf{e}_r + 4abt\mathbf{e}_\theta.\end{aligned}$$

1.4 The velocity of the particle is

$$\dot{\mathbf{r}} = \dot{r}\mathbf{e}_r + r\dot{\theta}\mathbf{e}_\theta,$$

and since $\mathbf{e}_r, \mathbf{e}_\theta$ are orthogonal unit vectors (with $\mathbf{e}_r \cdot \mathbf{e}_\theta = 0$ and $\mathbf{e}_r \cdot \mathbf{e}_r = \mathbf{e}_\theta \cdot \mathbf{e}_\theta = 1$) the kinetic energy is

$$\begin{aligned}T &= \tfrac{1}{2}m\dot{\mathbf{r}} \cdot \dot{\mathbf{r}}\\ &= \tfrac{1}{2}m(\dot{r}^2 + r^2\dot{\theta}^2).\end{aligned}$$

1.5 **(a)** The total force acting on the puck is $\mathbf{F} = -T\mathbf{e}_r$. Since r is a linear function of t, we have $\ddot{r} = 0$. Hence Newton's second law, in the form of Equations (1.5), gives

$$-mr\dot{\theta}^2 = -T \quad \text{and} \quad \frac{m}{r}\frac{d}{dt}(r^2\dot{\theta}) = 0.$$

These equations are equivalent to

$$mr\dot{\theta}^2 = T, \qquad (S.1)$$

$$\frac{d}{dt}(r^2\dot{\theta}) = 0. \qquad (S.2)$$

(b) From Equation (S.2), we know that $r^2\dot{\theta}$ is constant. Hence we have

$$r^2(t)\dot{\theta}(t) = r^2(0)\dot{\theta}(0).$$

This is used to substitute for $\dot{\theta}(t)$ in Equation (S.1), giving

$$\begin{aligned}T &= mr(t)\left(\frac{r^2(0)\dot{\theta}(0)}{r^2(t)}\right)^2 = \frac{mr^4(0)\dot{\theta}^2(0)}{r^3(t)}\\ &= \frac{mr^4(0)\dot{\theta}^2(0)}{(r(0) - kt)^3},\end{aligned}$$

as required.

(c) The string will break when $T = 500\,\text{N}$. From the answer to part (b), this occurs when

$$\frac{mr^4(0)\dot{\theta}^2(0)}{r^3} = 500,$$

or when

$$r = \left(mr^4(0)\dot{\theta}^2(0)/500\right)^{1/3}.$$

With $m = 0.1\,\text{kg}$, $r(0) = 1\,\text{m}$ and $\dot{\theta}(0) = 1\,\text{rad}\,\text{s}^{-1}$, this gives $r = (0.1/500)^{1/3} \simeq 0.06\,\text{m}$. The time at which the string breaks is then

$$t = (r(0) - r)/k = 60(1 - r) \simeq 60\,\text{s}.$$

(Note, from the form of the function for T, that for any finite breaking strength the string will break before the particle reaches the origin.)

1.6 Now

$$r = e^{kt}, \quad \theta = \omega t,$$

and so

$$\dot{r} = ke^{kt}, \quad \ddot{r} = k^2e^{kt} \quad \text{and} \quad \dot{\theta} = \omega.$$

Hence, using Equation (1.3), the velocity of the particle is

$$\begin{aligned}\dot{\mathbf{r}} &= \dot{r}\mathbf{e}_r + r\dot{\theta}\mathbf{e}_\theta\\ &= ke^{kt}\mathbf{e}_r + \omega e^{kt}\mathbf{e}_\theta.\end{aligned}$$

Using Equation (1.4), the acceleration is

$$\begin{aligned}\ddot{\mathbf{r}} &= (\ddot{r} - r\dot{\theta}^2)\mathbf{e}_r + \frac{1}{r}\frac{d}{dt}(r^2\dot{\theta})\mathbf{e}_\theta\\ &= (k^2e^{kt} - \omega^2e^{kt})\mathbf{e}_r + \frac{1}{e^{kt}}\frac{d}{dt}(\omega e^{2kt})\mathbf{e}_\theta\\ &= (k^2 - \omega^2)e^{kt}\mathbf{e}_r + 2k\omega e^{kt}\mathbf{e}_\theta.\end{aligned}$$

1.7 **(a)** Now

$$r = l(1 + e\cos\theta)^{-1}. \quad \text{(S.3)}$$

Differentiating this with respect to time, we obtain

$$\dot{r} = \frac{le\sin\theta}{(1 + e\cos\theta)^2}\dot{\theta}. \quad \text{(S.4)}$$

Now from Equation (1.7),

$$\dot{\theta} = \frac{L_z}{mr^2} = \frac{L_z}{ml^2}(1 + e\cos\theta)^2. \quad \text{(S.5)}$$

Substituting this in Equation (S.4), we obtain

$$\dot{r} = \frac{eL_z}{ml}\sin\theta, \quad \text{(S.6)}$$

as required. Differentiating this again with respect to time, we obtain

$$\ddot{r} = \frac{eL_z}{ml}\cos\theta\,\dot{\theta}.$$

Using Equations (S.5) and (S.3), this is equivalent to

$$\ddot{r} = \frac{eL_z^2}{m^2l^3}\cos\theta\,(1 + e\cos\theta)^2 = \frac{eL_z^2}{m^2l}\frac{\cos\theta}{r^2}. \quad \text{(S.7)}$$

(b) The force acting on the particle is

$$\mathbf{F} = m\ddot{\mathbf{r}} = m\left((\ddot{r} - r\dot{\theta}^2)\mathbf{e}_r + \frac{1}{r}\frac{d}{dt}(r^2\dot{\theta})\mathbf{e}_\theta\right).$$

Now, from Equation (1.7),

$$r^2\dot{\theta} = \frac{L_z}{m}.$$

So

$$\frac{d}{dt}(r^2\dot{\theta}) = 0$$

and

$$r\dot{\theta}^2 = \frac{L_z^2}{m^2r^3}.$$

Using these last two equations and Equation (S.7), we have

$$\mathbf{F} = m\Big(\frac{eL_z^2}{m^2l}\frac{\cos\theta}{r^2} - \frac{L_z^2}{m^2r^3}\Big)\mathbf{e}_r = \frac{L_z^2}{mlr^2}\Big(e\cos\theta - \frac{l}{r}\Big)\mathbf{e}_r = \frac{L_z^2}{mlr^2}[\,e\cos\theta - (1 + e\cos\theta)]\mathbf{e}_r = -\frac{L_z^2}{ml}\frac{1}{r^2}\mathbf{e}_r.$$

So the total force acting on the particle is an attractive force (this is shown by the minus sign) directed towards the origin (this is shown by $\mathbf{e}_r$) and its magnitude is inversely proportional to the square of the distance from the origin (this is shown by the $1/r^2$ factor).

Section 2

2.1 When $a = b$, the equation of the ellipse can be written as

$$X^2 + Y^2 = a^2.$$

This is the equation of a circle with radius a and centre the origin.

2.2 **(a)** The area A is twice the area of the upper half of the ellipse, namely

$$A = 2\int_{-a}^{a} Y(X)\,dX.$$

But from the definition of the ellipse (Equation (2.1)), the upper half of the ellipse (where $Y > 0$) has equation $Y = b\sqrt{1 - (X/a)^2}$. Thus the area is

$$A = 2b\int_{-a}^{a} \sqrt{1 - (X/a)^2}\,dX.$$

(b) Let $X = a\cos u$. When $X = -a$, $u = \pi$, when $X = a$, $u = 0$, and $dX = -a\sin u\,du$, so that the integral becomes

$$A = -2ab\int_{\pi}^{0} \sin^2 u\,du = 2ab\int_{0}^{\pi} \sin^2 u\,du = ab\int_{0}^{\pi} (1 - \cos 2u)\,du = \pi ab.$$

(Note that this becomes the familiar formula for the area of a circle if $a = b$.)

2.3 A circle corresponds to $a = b$, for which $q = 0$. Hence, for a circle, the foci coincide at the centre.

2.4 **(a)** When $b = a$ the eccentricity is $e = 0$.

(b) When $b = \frac{1}{2}a$, we have $e = \frac{1}{2}\sqrt{3} \simeq 0.8660$.

(c) When $b = \frac{1}{3}a$, we have $e = \frac{1}{3}\sqrt{8} \simeq 0.9428$.

The larger the semi-major axis a is compared to the semi-minor axis b, the more 'squashed' is the shape of the ellipse. This corresponds to larger values of the eccentricity e.

2.5 From Equation (2.4),

$$e^2 = 1 - \frac{b^2}{a^2},$$

which can be rearranged to give

$$b^2 = a^2(1 - e^2).$$

Hence, using Equation (2.5),

$$l = \frac{b^2}{a} = a(1 - e^2).$$

2.6 Refer to Figure 2.4 on page 143. During the interval $t_1 \leq t \leq t_2$, the planet is *closer* to the origin than it is during the interval $t_3 \leq t \leq t_4$. So to sweep through the same area (as it must do by Kepler's second law), it moves *faster* during the first interval.

2.7 If T is the period of a planet and a is the planet's semi-major axis, then Kepler's third law states that

$$T^2 = ka^3,$$

where k is a constant. If T_M, a_M are respectively the period and semi-major axis for Mars, and T_E, a_E are the corresponding parameters for the Earth, then we have

$$\left(\frac{T_M}{T_E}\right)^2 = \left(\frac{a_M}{a_E}\right)^3 \quad \text{or} \quad T_M = T_E\left(\frac{a_M}{a_E}\right)^{3/2}.$$

For the values given,

$$T_M = 365.256 \times (1.524)^{3/2} \simeq 687.2 \text{ days}.$$

2.8 **(a)** If $FF' > 2a$ then there can be no point P such that the sum of its distances from F and F' equals $2a$. If $FF' = 2a$, the point P must lie on the line segment FF', which gives us the trivial 'ellipse' consisting of the line segment FF'. So for a non-trivial ellipse we need $FF' < 2a$, that is, $FF' = 2ae$ for some number e with $0 < e < 1$.

(b) The position vector of P relative to F is $\mathbf{r}$; the position vector of F relative to F' is $2ae\mathbf{i}$; so by the triangle rule for adding vectors, the position vector of P relative to F' is $\mathbf{r} + 2ae\mathbf{i}$. Thus, from Equation (2.14),

$$|\mathbf{r}| + |\mathbf{r} + 2ae\mathbf{i}| = 2a,$$

which we can rewrite as

$$|\mathbf{r} + 2ae\mathbf{i}| = 2a - |\mathbf{r}|. \tag{S.8}$$

(c) Squaring both sides of Equation (S.8) we obtain

$$r^2 + 4ae(\mathbf{r} \cdot \mathbf{i}) + 4a^2e^2 = 4a^2 - 4ar + r^2.$$

Since $\mathbf{r} \cdot \mathbf{i} = r\cos\theta$, this leads to

$$a(1-e^2) = r(1 + e\cos\theta),$$

from which we obtain

$$\frac{l}{r} = 1 + e\cos\theta,$$

where $l = a(1-e^2)$.

2.9 From the equation of the ellipse, we see that $a = 13$ and $b = 12$. Using Equation (2.4), we have

$$e = \sqrt{1 - \frac{b^2}{a^2}} = \sqrt{1 - \frac{12^2}{13^2}} = \frac{5}{13}.$$

From Equation (2.5), we obtain

$$l = \frac{b^2}{a} = \frac{12^2}{13} = \frac{144}{13}.$$

So, from Equation (2.8), a polar representation of the ellipse is

$$\frac{144}{13r} = 1 + \frac{5}{13}\cos\theta,$$

or

$$\frac{1}{r} = \frac{1}{144}(13 + 5\cos\theta).$$

2.10 **(a)** Equation (2.6) is

$$l = a(1-e^2).$$

Rearranging this equation, we obtain

$$a = \frac{l}{1-e^2}. \tag{2.16}$$

Now, from Equation (2.5),

$$l = \frac{b^2}{a},$$

so that

$$b^2 = al = \frac{l^2}{1-e^2}.$$

Hence

$$b = \frac{l}{\sqrt{1-e^2}}, \tag{2.17}$$

where we have taken the positive square root because $a > 0$ and $b > 0$.

(b) The polar equation of the ellipse can be rearranged as

$$\frac{9}{5r} = 1 + \frac{4}{5}\cos\theta.$$

So $l = \frac{9}{5}$ and $e = \frac{4}{5}$. Hence

$$a = \frac{l}{1-e^2} = \frac{\frac{9}{5}}{1 - \frac{4^2}{5^2}} = 5$$

and

$$b = \frac{l}{\sqrt{1-e^2}} = \frac{\frac{9}{5}}{\sqrt{1 - \frac{4^2}{5^2}}} = 3.$$

Hence the Cartesian equation of the ellipse is

$$\frac{X^2}{5^2} + \frac{Y^2}{3^2} = 1.$$

Section 3

3.1 Equation (3.1) gives

$$\mathbf{F}_{ij} = -\frac{Gm_im_j}{|\mathbf{r}_i - \mathbf{r}_j|^3}(\mathbf{r}_i - \mathbf{r}_j)$$

as the force on a particle of mass m_i due to a particle of mass m_j. Hence, swapping the indices i and j, the force on a particle of mass m_j due to a particle of mass m_i is

$$\mathbf{F}_{ji} = -\frac{Gm_jm_i}{|\mathbf{r}_j - \mathbf{r}_i|^3}(\mathbf{r}_j - \mathbf{r}_i) = \frac{Gm_im_j}{|\mathbf{r}_i - \mathbf{r}_j|^3}(\mathbf{r}_i - \mathbf{r}_j),$$

where we have used the fact that $|\mathbf{r}_i - \mathbf{r}_j| = |\mathbf{r}_j - \mathbf{r}_i|$. Thus $\mathbf{F}_{ij} = -\mathbf{F}_{ji}$, and Newton's third law is satisfied by the gravitational force.

3.2 **(a)** The magnitude of the gravitational force on a particle of mass m at the Earth's surface (where $r = R$) is mg (from the simple model) and GmM/R^2 (from Newton's law of universal gravitation). Since these must be equal, we have $g = GM/R^2$.

(b) From the given values, we obtain

$$M = \frac{gR^2}{G} = \frac{9.81 \times (6.371 \times 10^6)^2}{6.673 \times 10^{-11}} \simeq 5.967 \times 10^{24} \text{ kg}.$$

(The accepted value for Earth's mass is 5.977×10^{24} kg.)

3.3 At height h above Earth's surface, the gravitational force on a particle of mass m has magnitude $GmM/(R+h)^2$, so that the gravitational acceleration at this height is

$$\frac{GM}{(R+h)^2} = \frac{gR^2}{(R+h)^2} = \frac{g}{(1+h/R)^2},$$

using the result $g = GM/R^2$ from Exercise 3.2(a).

With $g = 9.81\,\mathrm{m\,s^{-2}}$, $h = 10^4\,\mathrm{m}$ and $R = 6.371 \times 10^6\,\mathrm{m}$, this gives the value $9.78\,\mathrm{m\,s^{-2}}$ for the gravitational acceleration at a height of 10 km.

3.4 **(a)** Consider a particle of mass m on the surface of the Moon. If the radius and mass of the Moon are R and M respectively, the magnitude of the gravitational force acting on the particle is

$$F = \frac{GmM}{R^2}.$$

This force is equal to

$$F = mg_{\mathrm{M}},$$

where g_{M} is the magnitude of the acceleration due to gravity on the surface of the Moon. Hence

$$\begin{aligned} g_{\mathrm{M}} &= \frac{GM}{R^2} \\ &= \frac{(6.673 \times 10^{-11}) \times (7.353 \times 10^{22})}{(1.738 \times 10^6)^2} \\ &= 1.624\,\mathrm{m\,s^{-2}}. \end{aligned}$$

So the magnitude of the acceleration due to gravity on the surface of the Moon is $1.624\,\mathrm{m\,s^{-2}}$, which is $16\frac{1}{2}\%$ of its value on the surface of the Earth.

(b) The magnitude of the acceleration will be $0.9g_{\mathrm{M}}$ at a distance x from the centre of the Moon, given by

$$\frac{GmM}{x^2} = 0.9mg_{\mathrm{M}} = 0.9\frac{GmM}{R^2}.$$

Hence

$$x = \frac{1}{\sqrt{0.9}}R = 1.832 \times 10^6\,\mathrm{m}.$$

Subtracting the radius of the Moon, the magnitude of the acceleration due to gravity is 90% of its value at the surface at a height of $9.4 \times 10^4\,\mathrm{m} = 94\,\mathrm{km}$.

Section 4

4.1 Forces (i), (ii), (iii) and (vi) are central forces, since these are directed along $\mathbf{r}$ or along $-\mathbf{r}$, depending on the sign of the constant K (and, in the case of (iii), on the sign of x). (For force (vi), recall that $\mathbf{r} = x\mathbf{i} + y\mathbf{j} + z\mathbf{k}$.)

4.2 From Equation (3.2), the gravitational force acting on a particle of mass m is

$$\mathbf{F}(\mathbf{r}) = -\frac{GmM}{r^3}\mathbf{r},$$

giving $g(\mathbf{r}) = -GmM/r^3$.

4.3 **(a)** If the force is central, it has the form

$$\mathbf{F} = g(\mathbf{r})\mathbf{r},$$

and its torque about the origin is

$$\boldsymbol{\Gamma} = \mathbf{r} \times \mathbf{F} = g(\mathbf{r})\mathbf{r} \times \mathbf{r} = \mathbf{0}.$$

Hence, by the torque law, $\dot{\mathbf{L}} = \mathbf{0}$ and so

$$\mathbf{L} = \text{constant}.$$

In other words, the angular momentum of the particle about the origin is constant.

(b) By the definition of the cross product of two vectors (*Unit 4* Subsection 4.2), $\mathbf{L} = m\mathbf{r} \times \dot{\mathbf{r}}$ is perpendicular to $\mathbf{r}$ whenever $\mathbf{L} \neq \mathbf{0}$.

(c) If $\mathbf{L} = m\mathbf{r} \times \dot{\mathbf{r}} = \mathbf{0}$, then, by the definition of the cross product, $\mathbf{r}$ and $\dot{\mathbf{r}}$ must be parallel (or antiparallel) vectors.

4.4 The angular momentum of the particle is

$$\mathbf{L} = \mathbf{r} \times m\dot{\mathbf{r}},$$

but since the motion is in the (x,y)-plane, we may apply the equations

$$\mathbf{r} = r\mathbf{e}_r \quad \text{and} \quad \dot{\mathbf{r}} = \dot{r}\mathbf{e}_r + r\dot{\theta}\mathbf{e}_\theta$$

(Equations (1.1) and (1.3)). Since $\mathbf{e}_r \times \mathbf{e}_\theta = \mathbf{k}$, we obtain

$$\begin{aligned} \mathbf{L} &= r\mathbf{e}_r \times m\left(\dot{r}\mathbf{e}_r + r\dot{\theta}\mathbf{e}_\theta\right) \\ &= mr\dot{r}\mathbf{e}_r \times \mathbf{e}_r + mr^2\dot{\theta}\mathbf{e}_r \times \mathbf{e}_\theta = mr^2\dot{\theta}\mathbf{k}. \end{aligned}$$

Hence $\mathbf{L} = L_z\mathbf{k}$, where $L_z = mr^2\dot{\theta}$.

4.5 **(a)** Isotropic central forces have the form $\mathbf{F}(\mathbf{r}) = f(r)\mathbf{e}_r$. Of the forces listed in Exercise 4.1, the following are isotropic central forces:

(i) since $\mathbf{F}(\mathbf{r}) = Kr\mathbf{e}_r$;
(ii) since $\mathbf{F}(\mathbf{r}) = (K/r)\mathbf{e}_r$;
(vi) since $\mathbf{F}(\mathbf{r}) = K\mathbf{e}_r$.

(b) For the gravitational force we have

$$\mathbf{F}(\mathbf{r}) = -\frac{GmM}{r^3}\mathbf{r} = -\frac{GmM}{r^2}\mathbf{e}_r,$$

so this is an isotropic central force with $f(r) = -GmM/r^2$.

4.6 Using spherical polar coordinates, for an isotropic central force $\mathbf{F}(r,\theta,\phi) = f(r)\mathbf{e}_r$, we have

$$F_r = f(r), \quad F_\theta = 0 \quad \text{and} \quad F_\phi = 0.$$

Using the formula for $\mathbf{curl\,F}$ in spherical polar coordinates, we obtain

$$\begin{aligned} \mathbf{curl\,F} &= \frac{1}{r^2\sin\theta}\begin{vmatrix} \mathbf{e}_r & r\mathbf{e}_\theta & r\sin\theta\,\mathbf{e}_\phi \\ \dfrac{\partial}{\partial r} & \dfrac{\partial}{\partial\theta} & \dfrac{\partial}{\partial\phi} \\ f(r) & 0 & 0 \end{vmatrix} \\ &= \frac{1}{r\sin\theta}\frac{\partial}{\partial\phi}(f(r))\,\mathbf{e}_\theta - \frac{1}{r}\frac{\partial}{\partial\theta}(f(r))\,\mathbf{e}_\phi \\ &= \mathbf{0}. \end{aligned}$$

So by the curl test, isotropic central forces are conservative since the domain is sufficiently simple.

4.7 **(a)** The potential function $U(\mathbf{r})$ for a conservative field $\mathbf{F}(\mathbf{r})$ is defined by

$$\mathbf{grad}\, U = -\mathbf{F}.$$

Using spherical polar coordinates, for an isotropic central force $\mathbf{F}(\mathbf{r}) = f(r)\mathbf{e}_r$, this reduces to

$$\frac{\partial U}{\partial r}\mathbf{e}_r + \frac{1}{r}\frac{\partial U}{\partial \theta}\mathbf{e}_\theta + \frac{1}{r\sin\theta}\frac{\partial U}{\partial \phi}\mathbf{e}_\phi = -f(r)\mathbf{e}_r.$$

So

$$\frac{\partial U}{\partial r} = -f(r), \quad \frac{\partial U}{\partial \theta} = 0 \quad \text{and} \quad \frac{\partial U}{\partial \phi} = 0.$$

From the last two equations, we see that U is independent of θ and ϕ and is a function of r only. (You might have expected this from the symmetry of the force $\mathbf{F}$.) Integrating the first equation we obtain

$$U(r) = -\int f(r)dr.$$

(b) For the gravitational force, $f(r) = -GmM/r^2$ and

$$U(r) = \int \frac{GmM}{r^2}dr$$

$$= -\frac{GmM}{r} \quad (+\text{ constant}).$$

It is convenient to choose the constant as zero, so that the gravitational potential energy is zero at infinity. (In *Unit 24* we chose the datum for the gravitational potential of a spherical body to be at the body's surface.)

4.8 The conservation of total mechanical energy is

$$\tfrac{1}{2}m|\dot{\mathbf{r}}|^2 + U(r) = E.$$

Now, using Exercise 1.4, the kinetic energy is

$$T = \tfrac{1}{2}m|\dot{\mathbf{r}}|^2 = \tfrac{1}{2}m\left(\dot{r}^2 + r^2\dot{\theta}^2\right).$$

We can eliminate $\dot{\theta}$ from this expression by using the conservation of angular momentum, which gives

$$\dot{\theta} = L_z/(mr^2).$$

Hence

$$\tfrac{1}{2}m|\dot{\mathbf{r}}|^2 = \tfrac{1}{2}m\dot{r}^2 + \frac{L_z^2}{2mr^2},$$

and the conservation of total mechanical energy becomes

$$\tfrac{1}{2}m\dot{r}^2 + \frac{L_z^2}{2mr^2} + U(r) = E,$$

which is Equation (4.11).

4.9 **(a)** The effective potential energy function is

$$U^{\text{eff}}(r) = \frac{L_z^2}{2mr^2} - \frac{k}{r}.$$

Differentiation of this equation gives

$$\frac{dU^{\text{eff}}}{dr} = \frac{k}{r^2} - \frac{L_z^2}{mr^3}.$$

The value $r = a$ for which $dU^{\text{eff}}/dr = 0$ is therefore

$$a = \frac{L_z^2}{mk}.$$

It is clear from Figure 4.5(b) that this gives a minimum value of $U^{\text{eff}}(r)$, although this can be verified by finding the sign of d^2U^{eff}/dr^2 at $r = a$.

(b) So

$$E_0 = U^{\text{eff}}(a) = \frac{L_z^2}{2m}\left(\frac{mk}{L_z^2}\right)^2 - \frac{mk^2}{L_z^2}$$

$$= -\frac{mk^2}{2L_z^2}.$$

4.10 **(a)** Using Equation (4.6), with $GmM = 45$, the potential energy function is

$$U(r) = -\frac{45}{r}.$$

(b) From Equation (4.2), the particle's angular momentum is

$$\mathbf{L} = m\mathbf{r}(0) \times \dot{\mathbf{r}}(0) = 3(2\mathbf{i}) \times (3\mathbf{j}) = 18\mathbf{k},$$

whose magnitude is $L_z = 18$. Initially the particle's kinetic energy is $\frac{1}{2} \times 3 \times 3^2 = \frac{27}{2}$ and its potential energy is $-45/2 = -\frac{45}{2}$. So the particle's total mechanical energy is

$$E = \tfrac{27}{2} - \tfrac{45}{2} = -9.$$

(c) Using Equation (4.11), we have

$$\tfrac{1}{2}m\dot{r}^2 + \frac{L_z^2}{2mr^2} + U(r) = E,$$

i.e.

$$\tfrac{1}{2} \times 3\dot{r}^2 + \frac{18^2}{2 \times 3r^2} - \frac{45}{r} = -9.$$

Simplifying this equation, we obtain

$$\dot{r}^2 = -6 + \frac{30}{r} - \frac{36}{r^2},$$

as required.

(d) The radial turning points occur when $\dot{r} = 0$. Hence

$$-6 + \frac{30}{r} - \frac{36}{r^2} = 0,$$

which simplifies to

$$r^2 - 5r + 6 = 0,$$

i.e.

$$(r-2)(r-3) = 0,$$

which has solutions

$$r = 2 \quad \text{and} \quad r = 3.$$

So the particle's minimum and maximum distances from the origin are 2 m and 3 m, respectively.

4.11 **(a)** The angular momentum has magnitude $L_z = mr^2\dot{\theta}$. At the instant of launch we have $r = R$ and, since there is then no radial component of velocity, the initial speed is $u = R\dot{\theta}$. Hence $L_z = muR$.

(b) The total mechanical energy E is the sum of the kinetic and potential energies, and is constant. Initially, the kinetic energy is $\frac{1}{2}mu^2$ and the potential energy is $-GmM/R$. Hence, for all subsequent times, the total energy is

$$E = \tfrac{1}{2}mu^2 - \frac{GmM}{R}.$$

(c) From Figure 4.5(b), the motion is bound provided that $E < 0$. So for bound motion, we must have

$$\tfrac{1}{2}mu^2 - \frac{GmM}{R} < 0, \quad \text{or} \quad u^2 < \frac{2GM}{R}.$$

(d) Since $u^2 = GM/(2R)$, the total mechanical energy is

$$E = \tfrac{1}{2}mu^2 - \frac{GmM}{R} = \frac{GmM}{4R} - \frac{GmM}{R} = -\frac{3GmM}{4R}.$$

Since E is negative, the motion is bound.

(e) The equation for radial turning points is $E = U^{\text{eff}}(r)$, where

$$U^{\text{eff}}(r) = \frac{L_z^2}{2mr^2} - \frac{GmM}{r}.$$

From part (a), we have $L_z = muR$, so the equation for r_{min} and r_{max} is

$$\frac{(muR)^2}{2mr^2} - \frac{GmM}{r} = E = -\frac{3GmM}{4R}.$$

Putting $s = R/r$, the equation becomes

$$\frac{mu^2s^2}{2} - \frac{GmMs}{R} = -\frac{3GmM}{4R}.$$

The given condition $u^2 = GM/(2R)$ simplifies this to

$$\tfrac{1}{4}s^2 - s = -\tfrac{3}{4}, \quad \text{or} \quad s^2 - 4s + 3 = 0.$$

The solutions are $s = 1$ and $s = 3$, which correspond to $r_{\text{max}} = R$ and $r_{\text{min}} = \frac{1}{3}R$.

(We must assume here that the spherically symmetric body at the origin has a radius less than $\frac{1}{3}R$. Otherwise the orbiting particle would collide with it!)

4.12 **(a)** From Equation (4.5), we have

$$U(r) = \int 4r\,dr = 2r^2 \ (+\text{ constant}).$$

It seems sensible to take the constant to be zero, which corresponds to the potential energy function being zero at the origin. We then have a potential energy function

$$U(r) = 2r^2.$$

(b) Using the initial conditions,

$$\mathbf{L} = \mathbf{r}(0) \times m\dot{\mathbf{r}}(0) = \mathbf{i} \times (4\mathbf{j}) = 4\mathbf{k},$$

whose magnitude is $L_z = 4$.

The particle's total mechanical energy is

$$E = \tfrac{1}{2}m|\dot{\mathbf{r}}(0)|^2 + U(r(0)) = \tfrac{1}{2} \times 4^2 + 2 \times 1^2 = 10.$$

Equation (4.11) is

$$\tfrac{1}{2}m\dot{r}^2 + \frac{L_z^2}{2mr^2} + U(r) = E,$$

which, in this case, reduces to

$$\tfrac{1}{2}\dot{r}^2 + \frac{4^2}{2r^2} + 2r^2 = 10,$$

which simplifies to

$$\dot{r}^2 = 20 - 4r^2 - 16r^{-2}.$$

(c) The radial turning points are given by $\dot{r} = 0$, so

$$20 - 4r^2 - 16r^{-2} = 0,$$

or

$$r^4 - 5r^2 + 4 = 0.$$

Factorizing this quadratic equation in r^2, we have

$$(r^2 - 1)(r^2 - 4) = 0,$$

so

$$r^2 = 1 \quad \text{or} \quad r^2 = 4.$$

Ignoring the negative roots (because $r \geq 0$), we have $r = 1$ or $r = 2$. So the minimum and maximum distances of the particle from the origin are 1 m and 2 m, respectively.

Section 5

5.1 **(a)** The equation of orbits is

$$\frac{l}{r} = 1 + e\cos(\theta - \theta_0). \tag{5.8}$$

The right-hand side of this equation takes values between $1 - e$ and $1 + e$ (inclusive) as θ varies. The minimum value of r corresponds to the maximum value of the right-hand side, which is $1 + e$. Hence we have

$$r_{\text{min}} = \frac{l}{1+e}.$$

This occurs at $\theta = \theta_0$.

(b) If $e < 1$ then $1 - e > 0$, so the right-hand side of Equation (5.8) is always positive. Its minimum value $1 - e$ corresponds to the maximum value of r, giving

$$r_{\text{max}} = \frac{l}{1-e}.$$

This occurs at $\theta = \theta_0 + \pi$.

(c) If $e \geq 1$ then $1 - e \leq 0$ and the treatment of part (b) cannot apply, since r is always non-negative. The condition $r > 0$ is equivalent to

$$1 + e\cos(\theta - \theta_0) > 0,$$

which is satisfied by the range of angles

$$\theta_0 - \theta_a < \theta < \theta_0 + \theta_a,$$

where $\theta_a = \arccos(-e^{-1})$. For this range of values of θ there is no upper bound for the values of r, so the motion is unbound in this case. The corresponding orbits (for $e > 1$) are hyperbolas, as illustrated in the diagram below. For $e = 1$, the corresponding orbit is a parabola.

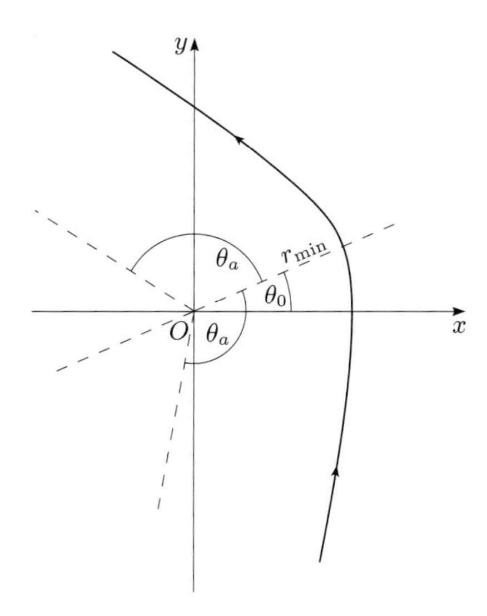

(d) Orbits are bound for $e < 1$ and unbound for $e \geq 1$.

5.2 **(a)** In a time T the whole area of the ellipse is swept out. Since $\dot{A}$ is constant, we then have

$$\pi ab = \dot{A}T = \frac{L_z T}{2m}.$$

Squaring both sides of this equation, and putting

$$b^2 = al = \frac{aL_z^2}{Gm^2M},$$

we obtain

$$T^2 = \left(\frac{4\pi^2}{GM}\right)a^3,$$

as required.

(b) Rearranging Kepler's third law, we obtain

$$M = \frac{4\pi^2 a^3}{GT^2}.$$

Now $a = 149.6 \times 10^9\,\mathrm{m}$, $G = 6.673 \times 10^{-11}\,\mathrm{m^3\,kg^{-1}\,s^{-2}}$ and $T = 365.256 \times 24 \times 60 \times 60\,\mathrm{s}$. So

$$M = \frac{4\pi^2 \times (149.6 \times 10^9)^3}{6.673 \times 10^{-11} \times (365.256 \times 24 \times 60 \times 60)^2}$$

$$= 1.989 \times 10^{30}\,\mathrm{kg}.$$

So the mass of the Sun is 1.989×10^{30} kg. (This agrees with the accepted value of 1.99×10^{30} kg.)

5.3 **(a)** If the orbit is bound, then we have

$$E = \frac{GmM}{2l}(e^2 - 1)$$

together with

$$l = \frac{b^2}{a} \quad \text{and} \quad e = \sqrt{1 - \frac{b^2}{a^2}}$$

(Equations (2.5) and (2.4)).

So $e^2 - 1 = -b^2/a^2 = -l/a$, giving

$$E = -\frac{GmM}{2a}.$$

(b) For any orbit, Exercise 5.1(a) gives the distance of closest approach as

$$r_{\min} = \frac{l}{1+e}.$$

Hence we obtain

$$E = \frac{GmM}{2r_{\min}}(e - 1).$$

5.4 **(a)** For bound motion, we have both

$$E = \tfrac{1}{2}mu^2 - \frac{GmM}{R}$$

and (from Exercise 5.3(a))

$$E = -\frac{GmM}{2a}.$$

On equating these expressions and solving for a, we obtain

$$a = \left(\frac{2}{R} - \frac{u^2}{GM}\right)^{-1}.$$

(b) From Equations (2.4) and (2.5), we have

$$e = \sqrt{1 - \frac{b^2}{a^2}} = \sqrt{1 - \frac{l}{a}}.$$

But from Equation (5.7) we also know that

$$l = \frac{L_z^2}{Gm^2M}.$$

Since $L_z = muR$ is given in the question, we have

$$l = \frac{u^2R^2}{GM}$$

and, using the result of part (a),

$$e = \left[1 - \frac{u^2R^2}{GM}\left(\frac{2}{R} - \frac{u^2}{GM}\right)\right]^{1/2}$$

$$= \left[1 - 2\left(\frac{u^2R}{GM}\right) + \left(\frac{u^2R}{GM}\right)^2\right]^{1/2}$$

or

$$e = \left|1 - \frac{u^2R}{GM}\right|,$$

where the magnitude has been taken to ensure that $e \geq 0$. (Note that the condition $e < 1$ must correspond to the given condition $u^2 < 2GM/R$ for bound motion.)

Alternatively, this result could have been obtained from the formula

$$E = \frac{GmM}{2l}(e^2 - 1).$$

5.5 **(a)** Using Equation (4.9), the equation of radial motion is

$$m\ddot{r} = \frac{k}{r^3} + \frac{L_z^2}{mr^3} = \left(k + \frac{L_z^2}{m}\right)\frac{1}{r^3}.$$

(b) From Equation (5.3), we have

$$\ddot{r} = -\frac{L_z^2}{m^2r^2}\frac{d^2}{d\theta^2}\left(\frac{1}{r}\right),$$

so

$$-\frac{L_z^2}{m}\frac{1}{r^2}\frac{d^2}{d\theta^2}\left(\frac{1}{r}\right) = \left(k + \frac{L_z^2}{m}\right)\frac{1}{r^3},$$

i.e.

$$\frac{d^2}{d\theta^2}\left(\frac{1}{r}\right) + \left(1 + \frac{mk}{L_z^2}\right)\frac{1}{r} = 0.$$

In terms of $u = 1/r$, we have

$$\frac{d^2u}{d\theta^2} + \omega^2 u = 0,$$

where

$$\omega^2 = 1 + \frac{mk}{L_z^2}.$$

(c) The solution of this differential equation is

$$u = A\cos\omega(\theta - \theta_0),$$

where A and θ_0 are constants of integration. By a suitable choice of the line $\theta = 0$, we can ensure that $\theta_0 = 0$, and so the path of the particle is

$$u = A\cos\omega\theta,$$

or

$$r = B\sec\omega\theta,$$

where $B = 1/A$. This orbit is unbound, as you might expect, with distance of closest approach B.

Index